THE END OF HOPE

THE END OF
HOPE

A Social-Clinical Study of Suicide

ARTHUR L. KOBLER

AND

EZRA STOTLAND

With the editorial assistance
of SUE DAVIDSON GOTTFRIED

The Free Press of Glencoe

Collier-Macmillan Limited, London

TO
ROSLYN AND MILDRED
AND
ROSE AND ISAAC

PREFACE

THE AUTHORS OF THIS VOLUME SHARE A FUNDA-
mental theoretical viewpoint: both have an orientation which
can be labeled psychosocial, field-theoretical, or transactional.
We believe that one cannot understand an individual, his behavior, or what has happened to him, without knowing the
setting, the significant aspects of the environment. To understand
a person in psychology one must look at the "life-space"; i.e.,
the person and the psychological environment as it exists for
him. Moreover, there are constant, shifting interactions within
the life space. Thus, Lawrence K. Frank (1957) has noted that
research must be concerned with "organized complexities," and:

« We need to think in terms of circular, reciprocal relations
and feed backs, both positive and negative, through which
the component members of the field participate in and
thereby create the field of the whole, which field in turn
regulates and patterns their individual activities. This is a
circular reciprocal relation, not a serial cause and effect,
stimulus and response relation.

It follows that we view the concept "mental illness," with
its implication of cause lying solely within the individual, as
inappropriate. And, of course, we cannot see suicide as "caused"
by a suicide drive. Emotionally disturbed behavior and suicide,
like any behavior, cannot be comprehended while disregarding
the setting in which the behavior takes place.

Within this theoretical framework, our research was undertaken in a small, private mental hospital emphasizing individual
psychotherapy and milieu therapy. It was initiated by an
epidemic of suicides, a series of four suicides among patients
which occurred within six months—three of them in three weeks
—after a period of nine years with only one suicide. Research
centered on the individuals who attempted or committed suicide,

vii

on their families, on the general hospital milieu prior to and during the period of the epidemic, and on the specific aspects of the milieu surrounding each patient of the suicide group.

We are convinced that in our examination of the suicides in the epidemic group we have been able to approach the implications of our field-theoretical, transactional orientation. The data permit us to know a great deal about the individuals; about the setting in which their suicides took place; about the character of all their important interpersonal contacts for a lengthy period preceding the suicides. The literature, which we discuss critically in the following chapter, consists largely of statistical studies of suicide; impersonal sociological investigations; or limited case histories stemming mainly from the point of view of the therapist alone.

Our unique data offer us, we believe, a unique look at the problem of suicide. We can then offer in this volume a study and a theory of suicide different from those which have appeared in the literature until now. In our minds our new view—in which we are not alone, but in a small minority—has important implications for the treatment of individuals now seen as suicide dangers and for the prevention of suicide.

A. L. K.

E. S.

ACKNOWLEDGMENTS

WE THANK FIRST THE MORE THAN EIGHTY PEOPLE who helped us so freely and openly with their time and thought, and without whose thorough cooperation this project could not have been accomplished: patients, aides, nurses, psychotherapists, consultant psychiatrists, members of the board of trustees, who, disguised, play major roles in our story.

Our deep gratitude to the families of patients whose generous cooperation—even when it was exceedingly painful to them—was based on their hope of helping others by helping us. Their aid was essential to the project.

This investigation was supported in part by Pubic Health Service Research Grant M-2858, from the National Institute of Mental Health, whose representatives offered useful guidance.

We thank Paul Bergman, Ralph Crawshaw, and Nathaniel S. Lehrman for their constructive criticism of parts of the manuscript, and Francis Hoague for his invaluable help in many ways.

Our special thanks to Sue Davidson Gottfried, our fine editor.

We thank Temple Kobler, Barbara S. Hilyer, Candace L. Hilyer, and especially Bruce W. Hilyer for their great help in reading proof.

We are most indebted to James C. Furlan whose efficiency, conscientiousness, responsible dedication, and kind, gentle presence was of inestimable value.

Finally, our deep thanks to our wives, Virginia and Patricia.

CONTENTS

THE END OF
HOPE

A VIEW
OF SUICIDE

WE HAVE CHARACTERIZED OUR APPROACH TO EMO-
tional disturbance, and particularly to suicide, as psychosocial,
as including environmental as well as intrapsychic factors. Our
conception views suicidal attempts and verbal or other communications of suicidal intent as efforts, however misdirected, to
solve problems of living, as frantic pleas for help and hope
from other people: help in solving the problems, and hope
that they can be solved. Whether the individual then actually
commits suicide—and this is our central concern—seems to
depend in large part on the nature of the response by other
people to his plea. If the response to the plea is hopeless and
helpless, suicide is more likely to occur. It is our conviction
that an implicit or explicit fear or expectation of suicide is
most often communicated by a hopeless, helpless response, and
that this communication is important in facilitating suicide.

Our approach is opposed to the view that suicide-proneness
is per se a sickness, existing as an autonomous force within the
individual. Seeking the answer within the individual is one
of the oldest and most consistently used frames of reference
for understanding suicide. Before the era of modern science,
explanations sometimes were derived from demonology, the
belief in a supernatural being who entered the body and soul
of the victim, driving him inevitably to suicide. Sometimes this
search within the person led to the condemnation of the suicide
as a self-willed sinner violating the Sixth Commandment.
But even more recently, the search within the person has led
to a conception of suicide as the outcome of a mysterious
"sickness" within the person. This approach to suicide is
implicit in the popular medical and psychological view that
suicide proneness in a person is to be identified as soon as

1

possible. Individuals so identified are viewed as being driven toward actual suicide unless the drive is alleviated through treatment. This concept of drive toward self-murder has been most pointedly formulated by Lindemann (1958), who endowed it with the name "hypereridism," defined as a "morbid state of hostile tension leading to suicide." This approach sometimes utilizes Freud's theory of a death-instinct, the striving of all living beings toward a state of nothingness (Freud, 1925). For example, Menninger (1938) describes the suicidal person as one who desires to kill, to be killed, and to die. Related versions of this approach postulate the complex process of the individual's incorporating a beloved but rejecting person into his own psyche, then destroying himself in order to destroy the beloved person and to punish himself in the same act.

Some have questioned this recent view as a pseudo-scientific version of the prescientific explanation of a devil as the cause of mental illness. Szasz (1960) states:

« The notion of mental illness provides an amoral and impersonal "thing" (an "illness") as an explanation for *problems in living*. We may recall in this connection that not so long ago it was devils and witches who were held responsible for man's problems in social living. The belief in mental illness, as something other than man's trouble in getting along with his fellow men, is the proper heir to the belief in demonology and witchcraft. Mental illness exists or is "real" in exactly the same sense in which witches existed or were "real."

Implicit in this "illness" point of view is the expectation that one can predict suicide on the basis of symptoms emanating from the person. In medical tradition and in medical actuality, symptoms generally permit a diagnosis which implies the course of an illness. But what are considered to be the symptoms predictive of suicide? Psychoanalysis has emphasized the importance of conditions of depression. In addition, Zilboorg quotes Freud as saying: "It is remarkable that in contradistinction to depressions, the compulsive neurotic never makes a suicidal attempt; he gives the impression of being immune against the danger of suicide, more so than the hysteric" (Zilboorg, 1936). Zilboorg comments:

« Patients with other than typical depressions are likely to commit suicide, and in the light of present day clinical experience Freud would not subscribe to his original statement that neurotic patients, particularly those with obsessional (compulsive) neuroses, appear to be immune to suicidal impulses.

He adds:

« Evidently there is no single clinical entity recognized in psychiatry that is immune to the suicidal drive . . . . While the fundamental mechanism which was described by Freud as characteristic of depressions is met in all instances of apparent depression, in some cases of suicide it is not possible to demonstrate that this mechanism is the only determining factor brought into full play in the act. Moreover, as has already been stated, the clinician observes a number of patients displaying the operation of this mechanism without the suicidal drive being either directly present or effectively operative when present. Hence, the presence or apparent absence of this mechanism cannot well serve as a reliable diagnostic or prognostic criteria.

Most studies of suicide have focused upon the presence of depression in the people who attempt or actually commit suicide. The presence of depressive symptoms must, however, be distinguished from the psychiatric diagnosis of depression. Levy and Southcombe (1953), for example, found that in a state mental hospital "depression seemed to be at work" in 55 per cent of the patients who committed suicide, but only 10 per cent had had a *diagnosis* of depression. Diagnoses of depression vary, depending upon many other aspects of the situation. In some cases, depression is a symptomatic diagnosis having little to do with the dynamic mechanisms implicit in psychoanalytic diagnoses. In some settings, those who tend to treat patients with electric shock will more often make a diagnosis of depression than those who tend to treat patients with psychotherapy, if only because the former view electric shock as helpful to depressed patients. Dorpat (1960), in his recent study of suicide in Seattle, noted that "all patients in this group had evidence of depression." Of 114 suicides, however, he gave only 19 a diagnosis of psychotic depression. Dorpat's attitude toward depression seemed to be important in his finding that all had symptoms of depression. He notes: "The examiners were especially assiduous in obtaining a history of depression." One might comment that assiduousness is scarcely required. It is a commonplace to assume that those who commit suicide are uncommonly unhappy; and severe unhappiness is itself a depressive symptom. With "assiduousness," how can one not find evidence of depression in suicides?

Must we not ask the question this way as well: How many of those who are depressed, or who have depressive symptoms, later commit suicide? We do not have direct data on which to base an answer, but there is evidence that the number may be surprisingly small. For example, Stengel and Cook (1958) report that in England and Wales, from 1920 to 1947, the average number of suicides per year in mental hospitals was one for every 2000 beds. Since many depressed patients would be in a mental hospital population, it appears in this connection, again, that depression is of small value in diagnosing the "suicide-prone" person.

What seems necessary, if depressive symptoms are to have any predictive significance for suicide, is that they must have an unequivocal meaning and indicate a distinct set of dynamics, directed specifically toward suicide. The literature on depression in suicide does not, thus far, reveal the presence of such a distinct set of dynamics.

Within this view of suicide as an illness, attempted suicide has also been seen as a precursor of actual suicide. There are many studies demonstrating that those who have attempted suicide are not, in fact, special suicide risks. In a series of five-year follow-up studies of several hundred persons who had attempted suicide, Stengel and Cook (1958) found that less than 4 per cent later suicided. Batchelor and Napier (1954) found that 2 per cent of those who had attempted suicide had killed themselves within a year. Hove (1958) found that 4.8 per cent had committed suicide in two to three years. Most impressively, Ringel (1952) at the University of Vienna Hospital reports that of 2879 patients seen because of attempted suicide in 1948, 1949, and 1950, only one had committed suicide by August 1951. While Ringel felt that the surprisingly small number of suicides was largely due to the treatment and attention offered, we feel that such results generally are not a consequence of intensive individual psychotherapy. On the contrary, as we will indicate later, in some situations where intensive treatment is carried out the actual suicide rate may be considerably higher.

One may explore the extent to which suicide-attempts are predictive of actual suicide by asking: How many of those who actually commit suicide had previously attempted suicide? Studies of actual suicides have reported that 14 to 33 per cent of their subjects had made previous suicide attempts (Dorpat & Ripley, 1960; Stengel & Cook, 1958). Or, to put it the other way, no previous attempts were discovered in from 67 to 86 per cent of the actual suicides. Although these data are not totally reliable, it seems clear that if previous attempts are used as an indicator of suicide-proneness, most of the actual suicides would remain unpredicted. Thus, an examination of attempted suicide confronts us with two issues which argue against the importance of autonomous self-destructive impulses in the motivation of the suicidal act. These are, say Stengel and Cook (1958), "the comparatively very small proportion of persons who having made suicidal attempts, finally kill themselves, even among those who frequently react with suicidal attempts to stressful situations; and the corresponding fact that among the suicides only a minority have attempted suicide before."

Clinicians may point out that many depressed people are not viewed as suicidal, nor are those whose suicide attempts are evaluated to be gestures. Few however would doubt that a "serious" or "severe" attempt implies the acute danger of actual suicide.

One effective study of severe suicidal attempts—done in England by Stengel and Cook (1958)—was based on a four- to five-year follow-up of a group of cases which they had classified into degrees of dangerousness, in terms of damage to the individual and an evaluation of intent. They report two pertinent findings: (1) "No grading for seriousness of large groups of suicidal acts can be really satisfactory.... Clearly the degree of danger to life is not a reliable measure of seriousness of intent." (2) "At this stage of research, no prognostic inference can be made in individual cases from the degree of dangerousness and intent of a particular attempt." And it should be recalled that in the studies of actual suicides, previous attempts ranged from 14 to 33 per cent. In all these studies anything that had the character of an attempt, whether gesture or serious, was so categorized. Thus, the number of those who had made severe attempts prior to actual suicide was relatively small.

It seems, then, that the popular and apparently reasonable indicators of potential suicide—depression, suicide attempt, and serious suicide attempt—do not stand up under examination. None of them seems to be effective in predicting suicide—in identifying the potentially suicidal individual.

Accordingly we conclude that the attempt to approach the understanding of suicide through the concept of a suicidal drive, a tendency toward suicide existing autonomously within the individual, has not proven fruitful. In our introduction we described our approach to emotional disturbance as field-theoretical and psychosocial. Emotional disturbance, we have suggested, cannot be understood except in terms of the field of which the disturbed individual is a part. Much of the data presented in the literature suggest that such a frame of reference may be considerably more fruitful in understanding attempted and actual suicide.

We view suicide attempts as frantic generalized cries for help. Stengel and Cook (1958), who studied many people who attempted suicide, state, ". . . in our society every suicidal warning or attempt has an appeal function whatever the mental state in which it is made." Shneidman and Farberow (1957) state: "Prevention of suicide lies in answering the individual's cry for help." Rubenstein, Moses, and Lidz (1958) summarized their study on attempted suicide with the statement, "We have come to regard attempted suicide not as an effort to die but rather as a communication to others in an effort to improve one's life."

The appeal nature of the attempted suicide is indicated by the fact that most often the person makes the attempt with an expectation and hope of being rescued. Jensen and Petty (1958) found that those who attempt suicide almost invariably have a fantasy of being rescued. Stengel and Cook (1958) found this fantasy relatively realistic; people often make a suicide attempt in situations in which they have a good chance of being rescued. Rubenstein, *et al.* (1958), described "a characteristic sequence of events":

« The patient was involved in a struggle with the persons important to him and sought a modification of their attitudes or a specific change in his relationships with them. After a crisis was reached in this struggle, the patient sought to effect these changes through a suicide attempt. These changes sought were sometimes described directly by the patient. At other times the patient was not conscious of his seeking these changes, or he denied them, but they were clearly revealed in his behavior. Patients sometimes told of seeking such changes prior to their suicide attempt, of seeking them

through the attempt, and by still other means afterward
. . . . We often found that a crisis had been reached in a
struggle between the patient and the same person toward
whom the attempt was directed.

Attempted suicide is a loud cry for help—and almost invariably people hear and respond. Stengel and Cook (1958) report
that the attempts often lead to significant changes in the
person's life through the intervention of other people, such
as would come about through medical and psychiatric care,
as well as to changes in the relationship with "a special person."
Rubenstein, *et al.* (1958), report that in 34 of 44 cases of attempted suicide "desired effects" were clearly brought about
through the attempt. They add: "We regard these 34 attempts
as successful in the sense that desired changes in the life situation of the patients occurred as a consequence of the attempt
. . . ." Moss and Hamilton (1957) stated, in evaluating factors
in recovery after suicide attempts:

« Success in recovered cases was most often attributable to the
therapist's active intervention in the patient's home environment. . . . We found consistently that recovery requires a
major change in the life situation. Only three recovered
patients returned to the same environment in which the
illness arose without fundamental changes in the employment situation or personal relationships.
   The most common changes, in order of frequency, were
(a) changes in occupation or retirement; (b) significant improvement in the marital relationship; (c) emancipation
from domineering and restricting parents; (d) breaking of
unsuitable engagements; (e) changes in psychosexual orientation . . .; (f) divorce of immature and sadistic mates . . .
and marriage . . .; (g) significant widening of social contacts, recreations, and hobbies.

The therapeutic effectiveness of a positive change in environment is further attested to by the fact that few of those persons
whose suicide attempts are followed by such change repeat the
attempt. Stengel and Cook (1958) found that no more than
17 per cent attempted suicide again within five years. Furthermore, as suggested by the data presented, these persons rarely
subsequently commit suicide.
How do we understand these results? Actual changes in the

individual's life situation mean that change is possible—that the world is not overwhelmingly and absolutely unchangeable, that hope is possible and warranted. The active response to the individual's plea demonstrates that he can hope. Furthermore, the concern in the response to the plea communicates the value and significance of the person—as one who is worthy of having hope, as one who deserves concern and active effort.

Our argument suggests that those who follow suicide attempts with actual suicide have made efforts, directly or indirectly, to elicit help from significant others in their world; and have received in response a hopeless expectation of suicide, a helpless answer. The evidence indeed supports this view. The vast majority of persons who commit suicide have told other people about their plans. Dorpat and Ripley (1960) reported that 83 per cent of 114 actual suicides had previously communicated, one-third by suicide attempts. Robins, Gassner, Kayes, Wilkinson, and Murphy (1959) found that 69 per cent of 134 similar cases so communicated, 29 per cent by attempts. Although these researchers were diligent in tracing down the people with whom the person had contact before his suicide to learn of possible communications of suicidal intent made to them, it is obvious that these percentages cannot fully represent the total number of such communications. Furthermore, both these researchers found that the communications were often made to several different people. Dorpat (1960) states: "The data indicate that people who commit suicide usually communicate their intention prior to the act and that they do so to different people and in different ways." Robins, *et al.* (1959), state:

« The mean number of ways per person of expressing suicidal ideas was 3.2. In the majority of instances, expressions of suicidal ideas were diverse even for individual persons. The ideas were communicated, on the average, to two different groups; and in two-thirds (67%) of instances the communications were repeated. Thus, not only did the communications occur in a high proportion of cases but they tended to be multiple, repeated, and expressed to a number of different persons.

They also add that "86% of the persons who were reported to have expressed suicidal ideas had recently expressed them for the first time or had shown recent intensification of these ideas." It is clear then that those who actually committed suicide had previously communicated regarding suicide.

The data also support our second contention that the response to the suicidal communication of those who later committed suicide was generally characterized by hopelessness and
helplessness. Robins, *et al.* (1959), in discussing the reactions
of the important people in the environment to those who
committed suicide, report:

« The chief characteristics of the audience relevant to the
present analysis are: whether those who received the suicidal
communications desired the death of the communicator, were
indifferent to it, or were distressed by it. As far as could
be ascertained from our interviews, only a very small minority of the respondents appeared to desire or welcome the
death of the suicidal person, or to be indifferent. The in-
difference did not appear to be complete; the suicide was
at least unwelcome and unpleasant to this group. By far the
largest number of respondents were genuinely distressed
and upset by the suicidal death. . . . The majority of the
respondents expressed a feeling of marked tension. They
were being repeatedly warned of the possible or even probable occurrence of a dire event about which they could do
nothing definitive. They did not feel able either to prevent
the suicidal act or to ameliorate the psychiatric illness. Nor
had they been able to turn total responsibility for the person over to anyone else.

They describe the respondents as denying and rejecting the
fear-arousing communications; as denying the possibility of real
suicide; or, lastly, "they rejected the significance of the communication."

« It was our impression that initially the critical considerations
here were whether the respondent had little or no idea of
what to do for the suicidal person or whether he believed he
should see a psychiatrist or other physician. In the cases
where a psychiatrist or other physician had examined the
suicidal person and had not hospitalized him or had hospitalized him only briefly, the respondents were left with the
problem of a communicator who was in part their responsibility and for whom they knew nothing definitive to do.
As a result, the original picture of themselves as being helpful
and effective in getting the suicidal person to a physician was
changed and they were left with an insoluble problem. It

should be pointed out that there is a lack of realistic information concerning what a respondent should do when confronted with this kind of situation. This is due to a lack of knowledge of the medical profession and not only of the respondents. No clear-cut information is available to physicians or to the public as to what should be done in this situation. A very real dilemma, therefore, confronts the respondent.

Thus the respondents to those people who did actually commit suicide were characterized as distressed, upset, using denial, and feeling helpless. (Obviously, the results were influenced by the fact that the study was done after the suicides had occurred.)

These findings present a sharp contrast to the quality of the responses reported by Rubenstein and his collaborators (1958) in cases where suicide was attempted but did not eventually occur. They attempted to assess the immediate reactions of others to the patient and to the attempt. They distinguished three major immediate responses: " (1) concerned and sympathetic, (2) calm and relatively indifferent, and (3) punitive and counter-aggressive." They state:

« These immediate responses are of importance in dealing with suicide attempts because of the indications they offer of whether or not a given attempt will be followed by desired change in the patient's life situation, and hence of whether or not the needs which brought about the attempt will continue to operate.

In 22 of the 35 attempts where the "desired effect" was achieved, the immediate response shown by at least one important person was concern and sympathy. . . . Of the only two cases in which a "desired effect" was discernible but not achieved, the response elicited was consistently calm and indifferent in one and consistently punitive and counter-aggressive in the other.

These studies suggest that when the response to attempted suicide was positive and active, only a small percentage (2 or 3 per cent) subsequently committed suicide. Conversely, there are strong indications that actual suicide follows upon a helpless, fearful response to communication of suicide intent. Two clinical examples with markedly different consequences seem to support our point of view. Wilmer (1958) used none of the "traditional measures" in dealing with suicide in his therapeutic community, "though over 10 per cent of our patients had made bona fide suicidal attempts prior to their admission and the risk was probably present in 25 per cent of the total patient sample." He states:

« The practice of writing "suicidal precautions" orders on patients' charts, it seems to me, is sometimes a "buck-passing" device that is not only ineffectual but has some very unfortunate results. If the staff is made to feel responsible for what the psychiatrist himself cannot prevent, their anxiety mounts. The doctor goes home. They are left with the orders, the responsibility, and the patient. They tensely watch him and follow him about, thereby isolating him from the patient community as a specially dangerous case; then, at the least provocation, they medicate and seclude him, primarily to protect or "cover" themselves.

Under these circumstances, the staff's fear becomes a disruptive element which can seriously interfere with care of the patient. Moreover, this fear communicates itself to the patient. If we expect that he is going to attempt suicide, our expectation is communicated to him by the elaborate precautions we are taking. This only increases the chances that he will do so. On the other hand, the firm expectation that he will not commit suicide can also be communicated to the patient, and can have an effect that will considerably reduce the risk.

In his ten-month experiment, two patients made suicide attempts and neither could be described as serious or well-planned.

An illustration of the outcome of a helpless, fearful response is found in a paper by Moss and Hamilton (1957). They viewed their patients—people who had attempted suicide—with the expectation that they would actually suicide unless they received therapy specifically directed to the elimination of the suicidal drive. They state: "Since in our series [of cases] only seriously suicidal patients were selected, therapy was often life-saving." While treating their patients with intensive psychotherapy, they expected a recurrence of suicidal impulses. "The reactivation phase must be anticipated. The patient and his relatives must be adequately warned and prepared for a return of suicidal urges and symptoms." Thus, their expectations were explicit. Their results were as follows. "Fifty per cent of our cases were

considered recovered and twenty per cent much improved. . . .
Four patients remained unimproved and permanently hospitalized. Eleven died by suicide." That is, 22 per cent of their total
group actually committed suicide, a figure strikingly higher
than any other report on follow-up of persons hospitalized as
a consequence of suicidal attempts.

Our view is that the expectation of suicide and feelings of
hopelessness and helplessness are facilitative of actual suicide.
The expectations of Moss and Hamilton, as they appear in their
statements, were clear; the relatives were warned of the suicidal
danger. It is noteworthy here that "four-fifths of all reactivations
occurred while the patient was on a day or overnight visit."
Further, "the characteristic reactivation of the suicidal drive
in over 90 per cent of the patients . . . occurred when the
patient was considered markedly improved and had the opportunity to come into contact once more with the environment
in which the illness began." We suggest that the families, faced
with the warning that their relatives were intense suicidal risks,
felt hopeless and helpless and expected suicide to occur. The
relatively high suicide rate in Moss and Hamilton's group may
be a consequence of the communication of the therapist's fears
and expectations.*

It is striking in this context to find that in discussing factors
in recovery, Moss and Hamilton report the crucial significance
of "fundamental changes in the employment situation or personal relationships." This emphasis on changes in the individual's life-space seems inconsistent with their general "illness"
approach and their emphasis on individual psychotherapy as
necessary to prevent suicide. In fact, their detailed study and
the conclusions quoted earlier can be seen as strongly supporting
our view that when positive changes are made in the field—in
the world of the disturbed individual—actual suicide does not
occur.

Sociological studies suggest that actual suicide tends to occur
when there is a process in which negative changes occur in the
individual's field, leading to a decrease of hope. Durkheim

---

* Moss and Hamilton argue that their high rate was a consequence of the
very seriousness of the previous attempts of these persons. Yet Stengel and
Cook, who attempted to predict suicide from the seriousness of the attempt,
found that they were unable to do so. Likewise, Rubenstein, *et al.*, feel that
seriousness of intent to kill oneself cannot be judged from the danger involved in the suicide attempt.

(1950), in his classic discussion of suicide, interpreted "egoistic" suicide" as an outcome of that loss of meaning in life which results from disintegration of the individual's relations with other persons and with social groups.

Henry and Short (1954) give figures on suicide as it is related to periods of economic depression—which would effect most profoundly, one might reasonably assume, the social roles of those whose lives are most affected by fluctuations in the business cycle. This assumption is supported by their findings which show that the rate of suicide among males (who lose jobs) goes up more in depression periods than does the suicide rate for females; that persons living in higher rental areas (who may have to leave them) show more increase in suicide rate during depressions than those in lower rental areas (who cannot leave their area); that white persons (who have more stable social roles in normal times) increase their rate of suiciding during depressions more than do Negroes. Other findings similarly support the connection between suicide and the loss of some significant aspect of life. The high rate among widows, widowers, and divorcees has been long and repeatedly noted. Older persons, especially those who have been separated from their families, have a high rate (Batchelor & Napier, 1954). Persons who have recently fallen into poverty have a high rate (Sainsbury, 1955), as do the newly unemployed.

It is interesting that Sainsbury (1955) finds that low income *per se* does not lead to a high rate of suicide (except for the poverty-stricken; many of the working class persons in his study lived in highly socially integrated and very stable communities. Sainsbury points out that in studies such as Cavan's (1926), which showed high suicide rates in the disorganized and poor sections of the city, the high rates may reflect instability rather than poverty.

These data strongly suggest that suicide and preoccupation with suicide are more likely to occur in response to a new experience involving the loss of a stable role. Suicide, then, is not made more likely solely by what may objectively be expected to be an "intolerable situation" but by a new set of circumstances which destroys the individual's entire sense of adequacy for dealing with the world as he knows and views it. The intolerability has to be viewed subjectively and not "objectively."

The experience, then, of an individual pushed to the point of making a suicidal communication is one of feeling that his

life situation has become impossible. His identity has been
undermined; his self-esteem sinks. In their review of the literature on suicide from 1945 to 1956, Vitanza, Church, and Offenkrantz (1957) find that one of the few points upon which researchers generally agree is that suicidal persons have self-
derogatory feelings, feelings of worthlessness and self-hatred.
Andics (1947), in a study of 100 persons who attempted suicide,
found them to have feelings of unworthiness as well as a sense
of meaninglessness.

Threatened with the loss of purpose and hope, and feeling as
a consequence that life is empty, what can such people do?
Obviously, they can seek new bases for hope. They are most
likely to seek it in their relationships with others, since these
relationships provided them with adequate and hopeful social
roles in the past. It is noteworthy that persons with low self-
esteem tend to depend upon others for guidance and to be more
responsive to their expectations (Stotland, Thorley, Thomas,
Cohen, & Zander, 1957). The work reported by Janis and his
co-workers (Janis, Hovland, Field, Linton, Graham, Cohen,
Rife, Abelson, Lesser, & King, 1959) suggests that persons of
low self-esteem are more persuasible than persons of high self-
esteem. Furthermore, Janis, *et al.*, report that mental patients
generally, with their low sense of adequacy, are more persuasible
than "normal people." Therefore, when people in such a state
appeal to others, the response provided them will have important, and sometimes crucial, effects. Crucial are the attitudes
and expectations of important people in the troubled individual's world: family members, treatment personnel, etc. It is this
aspect of our view which seems to offer an important clue to
the "why" of suicide as a solution, as contrasted with, let us
say, the development of a psychosis.

In our view, when the disturbed individual seeks an organiz-
ing principle or purpose he will be guided to a great extent
by his interpretation of the expectations of people significant
to him in his world. How others identify him seems crucial.
If the potential suicide is responded to with an expectation that
he will commit suicide, his suicide will be facilitated. He
grasps at the suicidal identity, and achieves a kind of equanimity
and stability of behavior. Many clinicians have noted that
patients act in an organized fashion, seem to be getting better,
seem to be calmed, prior to a suicidal act. It is putative that
when depressed patients organize they are in most danger of

suicide. This phenomenon was noted in the Moss and Hamilton study, as pointed out above. In such cases, people often deliberately and thoughtfully go about preparing for the end. Stengel and Cook (1958) have noted that they may even buy a plot in a cemetery and make wills at this time. In this somewhat bizarre fashion, life achieves a new goal: its own end.

It is also significant that when the clear purpose to commit suicide is grasped, the suicide is often done away from possible interference from other people. Stengel and Cook, and others, have found that most actual suicides are committed in isolation, in sharp contrast to attempted suicides, which are enacted in a social setting providing for rescue. Although in such cases the individual may be physically isolated, it is noteworthy that he is seldom socially indifferent. We refer here to the argument developed earlier, that those who commit suicide have made many prior communications of their intent. And many write suicide notes, which suggests again that they are not socially indifferent.

How is it possible that an individual comes to grasp an identity which inflicts upon him the ultimate punishment? The soundest basis for our total view of this problem seems to be offered by the theoretical formulations of Erik Erikson. Referring to adolescents, in whom he feels the state of identity diffusion is most often seen (although it is also seen in others in periods of emotional disability, and particularly when the identity is made diffuse through the recent or sudden loss of stability in the social world), Erikson (1959) notes the "act through which society 'identifies' its young members and thus contributes to their developing identity."

> «   If, for simplicity's sake, or in order to accommodate ingrown habits of law or psychiatry, they diagnose and treat as criminal, as a constitutional misfit, as a derelict doomed by his upbringing, or—indeed—as a deranged patient, a young person who, for reasons of personal or social marginality, is close to choosing a negative identity, *that young person may well put his energy into becoming exactly what the careless and fearful community expects him to be—and make a total job of it.* [Italics ours.]

It is our view that "society" can play a similar role with regard to suicide. Some desperately troubled, "marginal" individuals communicate explicitly—and we do not know why—their consideration of the alternative of suicide; others do not. Nevertheless, "society's" expectations are crucial in defining the choice of identity.

The case studies which follow, and which are described in detail, seem to us to supply dramatic illustration of the above point of view. Four patients killed themselves within six months —an epidemic of suicide—in a hospital where only one suicide had occurred since its opening nine years earlier. This group of people all came to the hospital with expectations of being helped. Some were actively considering suicide among other alternatives. In our view, the hospital and its personnel had the potential of providing a crucial source of expectation and identification. At the time when these patients were admitted to the hospital, the hospital staff's self-confidence was slowly deteriorating. The hospital and its personnel in this situation were incapable of providing the disturbed individuals with new goals, new social roles, new identities. In their hopeless and helpless state, and finding no meaning in life, the patients struggled still more desperately for purpose. As will be seen, what was offered in the environment of the hospital—in the disintegrating social atmosphere—was the expectation, the fear of suicide. The patients grasped at it as an identity.

REFERENCES

Andics, M. von. *Suicide and the Meaning of Life*. London, 1947.

Batchelor, I. R. C., and Napier, Margaret B. The Sequelæ and Short-Term Prognosis of Attempted Suicide. *Journal of Neurology, Neurosurgery and Psychiatry,* 17: 261-266, 1954.

Cavan, Ruth S. *Suicide*. Chicago: University of Chicago Press, 1926.

Dorpat, T. L., and Boswell, J. W. An Evaluation of Suicide Intent in Suicide Attempts. *Comprehensive Psychiatry,* 4: 117-125, 1963.

Dorpat, T. L., and Ripley, H. S. A Study of Suicide in the Seattle Area. *Comprehensive Psychiatry,* 1: 349-359, 1960.

Durkheim, E. *Suicide*. New York: Free Press, 1951.

Erikson, E. H. Identity and the Life Cycle. *Psychological Issues,* 1: 1959.

Farberow, N. L., and Shneidman, E. S. (Eds.), *The Cry for Help*. New York: McGraw-Hill, 1961.

Frank, Lawrence K. Research for What? *Journal of Social Issues,* Supplement Series No. 10, 1957.

Freud, S. Mourning and Melancholia. (In *Collected Papers,* Vol. IV), New York: Basic Books Publishing Co., 1957.

Henry, A. F., and Short, J. F. *Suicide and Homicide.* New York: Free Press, 1954.

Hove, H. In Stengel, E., and Cook, Nancy G., *Attempted Suicide: Its Social Significance and Effects.* London: Chapman-Hall, 1958.

Jackson, D. D. Theories of Suicide. In Shneidman, E., and Farberow, N., *Clues to Suicide.* New York: McGraw-Hill, 1957.

Jameison, G. R. Suicide and Mental Disease: A Clinical Analysis of One Hundred Cases. *Archives of Neurology and Psychiatry,* 36:1-12, 1936.

Janis, I. L., Hovland, C. I., Field, P. B., Linton, Harriet, Graham, Elaine, Cohen, A. R., Rife, D., Abelson, R. P., Lesser, G. S., and King, B. T. *Personality and Persuasibility.* New Haven: Yale University Press, 1959.

Jensen, V. W., and Petty, T. A. The Fantasy of Being Rescued in Suicide. *Psychoanalytic Quarterly,* 27: 327-339, 1958.

Levy, S., and Southcombe, R. Suicide in a State Hospital for the Mentally Ill. *Journal of Nervous and Mental Disease,* 117: 504-514, 1953.

Lindemann, E. In Stengel, E., and Cook, Nancy G., *Attempted Suicide: Its Social Significance and Effects.* London: Chapman-Hall, 1958.

Litman, R. E. Some Aspects of the Treatment of the Potentially Suicidal Patient. In Shneidman, E., and Farberow, N., *Clues to Suicide.* New York: McGraw-Hill, 1957.

Litman, R. E., Shneidman, E. S., and Farberow, N. L. A Suicide Prevention Center. *American Journal of Psychiatry,* 117: 1084-1087, 1961.

Menninger, K. A. *Man Against Himself.* New York: Harcourt, Brace, 1938.

Moss, L. M., and Hamilton, D. M. Psychotherapy of the Suicidal Patient. In Shneidman, E., and Farberow, N., *Clues to Suicide.* New York: McGraw-Hill, 1957.

Palmer, D. M. Factors in Suicidal Attempts: a Review of 25 Consecutive Cases. *Journal of Nervous and Mental Disease,* 93: 421-442, 1941.

Ringel, E. *Der Selbstmord.* Vienna: Maudrich, 1952.

Robins, E., Gassner, S., Kayes, J., Wilkinson, R. H., and Murphy, G. E. The Communication of Suicidal Intent: A Study of 134 Consecutive Cases of Successful (Completed) Suicide. *American Journal of Psychiatry,* 115: 724-733, 1959.

Rubenstein, R., Moses, R., and Lidz, T. On Attempted Suicide. *AMA Archives of Neurology and Psychiatry,* 79: 103-112, 1958.

Sainsbury, P. *Suicide in London.* London: Chapman-Hall, 1955.

Shneidman, E., and Farberow, N. *Clues to Suicide.* New York: McGraw-Hill, 1957.

Stengel, E., and Cook, Nancy G. *Attempted Suicide: Its Social Significance and Effects.* London: Chapman-Hall, 1958.

Stotland, E., Thorley, S., Thomas, E., Cohen, A. R., and Zander, A. The Effects of Group Expectations and Self-Esteem upon Self-Evaluation. *Journal of Abnormal and Social Psychology,* 54: 55-63, 1957.

Szasz, T. S. The Myth of Mental Illness. *American Psychologist,* 15: 113-118, 1960.

Teicher, J. D. A Study of Attempted Suicide. *Journal of Nervous and Mental Disease,* 105: 283-298, 1947.

Vitanza, A., Church, E., and Offenkrantz, W. Suicide: A Review of the Literature, 1945-1956. *International Record of Medicine,* 170: 678-683, 697-699, 1957.

Wall, J. H. The Psychiatric Problem of Suicide. *American Journal of Psychiatry,* 101: 404-406, 1944.

Wilmer, H. A. *Social Psychiatry in Action.* Springfield, Ill.: C. C Thomas, 1958.

Zilboorg, G. Differential Diagnostic Types of Suicide. *Archives of Neurology and Psychiatry,* 35: 270-291, 1936.

Chapter II

A SHORT HISTORY
OF CREST HOSPITAL

THE SUICIDE EPIDEMIC, WHICH IS THE SOURCE OF the basic data for our research, took place at Crest Hospital. Our reason for presenting this history is to show some of the facts which led us to our conception of the causal sequence leading to suicide. We have rejected an emphasis on an intrapsychic drive theory of suicide, and emphasized social expectations. This history shows that the expectations changed negatively prior to the beginning of the suicide epidemic; and that these changes occurred primarily as a consequence of conflict at the institutional level.*

Crest Hospital was a vigorous and respected institution for the care of mental patients, which opened in September 1950, nine and one-half years before the epidemic of suicides. During its early years, the hospital was a dynamic, dedicated, even inspired institution. In the years prior to the epidemic, however, the hospital staff steadily declined in morale, dynamism, and dedication. During this decline of hospital morale in the last years, the increasing hopelessness of the staff was transmitted to the patients.

The hospital, established in large part as a result of the efforts of two psychoanalysts in the community, was designed to function as a "psychoanalytic hospital," emphasizing individual psychotherapy and milieu therapy, and offering far better treatment than the already existing mental hospitals in the area. These two analysts were also among the senior partners of a private, psychoanalytic outpatient service, the Columbia Clinic, in the same community.

Crest Hospital was an independent, nonprofit corporation. The Columbia Clinic provided professional staff for the hospital, and psychoanalytic ideas about hospital treatment dominated.

---

* This history is more fully reported in our *The Life and Death of a Mental Hospital: A Social Psychological Case Study*, to be published by The University of Washington Press.

A local philanthropist, who was interested in helping to establish a psychiatric hospital to serve the general community, contributed a sizable amount toward the founding of Crest Hospital. Like all the original contributions, the gift was in the form of a loan, to be changed to a gift when the nonprofit status of the Foundation was established. There was some disagreement between this principal donor and the founding doctors about the long-range goals of the hospital; the founding doctors were interested in establishing a hospital offering a specific type of treatment and management; the principal donor was interested primarily in establishing a hospital to serve the entire psychiatric community. This underlying discrepancy in point of view was never resolved.

At the hospital itself the staff shared an enthusiastic belief that Crest was a unique and superior institution. The high level of enthusiasm of the staff was in part due to the emphasis on milieu treatment, i.e., concern for the potentially therapeutic value of all twenty-four hours of the patient's day in the hospital. This emphasis on milieu treatment was the result of the policies laid down by the part-time medical directors and consultants from the Columbia Clinic. Milieu treatment entailed full involvement of the ward staff in the treatment process; the particular form of milieu treatment that was emphasized was attitude therapy. This entailed the ward staff's behaving in certain ways toward each patient as prescribed by the physician. The ward staff, through constant and free communication with the doctors, was also drawn by the latter into the process of deciding what attitude to maintain for a given patient.

Morale was also raised in the early years by the dynamic personalities not only of the two founding psychoanalysts but also of the first part-time medical director and consultants. Furthermore, the director of nurses was an able, experienced, and respected psychiatric nurse, who gave the staff great support and guidance. The psychoanalytic community, holding her in high regard, soon came to have great respect for the ward staff as well. Because the medical director was at Crest only on a part-time basis, and the nursing director was so competent, the medical director depended upon her and delegated a large share of authority to her. This situation led, in the first years, to increasing autonomy for the hospital from the medical director and from the local psychiatric community in general. The ward staff was aware of this grant of autonomy and their self-confidence consequently rose.

The Crest staff came in time to believe that the hospital could cure anyone. The ward staff developed into a highly cohesive social group, both on and off the hospital grounds. The staff felt that Crest had a brilliant future of growth and achievement.

The combination of the hospital's growing autonomy and its dedication to milieu treatment made it increasingly difficult for the nonpsychoanalytic psychiatrists in the community to feel that they could treat their patients at Crest as they felt best. The few of them who had sent patients to Crest withdrew from the hospital, in some cases with bitterness on both sides.

Meanwhile, however, the disagreements between the Columbia Clinic and the leading philanthropist continued, with the latter maintaining his power over the hospital by refusing to change his loan into an outright gift. These difficulties led to the resignation of one of the founding psychoanalysts from the hospital board. With the support of the entire psychoanalytic community, a new, full-time director, who was not from Columbia, was appointed.

The new director, despite some initial but not repeated administrative and therapeutic blunders, continued to provide dynamic leadership for the hospital, planning and beginning to carry out further plans for development and expansion. Thus, morale at the hospital remained high. However, his expansionist plans and attempts to increase independence from the Columbia Clinic led him into conflict with the local professional community, which in turn led to his forced resignation within a year of his arrival, although his early administrative errors also played a role in this.

The resigning medical director was replaced by his young assistant, Dr. Dunn, who was also dynamic and expansionistic in his ideas, and for two years led and administered the hospital very well. Communication at the hospital among all levels of staff was good; responsibilities were appropriately delegated; the hospital grew in physical plant and personnel; morale remained high. The lay members of the Board of Trustees were highly impressed by Dr. Dunn. He told them of his plans to emphasize the treatment of adolescents and long-term patients. During his administration, "the Crest way," a devotion to "psychological treatment for the psychologically ill," blossomed. This philosophy emphasized the desirability of psychological treatment over physical therapies, such as drugs, sub-shock insulin, and electric shock, which had been used previously at Crest. This development did not receive the plaudits of the local psychoanalytic community, which still believed in the value of physical treatment in some cases. On the other hand, the involvement of the staff became even deeper.

Dr. Dunn, however, resigned during the third year of his administration. Because of a complex web of professional and personal relationships, his resignation explosively involved the psychoanalytic community, which was already split because of bitterness between the two psychoanalysts who had founded the hospital (although their disagreements were over other matters). All of this shocked the Board of Trustees. Referrals to the hospital from the Columbia Clinic began to fall off. The decline in referrals was also the result of the fact that many of the newer, younger doctors in the area found it economically advantageous to send their patients to other hospitals where the doctors would have both total treatment responsibility and financial rewards. The hospital census was somewhat sustained during this period by the referrals of adolescent patients from other parts of the country.

The search for a new medical director was begun at the time of Dr. Dunn's resignation. He was replaced by a temporary medical director, Dr. Dale, who had been an outstanding clinician and teacher of the ward staff, but who had no taste for administrative work. Meanwhile, the Board of Trustees turned to the local psychoanalytic community for help; the latter responded by assuming a more supervisory role over the hospital.

In the absence of a permanent or dedicated medical director, and with the loss of an outstanding medical leader and increasing loss of autonomy by the hospital, the morale of the ward staff declined. Moreover, the integrated group of professionals at the hospital which had sustained it during the latter part of Dunn's administration began to break up.

The ward staff began to lose much of its early involvement in milieu therapy. Staff members lost interest in the total institution, becoming more concerned with their own limited jobs. This led to a breakdown of the cohesiveness of the ward staff groups and a development of a status hierarchy among and between nurses and aides. The off-grounds social gatherings among the ward staff, which had been so frequent and so satisfactory in the early years of Crest, diminished in number, and changed in character. At one time, the aides threatened to strike.

The loss of morale among the ward staff and the weakness of professional leadership reduced the staff's ability to deal with difficulties with the patients. Consequently, the staff became unable to control the adolescent patients, who caused turmoil in the hospital to the point of semi-organized rebellion. The staff as a whole blamed its troubles on the "adolescent character disorders" in the hospital, but these were actually few in number. So severe did the difficulties become in a few months that it was decided to limit drastically the number of admissions of adolescents. The more difficult adolescent cases in the hospital soon left, with little staff resistance. The ward staff felt very strongly that as a group the doctors had failed to give them sufficient support, guidance, or leadership in coping with the adolescents. The morale of the hospital staff was, of course, very low.

Just as the hospital was recovering from its troubles with the adolescents, the staff received another blow: Dr. Dale announced his resignation as acting director, although in fact he continued to serve a short while after this announcement.

Because of the low number of referrals of patients from the local psychiatric community and the limited admission of adolescents, the financial difficulties of the hospital had become severe. The philanthropist who had played so large a part in the early years of the hospital had died meanwhile. The Board of Trustees, in turning to the local psychiatric community for help again, became enmeshed in the split among the local psychoanalysts. The latter, in turn, expanded their supervisory role over the hospital.

At the hospital, morale continued to decline. This decline was enhanced by the continuing loss of professional personnel, the death of a "mother-figure" laundress, the suicide of one ex-patient, and the suicide-like death of another.

By the time Dr. Dale left the hospital, the professional staff had dwindled from a high point of eleven professional people to one psychiatrist, one psychologist, and one social worker. In this situation, the psychiatrist, Dr. Preston, did an effective clinical job for the two and one-half months before the newly appointed permanent director was to arrive. Morale of the staff was sustained during this period by Dr. Preston's effectiveness and by the anticipated arrival of the new director.

The appointment of the new director, Dr. Doren, in May 1959—he was to arrive in September—was the culmination of a long, frustrating search for the proper person to fill the position. Dr. Doren was viewed by all—professional staff, ward staff, and the Board of Trustees—as a kind of a savior who could solve all the hospital's problems. The search for a new director had been first conducted by the Board of Trustees from the time Dr. Dunn announced his resignation in January 1958. When its long search proved fruitless, the consultants took it up and shortly thereafter secured the services of Dr. Doren. The shift from the Board of Trustees to the consultants as the prime movers in securing a new director also entailed a lessening of concern with the administrative experience of the new director, and an increased emphasis on his standing as a psychoanalyst.

After Dr. Doren's arrival, in September 1959, the financial situation of the hospital continued to deteriorate, as the stopgap measures that had carried the hospital financially began to run out. Referrals from the local psychiatrists were still limited and the patient census was below the financial break-even point. In fact, in January 1960, not long after Doren's arrival, stimulated by the chronic financial crisis, a committee of the consulting staff was appointed to study the place of Crest in the local psychiatric community. Meanwhile, Dr. Doren began to present plans to the Board of Trustees for expanding Crest in terms of its services and staff. To raise the additional funds needed, both for capital expenditures and for operations, the Board hired a public relations person. Doren did not prove able to raise money, as the Board had expected and hoped he would. One of the reasons for the difficulty of raising money was that, as a consequence of the uncertainty about the role of the hospital in early years, it was often viewed as a hospital for the very rich, since fees had continually risen over the years.

Even before Dr. Doren's arrival, he was regarded by the hospital staff as a potential savior. He made an excellent first impression and morale soon rose. However, it soon began to fall again. Doren showed little enthusiasm for the Crest way—emphasis on attitude therapy and psychological treatment in general—nor did he offer any exciting treatment alternatives. The staff felt disappointed in his failure to revive the failing image of Crest. Furthermore, he was not as prone as earlier directors to delegate responsibility to other professional persons or to ward personnel. This change tended to undermine the confidence of both groups and to undercut the administrative basis of milieu therapy; namely, the great significance of the ward personnel.

Another innovation was Dr. Doren's participation in the hospital treatment of patients, including those for whom he was not the managing physician. Previously, only the managing physician was directly involved in the hospital treatment of any patient. This shift further confused the ward staff. This problem was particularly serious because Dr. Doren and Dr. Preston, the other psychiatrist, differed a good deal in their approaches to hospital treatment.

Nevertheless, the staff, including Dr. Preston, was eager to find a way out of the poor state of affairs which existed; and many turned to Dr. Doren's more eclectic approach as potentially a more hopeful and reasonable way of treating patients. Dr. Doren's new approach was, inadvertently, put to the test in the case of one patient, Mr. Ullman. As will be described in Chapter IV, Ullman was the first patient in many years to receive shock treatment at Crest. Shortly after shock treatment was stopped after only three treatments, on December 23, 1959, he made an attempt to kill himself, but was saved. There followed the epidemic of suicides among patients described in the following chapters. In a period from January 1 to January 19, there were three actual suicides among patients. One more occurred in June.

Whatever hopefulness was present in the ward staff before Mr. Ullman's attempt disappeared afterwards—fear was in the air. Formal discussion among the staff about the suicides was continually postponed. Knowledge of the suicides was also limited outside the hospital; the executive committee of the Board received a full report, while others, Board members and consultants, got partial information through reports and rumors.

We believe that the hopefulness of the ward staff declined primarily because of these factors—described in the foregoing account—which were clearly independent of difficulties with patients. Of course, we recognize that once the difficulties with patients had increased beyond a certain point, they added to the decline in morale.

Chapter III

SUICIDE IN
THE HOSPITAL
The First Nine Years

OUR CENTRAL CONCERN IS WITH WHAT WE HAVE labeled an "epidemic of suicide" at a hospital during a given year. It is our thesis that the attitude of the hospital staff just prior to and during the epidemic period was strikingly different from what it had been in previous years, and that this change in atmosphere played a crucial part in bringing about the epidemic. During the nine years previous to the epidemic only three serious suicide attempts occurred and only one patient committed suicide while under care by the hospital staff. Immediately prior to and during the epidemic period—during which there was one serious suicide attempt, followed by three actual suicides in three weeks, and another actual suicide some months later—the staff expressed feelings of hopelessness and helplessness and a special and acute anxiety about those patients who could be viewed at all as suicidal. Such feelings of hopelessness and helplessness did not exist in the earlier nine years. In this chapter we shall try to communicate the quality of the atmosphere in which "suicidal" patients were dealt with during the first nine years.

We have noted our thesis that it was the change in the hospital atmosphere which produced the epidemic. One may ask, "Were there not significantly more suicidal people in Crest during the last year than in previous years?" Our evaluation of available evidence indicates that this was not the case.

To begin with, suicidal feelings or attempts were not among the criteria by which patients were selected or rejected at Crest.* Further, in order to compare the patient groups more system-

---

* Organically damaged, feeble-minded, and other custodial cases were not admitted.

atically, we have examined the admission histories of all patients who were in Crest Hospital on December 23—the date of the beginning of the epidemic proper—for the five years previous to 1959. From these histories we grouped patients into classifications labeled "Suicide," "Self-destruction," and "Depression." "Suicide" means that one or more of the following were reported in the history: suicide attempts; suicide threats; suicidal preoccupation; occasional suicidal ideas. "Self-destruction" means that serious self-destructive activity is mentioned in the history; for example, "history of impulsiveness with destructiveness directed toward self and toward others; indirect self-destructive trends such as serious automobile accidents." "Depression" means that depressive symptoms are noted as prominent. There is no overlap; if a patient fell into the "Suicide" group, he was not put in any other.

The data resulting from our classification must be dealt with cautiously in the light of our conviction that what are usually considered predictors of suicide—suicide attempts, talk, threats, depression—have little validity. Also, our categories must be questioned. For example, our examination showed only one person in 1959 who fitted the classification of depression; that is, a patient described as markedly depressed but for whom there was no mention of suicide. In 1954 there were seven so classified, and in each of 1956 and 1958 there were six who fit into the depression group. Since it is not very surprising to find hospitalized, markedly depressed people having suicidal thoughts, might it be that the staff's greater preoccupation with suicide in that last year produced the increase in mentions of suicide in the histories?

DECEMBER 23

	1954	1955	1956	1957	1958	1959
Hospital census	(30)	(23)	(30)	(24)	(24)	(23)
Suicide	7	7	7	4	3	10
Self-destruction	3	0	0	2	1	2
Depression	7	4	6	2	6	1
Total "Suicide danger"	17	11	13	8	10	13

Looking at the tabulation of "suicide danger" patients from 1954 to 1959, it appears doubtful that there was a genuine difference in the patient group on December 23, 1959, as compared with the groups in the hospital during the previous years. The "suicide danger" total for 1959—and we repeat that these data must be dealt with cautiously—is not larger than the totals for the earlier years. And while we have questioned the large "suicide" class in 1959, it is not markedly greater than those of 1954, 1955, and 1956. The difference is in what happened. Consider the total patient population on the 23rds of December; five of twenty-three patients in 1959 "acted suicidally" while under treatment by Crest's staff. This ratio, 5:23, must be contrasted with no such action in the 131 patients in Crest on December 23 of the five previous years, a ratio of 0:131.

We are convinced that this difference is a consequence not of a difference in patients but rather of the difference in the atmosphere in the hospital, particularly the lowering of the confidence of staff at all levels in their ability to deal with suicide. We will now try to illustrate the therapeutic atmosphere surrounding those patients who were considered to be suicidal dangers during the first nine years with which this chapter is concerned. For this purpose—as a base for comparison with the final year reported here—we have chosen another sample; we have drawn from the records of forty patients—all the "suicidal" patients from the earlier nine years that we could locate. Of the forty, twenty-three had pre-hospital histories which included suicide attempts, thoughts, threats, or preoccupation. The remaining seventeen had no such background, but suicide precautions were prescribed during their stay in the hospital. For all these patients, detailed daily nurses' notes were available. Interviews with staff members augment the data from patient records.*

Previous to the epidemic, the attitude of the staff—the nursing staff as well as the professional staff—had been one of confidence. This attitude was not a casual one; on the contrary it was, in the staff's view, a cautious one. They did not expect suicide; if danger of suicide should develop, they felt that they could control it. This attitude was almost unanimous. There are no interviews which seem to indicate that suicide was a preoccupation. One nurse, high in the hierarchy, reports that when she joined the staff she was told with pride that in the history of the hospital there had been only one, abortive, suicide attempt. "This

---

* The interviews were all held after the epidemic of suicide, in late 1960 and 1961. Staff members were asked generally about their attitudes and feelings about suicidal patients in the past, and discussed specific patients only if they had particular acquaintance with and memory of the case.

was the only suicide attempt they had. And they were pretty pleased about this; and this was one of the things I remember their telling of, that this was the only suicide attempt they had. And we had no suicide attempts in the early days of this thing that I can remember."

When asked whether there was any problem or preoccupation with the problem of suicide in his memory, an aide said: "No, I don't think there was. I can't remember. Well, if we knew someone was on 'S' precautions* we'd check them, but we weren't concerned about it—because we were in control of the situation. I think that is a different feeling than what existed later. I can remember that I wasn't concerned about somebody who was going to kill themselves. I never thought they would, because I was not going to let them. I mean, I felt in control. And I think this was a general feeling."

Other statements were in the same vein. "I think the staff was very confident and diligent." "On the locked ward we had control . . . on the wards I don't think anybody particularly worried that they could put it over on us. Either on the grounds, or off-grounds, maybe they could do it, but not when they were on the wards." Referring to the chief nurse, an aide observed: "She was a very shrewd psychiatric nurse who never, never let it slip, never let anybody become lulled into the feeling that suicide in the hospital was impossible just because the hospital happened to be Crest."

A recreational therapist added:

« Patients were sometimes put on suicide precautions; and I think that everybody was certainly cognizant of the patients who were considered very suicidal. But I don't think it was ever a real problem. I mean, I didn't have the feeling the people twitted about it. They knew it; and if—for instance, I used to at that time take patients to movies once a week; and if there was a patient who was considered suicidal, I certainly was aware of it, and I did things I felt were necessary. That is, I never permitted patients to go to the bathroom alone if we were at the movies or anything of this sort. If they were suicidal, I would be sure to put them in the middle in driving to town, and this kind of thing. But it didn't upset me. I felt like I had the situation in hand, and it was covered. I would take a male aide with me, and I

---

* "S" precautions means precautions against the danger of suicide.

would sit at one end of the row and he would sit at the other, and then we would know when anybody left; and automatically he would go with the men and I would go with the women; and we would let each other know that we were leaving for that short time.

The professional staff's views were similar. One psychiatrist stated:

« I never felt it was a particular problem. I always trusted the nursing staff. I felt that they were very careful. I felt that we had adequate restraints. I felt that the closed section was a pretty darn safe place, and I felt that if some people—if they are going to kill themselves under those circumstances, there just wasn't much you could do about it. And taking that attitude I figured we would do everything we can within reason imposed by the physical plant, and that was all we could do . . . I felt we could protect practically any patient who wasn't stronger than our aides, for example. If necessary we would tie their hands. And I never had any compunction about using ECT. . . . I mean, I felt if it had to be used, it was used. I mean, if this was necessary. I felt that it was handy. Never had any great reliance on it as a miracle treatment but —funny thing, I don't remember using it much.

He added that the situation did not seem to arise where it was necessary to use physical treatment because of concern with suicide.

A psychiatric resident, when asked about concern about suicide during the period he was at Crest, stated:

« Well there weren't any. The question that comes to my mind is how much did we think about it. I don't think we thought about it very much . . . looking at this in hindsight . . . probably the nursing staff anticipated this kind of thing and set up pretty good rules. There was, as I say, a rather conservative attitude, that when patients were sick they stayed put on the ward . . . And in trying to evaluate the ward function at that time, in that respect, I would say it was pretty optimistic atmosphere. It was sort of an atmosphere that, no matter what happens we ought to figure out something to do about it, which I think was conveyed to the patient, not in a sense of franticness . . . a conservative optimism.

The professional staff noted explicitly its confidence in the ward staff, and indicated that it was the nursing staff which really did the good job in this area. A number of the nursing staff reported on the efficiency of the training they received under the leadership of the director of nurses. In her interview, when asked about the confidence of the staff in controlling suicide, she stated:

« I don't know. This is funny, I can't tie this up with my feelings. I didn't have any concern about this because I felt myself very confident that if somebody was suicidal I didn't have any problem about thinking that I could tell the staff in a minute what they ought to be doing, and could spot it, and I didn't feel uncomfortable about it. [And the staff could carry it out?] Yes. I didn't feel that this was a problem about suicide. Never entered my head that I can recall.

There seems little doubt that the director of nurses was the major source of the confidence which spread downward through the ward staff and upward through the professional staff.

In examining in detail these case histories and treatment records, it was striking to find that in only two cases did there seem to be a particular anxiety on the part of the staff about the danger of suicide. One of these was the case of Mrs. Oslo, admitted in 1951. On admission, she stated that "she had been a bad girl and that she was harming everyone in her family and it would be better if she did not live." The patient was clearly paranoid and schizophrenic. She had extensive delusions about a coming revolution; she feared that her relatives would be executed in the future as a punishment for her failure to alert the FBI to the imminent revolution. It was reported that in the previous two years: "She thought of suicide many times and had a gun in her hand but did not know why she failed to do it."

Her course in the hospital was interesting. On the day after her admission she ". . . went down to the open section* for breakfast. Came back to closed section afterwards because too many people were in the open section." The following day she was put on suicide precautions and her privileges were restricted. The nurses' notes for that day state: "[Mrs. Oslo] was restless . . . resents having anyone escort her back and forth to buildings. She said, 'I'm not going to run away.' " She again went

---

* Crest hospital had three wards differing in atmosphere and stringency of procedures: a locked or closed ward, called the North Wing; a semi-open, semi-closed ward, called the Cottage; and an open section, the Lodge.

to the open section for supper, remained there all evening, and was fairly pleasant. She also spent the following evening in the open section, playing cards. It is noteworthy that this patient, who was felt to be in danger of suicide, and for whom suicide precautions had been prescribed, spent most of her evenings with the rest of the patients in the open section. This is a behavioral manifestation of the confidence of the staff in their ability to prevent suicide, as reported above.

The following day an order was written: "Suicide precautions to extend to not leaving the patient unobserved in [the Occupational Therapy shop], etc." She again spent the evening in the open section. Later that evening, in her bedroom, she was seen trying to hide an object in the bed; at length, she surrendered a badly-bent knitting needle.

The patient's talk the following day was full of suicidal and homicidal references. That evening, she swallowed something.

"Finally found it was a pin part of a ceramic pin. Also bits of ceramic were swallowed. Patient put to bed in belt restraints. Very delusional. Told of being persecuted by technocrats." It was noted later that "the patient called attendant and said she had swallowed a small open safety pin along with the pin mentioned above."

Two days later Mrs. Oslo underwent her first electric shock treatment. Two days following this she left, against medical advice, with her husband, to be transferred to another hospital.

This patient, who was at Crest in 1951, was, in our evaluation, one of two in the first nine years about whom special concern relating to suicide was manifest.* It is noteworthy that whereas ECT was an acceptable type of treatment at Crest till about 1955, it was rarely used on patients as a consequence of their having been considered a suicidal danger. Only two such patients, in addition to the one just described, received ECT. One of these patients talked of suicide often, but was never placed on suicide precautions. The ECT seemed to be used because of the patient's extremely manic behavior. The other patient was a young physician who was severely depressed, and about whom there was suicide concern. The choice of ECT, however, seemed to be based almost totally on his limited finances and the need for a quick resolution of the depression.

The use of suicide precautions varied; but in Crest's early

---

* The other "special concern" patient was in Crest in 1958, and is discussed in greater detail later in this chapter.

years they were rarely used for more than a short period of time. In many cases, including those in which suicide was a prominent consideration, suicide precautions were not used at all; for example, in the case of a 40-year-old woman admitted in 1953 with a prominent symptom of suicide preoccupations. Placed in the semi-closed ward, her behavior was noticeably manic; she "talked continuously all evening." The following morning she "ate very little because she talked so much and talked continuously." She was alternately angry and friendly with the staff. That day she hurled a glass of water into the hall, then threw herself on her bed and sobbed. "Conversation preceding this had been of suicide. The patient said she felt she had to commit suicide to 'prove to us'—'for our good,'" staff members reported. The patient declared that she knew a dozen ways to kill herself even should the staff take everything away from her. That evening she was transferred to the closed section of the hospital. Later that evening, the notes read, "Patient broke her glasses. Some suicide gestures noted by nurse."

The patient was markedly manic; and throughout the record there are notes of "talk of suicide" or "several suicidal remarks mixed with threatening statements and boastful talk."

One day the following took place:

« Walked down to the volleyball court where patient broke down the bank and ran north. Patient then turned northwest, ran and fought her way up the road. Patient made repeated attempts to hail passing cars. When this failed patient grabbed aide and attempted to throw both aide and herself in front of passing cars, *both in an attempt to stop cars and possibly as a suicide measure.* [Our italics.] Aide finally calmed patient down by stating that the two of them could go back down and make a telephone call at the grocery store. As the patient and aide [were on their way], second aide appeared in car. When patient recognized second aide she again attempted to *elope** by throwing self in front of cars. [Our italics.] Carload of evening shift happened along in time to help handle patient. Into car and returned to hospital.

We have been reporting this data in the context of the fact that suicide precautions were never used on this patient. It is noteworthy too that the aide, in reporting the foregoing incident,

---

* Elope means to run away from the hospital.

first suggested the possibility that the patient was making a suicide attempt, but in her second comment saw the incident as an elopement attempt. The underemphasis of the suicide possibility is in striking contrast to the way such incidents were regarded in a later period.

Another patient for whom suicide precautions were never prescribed was a successful business man, 70 years old, who was admitted to the hospital in December 1955. The admission note stated:

« Has made several suicide attempts. . . . Family relates there have been two suicidal attempts. However, one attempt was described as the time he was found in his room with a gun. The other attempt was last summer when he left home and was found floating in the water in an abandoned gravel pit. The family states that he has also talked about the fact the family would be better off if he were dead and has made many comments about killing himself.

On the occasion when the patient was found floating in the water of the gravel pit, he had left a suicide note. "On several occasions he has asked local store owners about buying a gun but without a permit was not sold one." The hospital physician wrote in his case history: "It is my feeling that suicide possibilities are still strong in him."

On admission, the patient entered the closed section. He resisted entering the hospital and needed to be "helped" in. He complained that he did not need to be in a mental hospital, that that was not what was wrong with him. The following day he was transferred to the semi-open ward. Three days later he was moving around alone between buildings; and shortly afterward he was free to move about the hospital. Thirteen days after his admission his wife came to the hospital and insisted that he leave. He signed out, against medical advice.

In another case, noteworthy because the referral to Crest was totally on the basis of severe suicidal preoccupations, suicide precautions were not used. The patient, a bright, 31-year-old woman, married to a real estate dealer, entered the hospital in September 1955. She had been treated psychotherapeutically in the past; had been hospitalized; and had been given ECT, all out of great concern about her suicidal preoccupations. These measures, however, had not brought about hoped-for improvement. The patient, referred to Crest "because of complaints of preoccupation and suicidal thoughts accompanied with depression," was "considered to be a serious suicidal risk." She was admitted to the semi-closed section of the hospital. After three days she was permitted to eat in the open dining room. Six days later she was permitted to leave the grounds with her husband. And not long after: "May walk 30 to 40 minutes alone." Clearly, in this case, in spite of the acute warnings of those who had treated her previously, the confidence of the hospital staff was high.

We have described a number of cases in which, although suicide attempts or preoccupations were prominent in the history, the hospital did not employ suicide precautions. When suicide precautions were used, although ostensibly certain specific "extra precautions" were to be observed, the general atmosphere in the hospital certainly influenced the manner in which these precautions were applied. The order book states:

« When "S" [suicide] precautions are ordered by the physician the following extra precautions should be observed; (1) Rounds must be made every 15 minutes. (2) Patient must be accompanied when eating. Must eat in room. May have silverware. (3) Patient must be accompanied in the bathroom; while bathing, using cosmetics, and the toilet. (4) Reading glasses must not be given to the patient unless accompanied by a staff member. (5) Patient must be accompanied while smoking. (6) Temperature should be taken rectally unless otherwise ordered by the physician. (7) Patient may not come into the clothes room.

Implicitly, in order to carry out these precautions thoroughly or even adequately, the patient on suicide precautions should be placed in the most secure section of the hospital. This certainly was done during the epidemic period. But in previous years, the semi-closed section was often used to house patients on suicide precautions.

For example, a patient was admitted in March 1954 "following a suicide attempt in which she cut herself three times on the scalp with a razor, slashed herself on the abdomen with a razor, got drunk on gin and tonic and took a dose of sedatol, then went to the garage, started the car motor and placed a coat over the exhaust lying under the coat." Her husband stated that "the only reason the suicide attempt was not successful was that he had had the car adjusted the day previously and the motor stopped shortly after the patient went to sleep."

On the first examination it was noted: "Although she was

tense and anxious, she stated that after she made the suicide attempt she felt a lot better and was not emotionally disturbed as she had been. She discussed her problem freely and expressed quite freely her hostility toward psychiatrists." She was diagnosed as a neurotic depressive with hysterical features, and the recommendation was hospitalization for "evaluation as to the exact nature and severity of depression."

This woman was put on suicide precautions on entering the hospital. On her first day in the hospital she seemed friendly and comfortable. The nurses' notes said: "Smilingly, while sewing, she said, 'I'm ready to spend the rest of my life here now.'" She slept well. The following morning, she sewed markers on her clothes in her room. By 11:00 A.M., she dressed and resumed the same project in the lounge, keeping at it till lunch. She talked easily to the other women patients in the lounge, and seemed to be adjusting herself to the hospital nicely. "She was pleasant and friendly. She went for a walk with the aide in the afternoon and seemed to like being out of doors. That evening she wrote letters and was gracious and pleasant and went to bed without sedation." The following day she again went for a walk and stated at one point: "I have an aversion to doctors. You know after you've gone for help and haven't received it several times you are a little skeptical." The patient also stated, "I have a new job starting Tuesday and I expect to be there." This was a Monday. That same day she was told by her physician that she was to call her prospective employer and did, saying that she was in the hospital with a high fever. At noon she left for an appointment with her psychotherapist in Columbia. She slept well and was discharged the following day, Wednesday.

The discharge note states that she was discharged against medical advice. It includes a summary of hospitalization which makes special mention of her pleasant, acceptable behavior in the sanitarium. The note continues:

« She requested discharge and stated she could not stay in the sanitarium the two weeks required for a work up. She had a job pending which would enable her to obtain funds so she could start psychotherapy on an out-patient basis. Following a consultation it was decided that the patient probably could with safety be discharged (*sic*) from Crest and be given psychotherapy . . . it was felt by both the consultant and myself that the patient probably would not make another suicide attempt and there was no great risk in discharging her.

It was noted that although there was little change in her condition, the prognosis was good with psychotherapy.

In May 1955, a young physician with a severe depression entered the hospital and was immediately placed on suicide precautions. Approximately two weeks after he had entered the hospital, he was permitted to spend his evenings in the open section. At about the same time, formal appointments for psychotherapy were set up for him. He was in the semi-closed section of the hospital. One noteworthy incident is as follows:

« A rusted table fork which looked as though it had been used to dig in the earth fell either out from under the patient's pillow or from the window. . . . Patient dressed and immediately went to the open section for lunch and then to OT [occupational therapy]. Played volleyball with tremendous enthusiasm, really knocked himself out. Very friendly. Dinner at the open section. Played bridge, wrote letters, etc. He discussed possible job openings [in the state] with the staff and said he would like to settle near Columbia.

A week later, still on suicide precautions, he "went out with the movie group" to one of the downtown theaters. Obviously, the discovery of the fork did not precipitate any drastic security measures on the part of the staff.

Interviews illustrate the Crest staff's attitudes toward suicide dangers. They expressed feelings of confidence in controlling suicidal dangers. But the specific character of their responses can be seen in the way they reacted to varying sorts of pressures surrounding suicide. One aide, in her interview, talked of the rusty fork incident described above. She indicated that there was no undue anxiety when the fork was discovered. There was "a little bit, but it just didn't flood the hospital and prevail for days and days and days. . . . He was not moved to the closed section, and I—sure, we were concerned, but like I say, as far as I personally was concerned, it was a passing thing."

Another patient "deliberately drove his automobile into a tree in what appeared to be a suicidal attempt," bringing about his admission to the hospital. Prior to that, "He had made a suicide attempt by taking twelve seconal tablets." The patient was not put on suicide precautions. This was in early 1956 and sedative drugs were often prescribed for patients to help them sleep. He was on the semi-closed ward and one evening he appeared to be very tense and afraid as to the effect sedation would have. At 1:30 in the morning he was in bed, but got up requesting more sedation. He talked to another patient about "killing himself." He said to an aide: "There is only one answer. I'm the sickest person in here. Is it true when people leave here they are well adjusted?" He was specialed by a male aide after taking a repeat sedation; and at this time he noted that there were "a lot of sharps around."

When questioned by the aide, the patient said that the "sharps" were razor blades, and that they were hidden. The patient expressed himself to the effect that life was useless; that he was the sickest patient at Crest; that he knew he was a bad person; that everyone except him was "smart" and "knew a lot"; that he was glad to be at Crest. He asked frequently for cigarettes, which were refused by the aide. Presently, his conversation became less melancholy; and at last, he fell asleep.

This patient constantly talked about suicide. At one point he asked an aide: "Has anybody ever committed suicide here?" The aide said not to his knowledge. The patient told the aide that he could easily commit suicide, for there were between thirty-five and forty razor blades in the OT building; he could easily get one, he said, as they were not checked. "As you know, if I slashed my wrists it would only take three minutes and I'm only checked every half-hour." The patient followed this up by saying: "I've tried to commit suicide many times; that's why I'm here." Then he requested permission to return to the open section for late TV, saying, while walking there; "I don't know why I say these things, I'm crazy I guess. I have to say them or I get all the more mixed up inside." Notice that after all this talk about suicide, the patient was permitted to go to the open section without question. A few days later, still on suicide precautions, he was allowed to go downtown with the movie group.

One evening, after being given some sedation, the patient asked the aide: "Are you mad at me?" The aide replied: "No." The patient said, "I've acted so funny all evening. I feel like throwing up. I feel like there was a glass jar in here some place." "I'll check," said the aide. The check revealed nothing unusual. The patient requested aide to come into the room to discuss suicide. "You don't want to do that," the aide said. The patient said: "I could sneak some broken glass into the bathroom and it would be all over before anybody found me. I've nothing to go on for. I just don't have the nerve." Later he came to the door, asked the aide what he was doing, and added: "I bet you write down everything I say." The aide did not reply. The following day: "He asked the staff where the arteries were and what could be done if he should cut them."

On another occasion this patient, at 8:15 in the evening, was sitting on his bed, dressed in his pajamas. He had been moving the screen on the window. He told the aide: "I can get my head through and wiggle through." The aide replied: "You can, so we check often." He had been picking a lock, and the aide told him to stop it. The patient replied: "I used to pick them just for kicks." The patient took the head off his electric razor, saying that the wheels felt awfully sharp. "Do you think I could cut myself with them?" The aide replied: "No, you couldn't. If you want to though, I'll put the razor in your sharp box." The patient said: "I believe you'd better."

This patient constantly pressed the suicide idea. At one point he pointed to a small pen clip he had sharpened to a point and asked the aide: "How about this?" The aide took the "sharp" and the emery board and the patient came into the hall and said: "Look what I did with that sharp object." There was a slight scratch across his wrist. He spoke that evening of having at one time taken fifty APC tablets. He bragged about having cut himself, showing his wrist scratch.

Shortly afterward, the patient was moved to the open section. Although he continued to talk of suicide, the "S" precautions for him were soon discontinued.

Another patient threatened suicide and was dealt with rather seriously for the moment. The anxiety about this person, however, was neither continued nor generalized. The patient, a 19-year-old boy, was diagnosed as a schizophrenic. The history states: "He had many impulsive suicide thoughts and had tried to act on these on several occasions, changing his mind at the last minute. Heavy drinking, thoughts of annihilating others; no longer trusts himself to drive a car." After six days in the hospital he was put on suicide precautions. Four days later his privileges were increased, and he was allowed to eat in the open section. Five days later he eloped from the hospital. Five days after he returned voluntarily, he was given "ground privileges"; that is, freedom to move around the hospital grounds as he wished. Three days later, again he eloped, but again returned by himself.

About two weeks later, as he sat smoking at about midnight in the lounge of the semi-open ward, he requested a repeat of his sedation. It was refused. He stopped a nurse as she was going through the lounge, asking her to call his doctor. This request was also refused. The nurse suggested that the patient go to bed and that she sit with him and rub his back. He refused, stating that he would not go back to his room. The patient was reported as appearing extremely tense and frightened. He absolutely refused to go to his room, saying he "cannot go." He asked again that the doctor be called, saying that he had only felt as he did that night on one other occasion; that he had talked to his doctor about it; that it had been very traumatic; and that he must have sedation. When told he should wait until the following day to talk over his need for sedation with his doctor, he replied: "When you find me hanging in the bathroom it will be too late to discuss it with your doctor." He spoke in a quiet, matter-of-fact tone of voice. The doctor was called, and he ordered an increase in sedation.

Later the patient again made reference to committing suicide by hanging himself. He was given some warm milk, drank it, and turned over for a back-rub. He continued to be tense and restless, turning frequently during the first part of the rub. Gradually, he seemed to relax. After the nurse had rubbed his back for ten minutes he suddenly said, in a quiet voice: "For all the abuse I've heaped on you I apologize." He slept shortly after this. The following morning his ground privileges were withdrawn, and his general privileges restricted. He felt this was "okay." Five days later, ground privileges were again allowed the patient. A short time after, he was given permission to leave the hospital for Christmas vacation. He decided not to return to the hospital.

The reactions of the staff in this earlier period to the one actual suicide and to one rather severe suicide attempt also are noteworthy. The patient who committed suicide in May 1954 had been in the hospital for approximately three weeks. She had been referred by a psychoanalyst who noted that she "presents a most curious psychiatric picture." He suggested that she appeared hysterical and, at times, paranoid. In one letter he stated: "In the last weeks there has been a change in her symptoms so that she shows apathy, loss of ability to concentrate and some memory defect. How much of this is part of a depression picture and how much is lack of motivation and inattention is very difficult to discover. . . ." A report of psychological tests stated that the "diagnostic picture . . . definitely favors a diagnosis of hysteria with marked compulsive features." No indications of possible suicide were noted.

On entering Crest she was still seen as a "confusing diagnostic problem."

« She is suspicious and defensively haughty. Her first days at Crest will be extremely important and . . . her ability to stay here will depend upon our aiding her in adjusting to the sanitarium. She should be treated with respect and friendliness, encouraged to visit the shop, grounds and open section, should eat in the open section whenever possible.

Admitted to the semi-closed section, she was moved to the open section of the hospital after nine days. There was a good deal of evidence of paranoid symptomatology. Her behavior varied. At times, she was quite active with fellow patients; at other times, she was withdrawn. This patient was puzzling to everyone; and the staff by and large felt unable really to contact her. The nurses' notes report her as being sometimes at ease, comfortable and pleased; at other times, disturbed, extremely uncomfortable, and talking in disconnected fashion.

On the day prior to her suicide, the patient's brother had visited her. The hospital view of the patient was discussed with the patient and with her brother. It was later elaborated in a letter to the referring physician:

« Diagnostically we were much in the same dilemma for specificity as you were. Our essential feeling was that the patient had to be considered a severely disturbed psychotic character disorder . . . our suggestion to her and her brother [was] that a guardian be appointed. It was our feeling that prolonged hospitalization was necessary while psychotherapy began and this recommendation was made.

It was noted in the letter that the suicide followed these recommendations "more than coincidentally."

Following the brother's visit and the discussion with the psychiatrist, the notes describe the patient's behavior.

« She talked of several automobile accidents she and her

husband had been in . . . "we were going bird hunting in Maine in a station wagon. It was a good thing we had the station wagon for it meant the difference between profit and loss." The patient couldn't seem to go on with the story, just stared off into space as though no one else was in the room. After a minute or two the patient seemed to come to and then continued talking but on another subject. Retired to room at 9:15 P.M. In another patient's room at 10:45, and then down to lounge at 11:00. Remarked to another patient, "I think I'm going to die tomorrow, I've such a funny feeling, my neck is so sore."* Ate cheese and crackers. Watched TV.

She slept soundly all night, and the next morning joined the recreation group at 10:30 A.M. She was later seen in the open section, and then returned to her room. She was pleasant, and seemed composed.

The nurses' notes continue: "Observed patient at 3:35 in what appeared to be a lifeless condition, although no sign of rigor mortis. Artificial respiration continually until 3:55, etc. The patient was pronounced dead at 4:00 P.M."

The patient had committed suicide in a closet of her room, strangling herself with a cord from her bathrobe.

In the interviews, most of the staff suggested that this incident did not have particularly disturbing consequences in the hospital. This may have been due, in part, to the patient's never having been felt part of the hospital, and to the absence of much real contact with her. Another aspect of the reaction to the suicide was reported by an aide:

« I came on duty as aide and they were still working on her upstairs. But it was to no avail. . . . They brought her downstairs and into an ambulance and off. All the patients were told. The director came into the office where a group was gathered and said, "Who is the aide on duty?" and I said I was and he said, "Good, well let's everybody else get the hell out of here and let the hospital go like it should, resume its normal function." . . . All the staff got out of there. And then the director told me that one patient was asleep and when she woke up he asked me if I would tell her what happened before she heard it from the other patients—which I did. So there is an indication maybe of

* Note the prior communication in a patient not suspected of suicide.

whether this medical staff had any confidence in the aides or not. And I told her. She took it very well I think.

What is noteworthy, again in comparison with what occurred later, was the director's prompt action to make certain that all the patients knew what had occurred. He acted with an apparent lack of anxiety, and in a self-confident manner. The suicides in the epidemic group, on the other hand, were kept "secret" and were not discussed generally.

An aide who was an employee of the hospital in varying capacities for many years reported on the reaction to another suicide attempt:

« I went into his [the patient's] room for no particular reason in the afternoon to offer him a cigarette and he reached out to take it and his hands were all covered with blood. He was lying on his bed and he had just a blanket over him. And I pulled the blanket off and he had cut both his wrists and I called the nurse, she came in and he had broken one lens of his glasses into five parts and we could only find four, so he said he had eaten the fifth one, swallowed it. I guess it was about an equal fifth to give you some idea how big it was.* So I sat in there and fed him mashed potatoes and white bread for an hour and he never suffered any ill effects from it. The only ill effects he suffered was that he became more depressed that he was not even able to do a good job of committing suicide. This was pretty much the impression he had of himself anyhow.

The confidence of the staff in handling suicidal problems is further evidenced in a number of cases where the patient was not felt to be a suicide danger while at the hospital, but was felt to be in danger of suicide if he were not in the hospital. Thus, in the case of the elderly man who had been found floating in water after having written a suicide note, no suicide precautions were used in the hospital, the patient being allowed to move about the hospital rather freely. But when, thirteen days after his admission, the patient's wife insisted upon removing him from the hospital, the staff expressed its belief that the patient would be a serious suicide risk away from the

---

* The checking on the pieces of glass, which was a routine procedure and which was carried on efficiently in this case, can be specifically compared with Mr. Ullman's suicide attempt. See Chapter IV.

hospital. The wife was so advised, but was not deterred; and the patient left the hospital against medical advice. This patient committed suicide about a month after his discharge.

Another patient, a girl in her late teens, entered the hospital following several previous hospitalizations. At one institution she had made hostile and combative outbursts and suicidal gestures, and had shown intense resentment for the hospital and her psychiatrist. The report states: ". . . in the hospital finally cut her wrists and jumped through a window about ten days before her transfer to here." As the result of that "suicide gesture," the patient bore a healing scar about two inches long over her left wrist when she entered Crest. It was noted that: "Further gestures of this nature may be anticipated but it does not appear that a genuine suicidal attempt is likely. . . . Suicidal attempts have been of the gesture variety." The patient was at Crest Hospital approximately six months. She was put on suicide precautions after four days in the hospital. The suicide precautions were removed about a month later. Originally placed in the closed section of the hospital, she was moved to the semi-closed section after about two and one-half months.

During the last five months of her stay in the hospital, the patient did not talk of suicide, nor did she make any suicide gestures. The problem of suicide ceased to be a concern in any way. The patient was in psychotherapy, and was seen as making significant progress. In the hospital, she was active and free to a large degree. Her discharge was forced by her parents, who could no longer continue financial support of hospital treatment. The patient was popular and was making progress; and the staff was unhappy about the precipitous discharge. The parents asked that arrangements be made for the patient to return to her home. One of the professional staff recalled:

« I remember we had this conference, and it was decided that the patient was going to go home. We were going to let her go home, and her managing physician was going to let her fly home on the airplane. In the middle of the conference I just said: "If we do she'll kill herself, if we do she will kill herself." And I remember that everybody was pretty unhappy; and I just said, "No, I don't think you can let this girl go home." And I remember sitting there saying, "This incident—this, this, and this makes me believe this girl is very suicidal—and I think you are making a mistake if you don't tell the family about this; and I think she will kill herself because you let her go, and particularly if she goes by herself. She will never make it home." Well, they didn't let her go home by herself. They made the family come and get her.

The parents were asked to come for the girl if they wished to take her home, and were told that she was a suicidal danger. The parents took the patient home. Within the following month or so the patient committed suicide.

These examples illustrate the staff's feeling of confidence in the *hospital's* ability to deal with people who were considered suicide risks in other settings. The staff recognized the significance of the hospital milieu for these cases, as for any other cases. However, the concept of the effects of the milieu was not extended to the post-hospital period. One may speculate that, in both these cases, the intense warning that the patients were suicidal had a strong effect on the way the family members treated the ex-patients, and may have facilitated, rather than inhibited, the suicides. Once out of the confident atmosphere of the hospital, these patients found themselves in a world pervaded by the prediction and expectation of suicide, where "others" could only feel helpless in relation to the danger of suicide. Such a situation fulfills the requirements for actual suicide outlined earlier.*

We stated earlier that there were two persons in the nine-year-period preceding the epidemic for whom suicide in the hospital was felt to be a real danger. We have mentioned only one, Mrs. Oslo. The second, who entered Crest August 1, 1958, was a person who was felt to be very similar to Mr. Ullman, who later made the suicide attempt which preceded the actual suicide epidemic. The treatment of this patient can be more specifically compared with the patients in the epidemic group; in spite of anxiety, and the fact that this was 1958, the attitudes and treatment were clearly strikingly different.

The admission note described Mr. Agard as a 47-year-old researcher referred to Crest by a psychiatrist "who has been treating him intermittently over the past year for a mixed neurotic illness."

---

* See Chapter I, particularly our discussion of the Moss and Hamilton paper.

« Mr. Agard was accompanied to the hospital by his wife, a controlling, rather rigid person. Mr. Agard was referred because of mounting disturbance in his subjective feelings and social behavior over the past two months. The patient, the family, and the referring psychiatrist have in mind a short-term milieu therapy and evaluation as the primary reason for hospitalization. At present it is felt that long-term hospitalization and treatment at Crest cannot be considered for financial reasons.

The patient's neurotic symptoms date back to early childhood. . . . Over the years he has had innumerable consultations, electro-encephalographs, electro-cardiograms, etc., trying every new medication and treatment that came to his attention. In spite of his numerous symptoms, he has achieved success both academically and in research. . . . Until the last year the patient has done fairly successful research, and has been described as a compulsive, driving, very determined person, who is unable to delegate responsibility. In March 1957, he was referred to a psychiatrist by an internist, but was unable to tolerate any other explanation than "physiological organic process." However, by Christmas time, his anxiety had increased and he again sought help from the psychiatrist. This time he was referred to [another psychiatrist] for consultation as the psychiatrist considered the possibility of an emergent schizophrenic process. Psychological testing was performed without an indication being obtained of an underlying schizophrenic process. In January, psychotherapy was started at two-hour-a-week intervals, has been characterized by extreme defensiveness on the part of the patient, who has not been able to talk about his current feelings, past family experiences, other than to relate his dissatisfaction at not having achieved more in his profession than he desired. He had been working extra long hours until May of this year, when his compulsive defenses seemed to fall apart. He lost interest in his work, was unable to concentrate on either his research or his hobbies. He has had to be hospitalized about six times in the last two months with feelings of depersonalization, unreality, distortions of body image and mounting anxiety. During the past six months there has been a severe struggle between psychiatrist and patient over medication. The patient has been on innumerable drugs and has frequently complained that they have been poisoning him.

The initial diagnostic impression was: "Borderline psychotic condition with decompensating mixed neurosis, obsessive compulsive and anxiety type." This was later changed to schizophrenia "with clearly defined paranoid symptoms."

In a very short while Mr. Agard began doing things which caused the staff to be concerned about suicide. At the request of an aide, Mr. Agard turned over the sharp objects in his possession, claiming, however, that he could not find his tweezers or scissors. While searching through the dresser, the aide thought he saw the patient putting something in his pocket. The aide said, "We've looked everywhere and still can't find them. We have to turn them in. How about the clothes you are wearing. Did you look there?" The patient replied, in a casual voice, "Yes, and I don't have them." Asked a little later about the items, Mr. Agard said, "Let's go look in the room again." The aide countered with, "Let's go through your pockets again." The patient started to walk away, but the aide called him back. At this point, Mr. Agard exclaimed, "Oh! here are the tweezers; they were in my cigarettes." Further search revealed a dining room knife in his pocket.

The next morning when the nurse was making rounds, she noticed that the patient was bent over his bed, apparently meddling at the bedsprings in some way. The staff checked the locks on the bedsprings. That afternoon, before shift change, the aide made a search of his room and found a dinner knife under the mattress on the bedsprings. When the nurse confronted patient with this discovery, the patient said, "Oh, I was using that for a straight edge." The nurse said, "You know you aren't allowed to keep silverware on the ward. As for a straight edge, you can borrow a ruler from the office." The patient chuckled in a forced manner and said, "Oh I was just keeping that to tease Walt." "Oh come now, Mr. Agard," replied the nurse. Later the aide went in, saying, "I want to make a check of your room. I found a dinner knife in here." The patient paced around but tried to appear matter-of-fact, and said, "I was just using that for a straight edge, that's all you'll find." On this day the following order was written: "Spoon only. To be accompanied with all sharps including pencils. Fifteen-minute-rounds." And the following day, his fourteenth in the hospital, he was put on suicide precautions.

At the case conference, after two and one-half weeks of hospitalization, the prognosis was seen as "fairly good," although "one of the important aspects of his treatment was felt to be the prevention of impulsive suicide which his present intense anxiety and disorganization as well as his repeated suicidal maneuvers intimated."

Mr. Agard's course in the hospital was downhill. The staff, including the professional members, was concerned about its own attitudes and reactions towards this patient, deeming itself responsible. For example, on September 1, after one month in the hospital, Dr. Rhodes wrote an Attitude and Management note for the ward staff's consideration and guidance. It said in part:

« It would seem at this point essential for the whole hospital staff who work with Mr. Agard to give careful thought to the difficulties with him. This seems necessitated by the repeated slip-ups in his management, which have been too frequent to be accidental. Examples are: His loosening the locks on his window, and while this was known to the ward personnel, no report of it or request for further elopement precautions was made. He had managed to secure a knife, a broken spoon, and possibly other sharp instruments and hide them in the room while under full suicidal precautions and while being specialed. On another occasion the nurses' notes reported that he had a belt on and was going through some rather dramatic gestures to draw the attention of the staff to this. Another troublesome thing seems to be the feeling of awe, strangeness, with which he is regarded by most of those who work with him. It seems also that no one is able to develop any close feelings for this patient; though he has been specialed for two weeks, there seems to be almost no interpersonal reaction, at least none that is reported. There can be no doubt that Mr. Agard is suffering a great deal from the terrible sensation of having his personality fall apart; in spite of his literal requests for this or that medication, what he really needs and what he is asking for through symptoms is a human understanding and relationship. Yet these same symptoms, through their repetitious compelling and demanding of more than those around him feel able to give, result in further isolation and more intense need. At this point it would seem well for the staff to realize that we are going to, to the best of our ability, fulfill his needs and help him get well, but that we certainly will not be able to do it as quickly and as easily as he would like. Therefore there is bound to be a discrepancy between what he wants and what we can give. Realizing this, there is no need to feel impelled to a course of blind action in response to his requests.

The compulsive schedule so far has seemed to have been of little use to this patient as he has apparently been too sick to carry it out. However, I think it should be available to him so that he can have it as soon as he is able to use it. In view of this, I do not feel that the staff should be too forceful concerning the schedule, but rather offer it to him when you think it is appropriate, rather than blindly pushing it because it is an order. I think in answer to Mr. Agard's request that something be done, or that he be given something, you can offer him your time, your understanding that he is ill and that he is suffering, and participation in a card game, putting together a puzzle or conversation. At other times you may wish to give him a glass of warm milk, cup of coffee, or something of this nature. There is no point in dealing with his problems in his terms of physical disturbance and medication. Rather [interpret] to yourself what he is driving at, what the underlying need is, and in some way, real or symbolic, attempt to meet it. Mr. Agard does possess a sense of humor and even since his admission here has been able to carry on fairly warm and adequate conversations with visitors, so it would seem that he is capable of doing likewise with the staff, if we are able to find a way of adequately relating to him.

It would seem that strict suicide precautions will have to be maintained for a considerable period of time.

The emphasis on hope and confidence remained. Part of another note read:

« You act in such a way that there is in fact no possible way of his harming himself, or leaving you in doubt that he could. You act in such a way that he has virtually no choice but to get on with the business of living, which is getting up to wash, toilet, eat, work, lie down for sleep. Talking is less important for now.

And another:

« I feel it may be helpful for those of you who sit with Mr. Agard for long intervals to think at times that behind his more bizarre statements, he still has extensive capacity for reasonable discussion and behavior and to a certain degree your job is to appeal to this reasonable part of his personality and attempt to deal with it. This may perhaps prove more useful than trying to counteract pathological features that he demonstrates.

Such concern with the staff-patient relationship, such effort to change the relationship in order to better help the patient, was absent during the epidemic period. Moreover, the hospital staff's investment in psychological treatment, and their expectation that in spite of the difficulty with Mr. Agard he could be helped through the "Crest way," was made most clear at a later conference with a consultant. The report reads in part:

« Over the last two months there has been a fairly steady progression of Mr. Agard's illness. This has been manifest by an increasing thought disorder and delusional preoccupation as well as more open expressions of suicidal wishes and frank self-destructive attempts. In September while out on a walk he jumped off an eight-foot cliff but did not succeed in doing any damage to himself; this resulted in walks being discontinued. However, he still managed without incident to go accompanied to therapy to Dr. Preston's office until approximately two weeks ago, when he became more agitated, combative, and self-destructive on the ward, especially during the evening shift, and subsequently was placed in restraint. Even in belt restraint the patient attempted to jab a pencil in his eye, to tie pillow cases and sheets around his neck and in banging his head against the wall. For this reason he has been in arm restraint except for short periods during the day since. . . .

In spite of the increase in the patient's symptoms, there has been in the last few weeks growing optimism on the part of those who work with Mr. Agard in regard to his treatment, that he seems to be better understood and, since he has been in restraint, frequently much more rational and less agitated.

Because of the apparent worsening of Mr. Agard's condition, he was presented to the consultant at staff meeting. This was one of the most active meetings held this year;

discussion lasted for approximately two hours. It was the consultant's opinion that somatic treatment was indicated —either shock or drug therapy. . . . However, this feeling was not shared by several of those who work with Mr. Agard in the hospital including the administrative physician, therapist and the clinical director.*

Physical treatment was not utilized.

After four months at Crest, Mr. Agard was transferred to a state hospital, because of his family's limited financial resources. The period during which he was at Crest was a difficult one for the hospital as a whole, largely because of serious administrative problems. Nevertheless, hope remained, and the threat of suicide, though it evoked serious concern, did not give rise to feelings of fear, helplessness, and an expectation of actual suicide.

We have attempted in this chapter to communicate the character and quality of the atmosphere surrounding suicide in Crest during its first nine years. We turn now to the epidemic period, when the atmosphere was markedly different.

THE EPIDEMIC

On December 23, 1959, before noon, Mr. Joseph Ullman, a patient in Crest Hospital, was found in his room bleeding profusely from deep cuts on his throat and wrists. He was rescued from his suicide attempt. On January 1, 1960, Mr. Harry Einston, a student in his early twenties who had been in treatment at Crest for nine months, and who was out on a pass for the New Year holiday, killed himself by cutting his wrists. He was found dead a few days later in his car on a lonely road. On January 16, 1960, Mr. William Oakson, a man of over 50 years who had become an outpatient nine days previously, and who was due at Crest Hospital for a therapy appointment that day, killed himself by carbon monoxide poisoning in the early morning in the garage at his home. On January 19, 1960, Mrs. Virginia Arlington, in her thirties, a patient in the hospital on suicide precautions, was found dead by strangulation in her

---

* See Chapter IV, concerning the use of ECT as a consequence of the helplessness surrounding the treatment of Mr. Ullman after less than two weeks of hospitalization.

room at change of shift time in the late afternoon. She had choked herself with strips of a sheet. On June 16, 1960, Mrs. Miriam Irwin, a divorcee, 35 years old, a patient on suicide precautions who was felt to be very self-destructive, escaped from the hospital's locked ward. On June 22 she was reported to have been found in a bathtub in a hotel room in a distant state, after having taken an overdose of nonprescription sleeping pills.

These were the persons who were involved in the suicide epidemic. The personalities, and life histories of each will be described in detail in the following chapters. During this same period, there was one more death by suicide. This suicide in our view does not belong with the epidemic group, although the death influenced the very vulnerable hospital staff and atmosphere. Mrs. Doris Ives had been admitted to Crest Hospital on January 3, 1960, "because of a depression (accompanied by suicidal ideas) of approximately two months duration, more acute during the week or two weeks preceding hospitalization." She had been referred by a psychoanalyst on Crest's consultant staff who continued to see her in psychotherapy.

In the hospital, according to the discharge note of March 17, 1960:

« Although initially moderately depressed, the patient quickly entered most of the activities in the hospital, carrying them out productively and with some evidence of lift in her mood. However, she continued to complain of depression and despair. As her hospitalization continued it became financially necessary to consider early discharge and this was carried out after a trial period, during which the patient had her automobile at the hospital, visited her house frequently, and went off grounds with friends. She was discharged on March 17, 1960, to continue her treatment.

On April 16, 1960, on her way to a therapy hour, Mrs. Ives shot herself in the head. She was hospitalized, and died from the effects of the wound one month later.

We use the term "epidemic" as defined in Webster: "Common to, or affecting at the same time, many in a community." We see the source of the epidemic in the hospital community and its members. While the life-space of each of the individuals who attempted or committed suicide was unique, they all shared the Crest hospital staff members and atmosphere as part of their field. We believe that in the detailed case studies which follow one can see the interactional processes in the "organized complexity" which resulted in each individual's choice of action. Each study illustrates different processes, although, as we shall try to show in our concluding chapter, all seem to be consistent with the theoretical framework elaborated in the first chapter of this volume. Throughout, in each case, the hospital played a crucial part. Prior to the epidemic the hospital staff had suffered considerable loss of confidence. As time moved on, the cumulative effect of the suicides and other factors caused a massive increase in anxiety and feelings of helplessness, and a deterioration of therapeutic effectiveness. The hospital was a necessary, if not sufficient, part of the causal nexus which resulted in each suicide, and thus may be seen as the source of epidemiological nature of the group of suicides.

Chapter IV

JOSEPH
ULLMAN

MR. JOSEPH ULLMAN, A MAN IN HIS EARLY THIRTIES, was admitted to the hospital on December 4, 1959, suffering with anxiety, depression, and a conviction of worthlessness which centered about the impending holiday, as well as about his wish to make a career change.

Ullman's father was an immigrant who, with his brother, had built a successful business from the ground up. The father was described by the patient's sibling, a brother seven years his senior, as extremely difficult to get along with; "impossible," set in his ways, dogmatic, hard to talk to, stubborn. He had an unpleasant habit of reviewing and "rubbing in" the mistakes he believed others made, while refusing to take any blame upon himself. Yet in spite of these characteristics, and although he was often gruff and distant, the senior Ullman was felt to be essentially goodhearted and warm. His sister-in-law described him as a volatile, hot-headed man, who argued easily, loved easily, and got upset easily.

Ullman's mother was described as ambitious, perfectionist, and rather nervous. She was an immaculate woman, a fine housekeeper, and an accomplished cook. Her concern about the health of her son Joseph, whom she had always felt to be "sickly," was extreme. It was felt generally in the family that Joseph was not very close to his father, but that the relationship with his mother was intense. The family structure was in many ways a close one; there were many relatives in the area, with multifaceted business and social relationships.

Mrs. Ullman had been very anxious about her first son, Irving, during Irving's infancy. She often called for help upon her own mother, who finally suggested that she and her family move into the mother's home, as she could not continually respond to calls from a distance. For about three years thereafter, the Ullman's lived with Mrs. Ullman's parents and bachelor brother, all of whom interfered with the handling of the first son. In part because of this, Mrs. Ullman did not wish to be pregnant again. When she found herself pregnant with Joseph she fretted for a long time about it. He states that as long as he can remember he was aware of his being premature. He was also aware that his mother had tried to induce an abortion at around the fifth month. The idea of his not being wanted seemed firmly implanted in his mind. Joseph was born of a difficult labor. The mother was critically ill at the time of his birth, and there was question as to whether either mother or infant would survive. When the doctor asked the father whom he should save, the father asked him to save the mother. The father was later totally surprised when the doctor asked him if he wanted to see his son. The family story is that they were surprised and delighted that both lived. Joseph was known in the family as a "happy accident" and "the little boy who never should have been."

Throughout his infancy and childhood Joseph was treated by his mother as if he were an extremely sickly youngster. The exaggerated maternal solicitude had the effect of convincing him that he was weak and different from other children. Fatigue and undue strain were expected in him if he carried on normal childhood activities. He was taken to a distant clinic when he was four years old, and again when he was eight. In referring to the last examination, a note states:

« The chief problems were headache, enuresis, anorexia, and a vague discomfort in the chest. A note was made at that time that the boy was very bright and alert but that he probably carried an overload in and out of school. His complaints were thought to be functional and we suggested a regime be arranged by which he would be permitted adequate rest and avoidance of fatigue.

This suggestion, of course, reinforced the solicitude and overprotectiveness with which Joseph was treated. Even though he was repeatedly removed from school by his mother because of fancied invalidism, Joseph was extremely well-liked at school. He was an athlete, and a distinguished scholar. He was described by his family as a bright, well-behaved, adorable, easy-to-raise child, sweet and docile. At a very early age he was an accomplished pianist; and by the time he was eight, he was reading adult books, to the awe of his family. Moreover, he had many friends. He was allowed to attend school only half-days in the seventh and eighth grades, because of headaches, although he does not remember having had headaches at all.

His older brother, Irving, a figure of great importance in Joseph's life, was an outstanding high school student, with a record of academic brilliance and success in athletic and social activities. In all respects Joseph equalled his older brother's high school achievements: class president, class valedictorian, and voted the most popular boy in his class. He played on the high school basketball team until, in his senior year, his best effort was cut short by a bout of pneumonia; thereafter, his mother refused to allow him to continue athletic participation. Joseph's older brother was apparently very protective of him; and Joseph seemed to be proud of his brother and to have great confidence in him. It seems clear that throughout his early days Joseph idolized Irving and, in spite of his own achievements, felt himself inferior to his brother. The two boys shared a room during Joseph's first twelve years.

Off and on during his life he had a difficulty that was called "restless legs." These attacks consisted of painful muscular spasms, primarily restricted to the quadriceps, which would generally awaken him. When he was twelve or thirteen years old, he and his mother went on a trip, a not uncommon occurrence. During one night they shared a lower berth. He awakened the next morning with a stiff, sore back and paralyzed legs. After three days of observation in a university hospital, poliomyelitis was ruled out, and he had an uneventful recovery. One of his most vivid impressions is that of being carried on a stretcher, and of his father's arriving later, showing great concern. He reported that, somewhere about this time, he had an outbreak of overt incestuous dreams. He began to masturbate about a year later, with fantasies of being the slave of various female classmates and of being beaten by them across the back and legs. In this same period, Joseph and a chum were staying at a summer cottage. They arranged a post-midnight rendezvous with two girls from a nearby camp. Joseph went to bed greatly excited. But when his friend tried to arouse him for their clandestine appointment, he refused to awaken. He recalled that he had severe abdominal cramps the next morning and that his brother came for him, carrying him in his arms to the car.

After high school, he was in the service for approximately two years, part of the time overseas. He remembered being inept at the mechanical and electrical work required in his job. Following discharge, he enrolled at a university, majoring in chemistry, with a plan of becoming a technical partner in the family business. His older brother had obtained a business degree, and by the time of Joseph's entry into college was becoming firmly entrenched in the family enterprise. For many years, the two brothers had been quite close. Because of his inability to deal with his parents, particularly his father, Joseph often used Irving as a parent surrogate.

At college, Joseph made an admirable academic record, placing close to the top of his class. But as his graduation approached, he began to be concerned about succeeding in the family business. He was aware of the subtle, grinding competitiveness between himself and his brother, in which his brother seemed to him the more successful, and he felt intimidated by it.

A letter written by Joseph to his brother in May, 1953, illustrates the quality of this competitiveness, as well as some of the other problems he was dealing with at this time. The letter is concerned with the "meaning of a religious philosophy." He wrote of his attempt to obtain a "religious" attitude, in order to feel some hope and find some meaning in life, and quoted from Erich Fromm at length. "I want to make it clear that I have not yet attained this 'religious' attitude. I have merely gained sufficient understanding of its many implications to realize that therein lies the hope of the world and of individual man. Not his 'salvation,' but his 'preservation.'" The letter also contains "my analysis of your life to date. . . . Your approach to life has been pretty much what Fromm calls the 'marketing orientation.' I believe he has outlined his attitude rather well in his book, and I have copied a portion of it and attached it to this letter. You might read it at this time." The brother had written that he had decided to sell his shares in the business. Joseph commented: "I likewise don't know what was behind your letter. (What influence could your decision to sell the business in September have on my decision *not* to return to the business?) In any event, just as you don't want to influence me, so I don't want to influence you. Maybe we're both getting smarter."

That spring, he attended a brief seminar, where the group discussed man's problems in the contemporary world. The discussion centered around statements credited to Jesus.

During the summer of 1953, Ullman went with some friends on a trip to Montana, remaining there most of the summer. When he returned home, it was to face the problem of making a vocational choice. Throughout his college years, tremendous pressure had been brought upon Joseph by his father, his uncle, and his brother to enter the family business. Joseph's severe misgivings about such a move, his feelings of inferiority and inadequacy, particularly in relation to his brother, still persisted. Beyond this, he had now become engaged to a girl not of his religious denomination, of whom the family strongly disapproved. Upon his return, therefore, he was determined to make a stand against being forced into the business and to free himself to pursue another vocation. But he felt frightened, confused, and in need of support. He expressed feelings of worthlessness. The family saw him as depressed, anxious, agitated. A few days after his arrival home, he had the following experience: "I thought I dreamed that I got out of bed, went into the kitchen and got a glass of water, put it on the buffet in the dining room, and then went back to bed. In the morning when I saw the glass of water where I had placed it on the buffet, I realized I must have walked in my sleep."

Ullman went on to say that he subsequently queried his mother, who told him he had never been known to sleepwalk. In the days immediately following the sleepwalking incident, he became more and more disturbed. His mother suggested that he might sleep more restfully with her. The first night this arrangement was carried out, he lay awake terrified, with thoughts of murder and suicide. In the morning his brother phoned a psychiatrist, asking urgently for an appointment. The psychiatrist wrote: "I found the patient to be definitely depressed and also to be expressing some ideas of unreality and some suspicions that his family were trying to play a trick on him." He was openly delusional at the time.

« While we were trying to figure out just how to handle this patient's immediate condition, he got away from his brother, who was supposed to be watching him in the waiting room of my office, squeezed through a narrow window opening on the third floor, and jumped. He just barely skimmed over a sharp picket fence adjacent to a cement sidewalk.

Fortunately, the sod was soft from recent rains and the only thing he broke was his glasses. He seemed a little confused . . . but he did not appear to have any head injuries of consequence. He was up and walking a few steps within five minutes.

He was taken to a hospital, where he was given six electroshock treatments, received individual psychotherapy, and attended one group therapy session. "His depression seemed to clear up nicely in about a week's time, but his brother took him away from the hospital a little prematurely." He was not brought back for what the psychiatrist considered to be advisable follow-up supportive psychotherapy. The psychiatrist noted too: "We had quite a problem with different members of the family and the patient's fiancée, all of whom persisted in swarming in on him."

The psychiatrist suggested that the difficulty Ullman was having, which was diagnosed as a psychoneurosis with depression, was the result of an accumulation of painful conflicts over the years. First, basic inferiority feelings; second, unfavorable comparison with his older brother; third, ambivalence toward his father, with the particular pressure to enter the family business in spite of his lack of desire to do so; fourth, ambivalence toward his mother, with particular concern about her objection to his planned marriage; fifth, confusion over the seminar on religion he had attended, and concern over religion and philosophy.

Following this experience Joseph returned to the university to complete his final term while being taken care of by his brother. During the time of this final term of college he took an apartment very close to that of his brother, who, together with his wife, Joseph's fiancée, and two friends, accompanied him during the times that he was not actually in class. He had a close relationship with his brother's wife, who, he felt, understood him. Apparently aware that Joseph was lonely, she gave him a shepherd dog. He treasured this dog, deriving much satisfaction from owning and training it.

During this period Joseph was taken by his brother to a psychoanalyst "for hypnotic treatment." The doctor later wrote, "I had a difficult time convincing his brother that hypnosis was not the answer. As a result of psychotherapy Joseph became more independent within a few months, and his brother left in a huff." (This unexpanded upon comment gains significance in the context of an incident that occurred seven years later, when Joseph was admitted to Crest; Irving then remarked to Crest's social worker that Joseph had idolized him until he was analyzed.)

The analyst reported that Joseph became more independent in a relatively short while. There followed a long period of "very mutually hateful and dependent" involvement with his fiancée. "Following his breaking off with her she became temporarily psychotic." Joseph made slow but steady progress for the next two years; most significantly, he took a job, where he acquitted himself successfully. He finally left this job to study at the university, with the object of fulfilling a long-frustrated ambition to become a writer.

He interrupted therapy in June 1958 to take a trip to Europe, remaining out of therapy for nine or ten months. In the early summer of 1959, he returned to therapy on a twice-weekly basis. "Our main topic of conversation since then and until the present has been his fear and sabotage of his own attempts to be independent and successful. Whenever he takes a step forward he inevitably has to take three quarters of a step back."

The analyst encourged Ullman to enter group therapy, feeling that this would help him with his problems in socializing and with women. He wrote that this was not useful, and added: "If anything contributed to his recent regression [the one which brought him to Crest Hospital], it seems to me it was an attitude on my part and on that of several of his friends and the therapists in the group that he was able to do more than he was doing. This is not meant in the sense of 'activity'. . . ." What the members of the group felt, according to the analyst, was that Ullman had "a certain . . . strength" to give them, which he was denying them. Ullman was attacked in the group several times because of this sense of his denial or withholding. He was much upset by these attacks.

In the view of the analyst, another debilitating occurrence arose out of Ullman's becoming financially independent of his family at this time, over strong family protest. This came about in mid-1959, with Ullman's demand that his share in the family business be liquidated and presented to him in cash. He invested this cash, and quickly lost about $20,000 in paper profits.

What the analyst considered most important in precipitating the illness which brought Ullman to Crest, however, was the situation which developed out of Ullman's becoming interested in psychology as a possible vocation. "The idea that he might want to be in a field related to the one I was in was intriguing and anxiety-provoking." Ullman became involved in a psychological research project with which the analyst was connected; and although he made a successful beginning, he nevertheless became increasingly convinced of his basic worthlessness. From that point on, it was a downhill progression. "If there is anything that is basic to the immediate situation I would say it is the repetition in the situation of his old relationship to his brother."

As the Christmas holidays approached, Ullman became more and more concerned about how he would spend this large amount of time. His depression and anxiety grew; and in a mounting panic he turned once more for help to his brother, whom he had not seen for some time. Upon Irving's arrival, the brothers decided on hospitalization for Joseph. After arrangements for admission had been made, he was brought to Columbia by his brother and sister-in-law. He spent the night in a downtown hotel, and was admitted to Crest the next afternoon, December 4. Joseph says that during the night he spent at the hotel, he thought of jumping out of the ninth-floor window.

Joseph's referring analyst stated that Joseph had felt strong alternating dependency toward his mother and older brother. Toward his father he was hostile and contemptuous, but fearful. His mother was overprotective and seductive with him. It seems clear that the patient was forced to develop, early in life, what may be called a "magic cloak of helplessness." He managed to remain especially uninformed in business matters. As he grew older, he identified himself with his brother and was protected by him. This allowed greater freedom from his mother and a certain contemptuousness toward her. The analyst noted that there was a "conflict in the patient between his desires for his mother and the dangers of her bed."

« It seems likely, further, that this conflict was in a sense ameliorated by a close feeling toward his brother so that while his brother [or substitute] was present, the conflict was less apt to become unmanageable. This is not to say that the protective relationship of the brother did not produce its own peculiar difficulties. The nature of the incestuous mother and brother relationships has been seen during treatment.

In childhood, illness proved to be a carte blanche to the mother's bed (as well as arousing affection and concern) and a shield from his father's wrath. Since puberty he was subject to hypomanic attacks which customarily began following some small success or minor triumph. The accompanying fantasy would include ideas of being so great that he would be free of the parents, more important than the brother, and at the same time endear himself to the family, win their respect, and secure the girl of his choice. For the duration of the excitement he would also recognize a definite fear.

Again:

« In the patient's situation there was a remarkable emotional distance between the parents, and the mother took her son on long vacation trips. She exploited his dependency to the extent of making a hypochondriac of him, and in his early life, when he awakened with a need to urinate, would take him to the bathroom and then to her bed. The patient felt that occasionally he feigned illness to be taken to the parents' bedroom. The advent of genital sexuality increased the dangerous aspects of his relationships to his mother and hence increased the need to be free of her and strengthened the tie to his brother.

The analyst speculated that the psychosis of 1953:

« Dawned under the impact of freeing himself from the family and aligning himself with another woman; the early feelings toward the mother were revived. During this period he consciously avoided her. . . . The "last straw" for his mental economy seemed to be the night that he actually slept in his mother's bed. The horrifying aspects of his dependency broke through in the psychotic form of "kill" or "be killed."

Certain aspects of Mr. Ullman's personality at the time of his entering the hospital are worthy of re-emphasis. He had particular problems with his passivity and with his tendency to be dependent. The latter had often been manifest in his identifying with father-figures such as his brother and his analyst. Also, Ullman's identity was vague and confused; and he seemed particularly vulnerable to suggestion. Ullman later reported his view of the hospital staff: "As far as I was concerned these people were gods. They knew what was best. I was willing to go along with anything."*

---

* Personal interview, August, 1962.

Mr. Ullman entered the hospital with a somewhat special aura. One nurse high in the hierarchy elaborated this in her interview:

« I remember about Ullman before his admission, that somehow this patient took on the character of a special patient. I was at a loss to figure this, really. . . . It was obvious, at least to me, from the minute Ullman got into the hospital he meant something particular to Dr. Doren.* He was important in an unusual way.

Another nurse described the peculiar expectations aroused about Ullman in this way:

« They talked about his having been hospitalized before and said he was a severe suicidal risk. They talked some about his involvement with his brother, some of his feelings toward his brother, and sort of created an atmosphere of a dislike of the brother; and somehow this got mixed up with the patient, I think, when he first came in here.

Dr. Doren remarked:

« When he first came in I was very much impressed by the relationship between these brothers and had a feeling, more than an accurate knowledge based on factual and objective observation, of something really being involved and sick here.

Although the emphasis was on the importance of his successful brother, there were other factors which helped to make Ullman a "special" sort of patient. He was a bright, capable, intellectual young fellow in his early thirties, the kind of patient who is most interesting to young, dynamic psychotherapists. In addition, he had had lengthy treatment—analysis—and after a "failure" in treatment, it is often a challenge to the new treating people to show up the old. However, as will become apparent shortly, the emphasis upon the brother was appropriately placed. Although the brother was on the hospital grounds only twice, his influence upon the attitudes toward the patient and the subsequent handling of him proved considerable.

The concern about Ullman as a special patient did not reach all of the ward staff immediately. He was admitted on December 4 to the semi-closed unit of the hospital. The aide who admitted him stated:

---

* Medical director at that time.

« I didn't know anything about him . . . Well, when he first was there I stayed with him quite a bit. He was quite shaky. I felt he was very anxious and I just felt that he was very uncomfortable in the situation as a lot of people are when they first arrive. But at the time I didn't feel that, you know, I didn't know if he was suicidal or not.

The nurses' notes report that the first locus of Ullman's fear was the hospital itself. "He said he was frightened about what the hospital was like," and asked many questions about it. He was kept busy playing cards for awhile. Then, at his own request, he saw Dr. Preston. (Dr. Preston was the patient's managing doctor; that is, he was nominally responsible for the patient's hospital treatment. At this point, however, both Dr. Preston and Dr. Doren were seeing the patient in the hospital situation; later, after the initial period of observation and evaluation, which in this case lasted about two weeks, Dr. Preston was appointed the patient's therapist. This meant that he would see the patient on a formal schedule of therapy appointments, for which the patient would be additionally charged. During the evaluation period, a patient would see a psychiatrist—his managing doctor—often; since Dr. Doren's coming, patients also saw the director, but at irregular times.)

His brother and sister-in-law visited him for five or ten minutes, at about four in the afternoon. He was then seen again by the doctor; an activity schedule was developed for him; and he was accompanied a good deal by the staff, playing cards and Scrabble. Obviously tense, he nevertheless seemed to concentrate well and to appreciate the staff's time. He was reported as being warm and spontaneous in his interaction with staff members.

But that night he had difficulty in sleeping; indeed, he lay awake most of the night. The patient later stated: "My brother was talking about it [*i.e.*, suicide] from the beginning. He brought it up with my doctor at home . . . Until he mentioned it, I had not been thinking about it at all." On the night following his admission to the hospital, "feeling so much alone, feeling like a prisoner . . . I had a miserable night, didn't sleep at all." By early next morning, "the thought was coming more frequently. Preston came in sometime during that next day and asked if I had thought about it [suicide], and I said 'yes.' "

The following morning, Ullman was pleasant, his behavior unremarkable, until he saw his relatives drive up in a taxi. He then expressed his fear "that his relatives would take him away from here." When it was explained to him that it was routine for relatives to make several visits to the hospital, he was reassured. He was taken on an orientation walk around the hospital and seemed less anxious in the afternoon. By late afternoon, however, he was reported as extremely depressed and agitated. He said, "What have I done, what have I done?" After talking a bit about the doctor, he said: "I wish they'd let me die." The nurses' notes report him: "Trembling. On the verge of tears. Most apprehensive. Seems very frightened." At this point the patient was transferred to the closed section of the hospital. The order was written as follows: "Transfer to closed section immediately. S precautions." The order of suicide precautions was the first open communication to the ward staff that Ullman was considered a suicide danger.

The order of suicide precautions at this point appears unusual. The patient's only suicide attempt had occurred more than six years previously; in the years since then he had received a great deal of treatment. He had made no suicide attempt since entering the hospital. Although he had verbalized the idea of suicide, this had apparently been in response to direct questioning by the doctor.

The brother's influence here appears to be crucial. In an interview, Dr. Preston, who wrote the order, stated that to the best of his recollection, he felt that a suicide danger was indicated in some of Ullman's remarks on his second day in the hospital. The brother, he noted, visited on the first day. On the second day, following a talk with the patient in which he learned something about his feelings toward his brother, Dr. Preston decided that the brother was not to visit any more and so informed the brother. During this exchange, the brother stated strongly and explicitly to Dr. Preston that "we had better keep an eye on the patient, because he can kill himself while looking you straight in the eye." Dr. Preston felt, in retrospect, that without the pressures from the brother, there might have been no suicide precautions ordered for the patient. Dr. Preston's own reaction to the brother's warning was a feeling that he must be especially careful with this case.

Dr. Preston was not the only staff member to whom the brother communicated the danger of suicide. The social worker who saw the patient's brother at the time the patient was admitted wrote in her note: "The brother over and again ex-

pressed his concern about the patient's suicidal tendencies.
. . . The brother was concerned about any suggestion that it
would not be necessary to remain in Columbia longer than
a day or two, because he so feared that should he leave town
his brother would become more suicidal."

Dr. Doren stated:

« The brother, being seen the next morning, made some statement to the effect, "Well, I don't know if I should stay
around?" . . . I asked why, or said, "No, there is no need to."
He said, "Well, I suppose that's right. If I stay around here,
he could commit suicide while I'm sitting right here in
your office." He was very much aware of the suicidal possibility. . . . I think the point was that certainly suicide
was very prominent in the brother's mind; much more so
than it was overtly in Ullman's mind, until he got well along
in his regression.

The implications of the move to the closed section of the
hospital, quite apart from the suicide precautions, were also
significant. Dr. Doren suggested that Ullman's anxiety seemed
to be most especially about the temptation toward regression
that the hospital provided. There appeared to be general agreement that this patient was "falling to pieces" and that therefore
he should be moved to the more secure section. In the light of
the patient's questions about the hospital and his fear of regression, the definition of him as an extremely sick and suicidal
person may have been crucial. To our mind, and we shall
elaborate this further, the pressure on Ullman to conceive of
himself as extremely sick was intense.

Dr. Doren, in a letter to Ullman's analyst, the referring physician, written three days after Ullman's suicide attempt, stated:

« He was admitted to a semi-closed ward. However, by the
second day it was deemed advisable to move him to the more
secure ward because of his state of agitation and his expressed fear of his "falling apart" and "going clear down
to the bottom and having to work up from there." Though
he expressed at the beginning no direct suicidal intentions,
the nature of his agitation was such as to keep the experienced
ward personnel constantly in doubt. His brother Irving
repeatedly admonished us to keep a very close surveillance,
because "this guy can kill himself looking you right in
the eye."

There was no indication that at this time the ward personnel were concerned about suicidal intentions in Mr. Ullman. There was a very definite concern among those who had had contact with the brother: Dr. Preston and Dr. Doren, the two physicians who were involved with the patient.

Ullman appeared to organize fairly well on the closed section, in a quiet but pleasant way. He slept poorly again. The following morning he requested his glasses. He was told that the staff was too busy to accompany him with his glasses at that point. This was the first time that his glasses were refused him. On the same day an order was written that the patient "may wear glasses in lounge only, unaccompanied, and may wear belt." This is obviously an easing of the suicide precautions. It is noteworthy that the glasses were chosen as focus of easing; for, as will be seen later, the glasses became an issue of great conflict and anxiety, and were finally the instrument used by the patient in his suicide attempt. During the day Ullman's course was up and down. At times he seemed rather confused and helpless; at other times he was quite organized.

On his fourth day in the hospital, the nurses' notes reported that Ullman seemed quite agitated and "banged his head against his bed, apparently as a suicide attempt." Later that same day he asked for a bath after lunch and: "Attempted to drown self in tub, though the water was running out and there were only a few inches of water left and aide had just stepped out for about thirty seconds." The reaction to this behavior appears in the following orders: "Return to unmodified S precautions. Must be accompanied with glasses," and, "May remove patient's bed for tonight."

The paradigm of the course that was to obtain during the patient's time in the hospital seems to be elaborated here. The patient banged his head against the bedstead and put his head under the water while it was running out. Both these actions were labeled by the aide who was working with him as "suicide attempts." The physician in charge of his treatment reacted by dealing with the patient as if these were real suicide attempts. Clearly, in both cases, they were not attempts at suicide. The patient could not have killed himself and, in fact, could hardly have hurt himself had he banged his head against the bedstead in the presence of an aide.

As to the experience in the bathtub, a note the following day elaborated this interestingly. The nurses' notes read: "Also talked freely about his 'suicide attempt.' Seemed to think I moved pretty slowly when he was trying to drown himself in the bathtub yesterday. I told him that it would take a couple of minutes to drown and since the water was running out of the tub I didn't feel any real danger in the situation." It is noteworthy here that the aide stated to the patient that he did not feel any real danger in the situation. Yet he had communicated to the rest of the staff and the physician in charge that there was a great danger, and the physician had acted on this communication. Constantly throughout Mr. Ullman's stay in the hospital the most severe interpretation was put on his symptomatic actions. And, to the patient, the qualification by the aide that there was no danger was certainly of less significance than the fact that he no longer could have his glasses, and that strict suicide precautions were again applied.

Mr. Ullman later stated, in an interview, that he was at this time suffering from a "wave of anxiety." "I couldn't help myself. . . . I requested that they take the bed out—just leave the mattress—so that at least I couldn't do that to myself"—referring to his action of banging his head against the bedstead.

After the glasses were removed, Ullman's eyes became the object of his attack. On his sixth day, while being accompanied to the bathroom, he "suddenly leaned down and banged his head against the faucet of the wash basin, making a cut below his right eye." A little later the patient hit at himself with his slippers. The slippers were taken away. He was lying in a rigid position for some time, not saying a word. Then:

« Presently he lifted his arm over his head, stuck his finger out and jammed it into his eye. I am sure he closed his eye before striking himself. Aide then directed patient to leave his arms at his side. After approximately fifteen minutes patient made a half-hearted attempt to gouge his eye with thumb. There was a short scuffle and aide then directed patient to leave his hands under the covers (with the idea that he would have to be accompanied until asleep) but patient again tried to gouge his eye, this time in earnest, and was somewhat resistive to aide when aide stopped him.

The doctor was called, and Ullman was put in waist and wrist restraints, in order "to keep the patient's hands away from his face." Since a bed is necessary for fastening restraints, and Ullman's bed had earlier been removed from his room, he was transferred to the ward lounge for the night. He was told that "we were not going to let him hurt himself."

Later that evening, when a nurse went in to look at his eye, the patient remarked, "I didn't hurt it much." In answer to the nurse's query, he said that he felt all right; when the nurse left him, he called out, "Goodnight."

From this time on, three themes dominated the patient-staff interaction. There was first of all the preoccupation with the patient's eyes as a target for self-injury, related to staff anxiety over the problem of the patient's glasses. The patient kept picking at his eye with various instruments—his glasses when he had them (always accompanied) or a spoon while he was eating (always accompanied). It was never clear whether he was trying to hurt himself badly or not. It was noted earlier that he had closed his eye before he tried to stick his finger into it. At another point, an aide reported, he "suddenly and with a great swooping gesture dashed a spoon to his eye without making contact, but easily could have before I grabbed the spoon away." From the notes it is not at all clear what the facts were; whether the patient would have hurt himself in any serious way at all. He was constantly accompanied, and most of his gestures were stopped before their conclusion by the extremely alert and anxious aides; in a few cases where this was not possible, there were statements indicating that he restrained himself enough to prevent injury. Whether or not he intended to injure himself, it appears clear that Ullman's choice of his eyes as a target followed staff anxiety over his glasses. Mr. Ullman verified this. He stated in his interview:

« This business of taking them away and giving them back: as I say, it seemed to me they were trying to tell me something . . . to my mind they were trying to draw attention to my glasses, they were trying to tell me something about the glasses, and I hate to say these things because they are so screwy—but the way I felt then, they were trying to tell me I should kill myself, they draw attention to the glasses, so they are saying: here is the way you can do it.

So I started thinking about how can I do it, how can I use my glasses to do it? I think after I got the first idea about running something through the eye—now once I got that idea, it seemed to me I could use something else, it didn't have to be the glasses. But I think the reason that I kept doing that type of thing—I'm not sure of this, but I think my attention being drawn to that particular way of hurting myself was the result of their concern about my glasses—they would take them away and give them back.

The second theme was the constant communication to the patient of the nurses' and aides' concern that he would continue attempts to harm himself. When, for example, Ullman asked the head nurse on the sixth day, "Are you sure you won't let anything happen to me?" the reply was, "That's right, we will do all we can to prevent you from hurting yourself and anyone else." Later that day, the aide who brought in the supper-tray said he would accompany the patient while he was eating, to make sure that he wouldn't hurt himself. Ullman continued to test. During the same evening meal he put a lighted cigarette in his mouth. The aide extracted the cigarette, noting that it was extinguished when it came out. The patient was immediately put back in full restraints and was told that the aide would prevent him from hurting himself. Ullman next succeeded in inflicting two surface lacerations on the inside of his right wrist by rubbing it on the side of the bed. This was on the eighth day. On the morning following this incident, his wrists were carefully re-examined for signs of further laceration. When, after this examination, Ullman asked for a cigarette, the aide refused him. " 'No, you had a rough time handling this last one.' The patient said, 'That was yesterday.' There was no comment."

The third theme was the staff's communication to the patient of its qualifications and doubts about its ability to control him. For example, an entry of one typical comment to Ullman read: "We are not going to let you hurt yourself *if we can help it.*" Again, in one of the early incidents described above, the nurse had said, "We will do *all we can.*" The suggestion that this "all" might not be sufficient is reflected in Ullman's doubtful response: "Thanks a lot for trying to help me." In other ways, Ullman indicated awareness that the staff did not have confidence in its ability to handle the situation. He continually played upon the fears he sensed. He told the staff, for example, that the restraints "don't make sense to me. I thought they were supposed to keep me from hurting myself." He then demonstrated that he could move his hands to his face. His attempts to test the staff's confidence, and the staff's uncertain responses to these tests, were illustrated in other ways. For example, when an aide brought Ullman some refreshment, at his own request, Ullman said, "I'll make a deal with you. I'll drink that if I can have a cigarette." The aide's reply was, "Not at this time." Ullman next pointed out to the aide that his head was close enough to the bedstead for him to crack his skull. The aide directed the patient to move down.

Ullman was given electroshock therapy [ECT] on the morning of his ninth day in the hospital. The use of ECT in a case of this sort might, in many institutions, be considered routine; but at Crest it was a rather dramatic occurrence. Crest's strongly held philosophy was "psychological treatment for the psychologically ill." From time to time, with particularly difficult patients, tranquilizing drugs had been used, but always with some ambivalent feelings on the part of the staff about such use. Actually, for a long period of time, no drugs at all were used in the hospital. Shock had not been used since October, 1957, when it was given once to a woman of over 60 years, who had received more than a year's treatment without showing any progress. ECT had been used very rarely, if at all, in the two years prior to 1957. The use of shock for a man of Ullman's age and intellectual capacity was strikingly inconsistent with the staff's beliefs.

Dr. Doren, the new director, commented on this. He said:

« The badge, so to speak, was no shock treatment; the other, no drugs, and so on. And yet this was not altogether true, because in Crest's history there have been shock treatments used, and in other instances there have been drugs used. So it was in part kind of a banner—but on the other hand it wasn't altogether so.

The conference held on Ullman, where the use of shock was decided upon, was one in which the over-riding attitude was one of helplessness. In retrospect it is striking to note that helplessness of such an extreme sort had set in in such a short time, less than a week after Ullman's admission. One staff member reported:

« We had a conference, a staff administrative conference on Tuesday morning, devoted to Ullman, and at that conference the feeling was expressed that we were helpless in dealing with this man. He was forcing us to treat him in such a regressed way, that is, to facilitate his regression, that we had a choice of either regressing him all the way or doing something to break up this pattern. It was a feeling of helplessness, and the expression was repeated that he had us over a barrel; and it was at that time that ECT was raised and agreed on by most everybody, including I even think myself, although begrudgingly—but then I wasn't in touch with the thing. But I think everybody agreed, in frustration.

A factor which cannot be overlooked in this case was the pressure from the relatives. Mr. Ullman stated: "This was another big area of conflict between my brother and the staff." Both physicians discussed this. Dr. Doren spoke of the patient's father and uncle telephoning, "pressuring us into giving electroshock." This occurred:

« Almost from the beginning. This was pressure, but I am quite certain in my own mind that this had very little to do, if anything, with our deciding to give it. This is one of the reasons why it was presented to the whole staff for consideration and decision—to minimize the factor of the family—because Dr. Preston was the one getting the family pressure. I got some of it myself, but he was the one getting most of it.

Dr. Preston's view is somewhat different. After agreeing that the staff felt helpless, he added:

« We were in a box. The important relatives were saying, "By God, the only way to treat him was with ECT," and it's malpractice if you don't, because ECT will help him. And Doren was strongly considering ECT. I wasn't concerned terribly that this man was going to kill himself, but I felt like I'd be in a hell of a spot if he did anything to himself and I hadn't given him ECT.

Dr. Preston referred to patient Agard who, it was felt, was in many ways similar to Ullman, and who had been worked with for three months. There were periodic feelings of helplessness around the treatment of Agard, but the actions taken in relation to the helplessness were conferences between the physicians and the staff attempting to resolve the staff's difficulty in working with Agard. Attitude and management notes were written often and at length. It is striking that none of this was done in the case of Ullman. The first note in Ullman's record was a letter of December 26, three days after his suicide attempt, to the referring analyst.

Some of the nursing staff felt the use of electroshock to be primarily for the staff, not the patient. One aide said, in explaining her view of the difficulty in the treatment with Ullman:

« No communication between the doctor and the individual that was working with the patient and was assigned to the patient all the time, and that was me. And speaking of him, it is a very peculiar thing that I, of all people on the closed section, should have been assigned to Mr. Ullman, because I disagreed with his treatment from the very beginning. His treatment—electric shock treatment. To me, Mr. Ullman's electric shock treatment was not for Mr. Ullman; it was for certain ward staff, or doctors, or whoever. It was for their anxiety. We were treating anxiety but not the patient. That is the way I felt about it.

A head nurse on the closed section stated:

« Let's admit it, this is something a lot of people can't do. We as personnel on the ward can only go so far and then you have to use a gimmick to help us, whether it be tranquilizers, sub-coma insulin, or ECT . . . If it helps the staff it helps the patient. I think everything is so closely connected that you can't just separate it.

The staff was divided about the issue of shock. A head nurse on the ward stated that her personnel "were very much against it." The Director of Nurses said: "Most of us felt that if shock were indicated, that this probably was the time." In the individual interviews, the nurses and aides who worked with Ullman presented varied points of view. Some felt that shock was called for; others felt that if the doctors decided for it, that was fine; and others felt strongly opposed to it. Certainly, in the light of Crest's history and philosophy, ECT could be used only with ambivalence on the part of the staff.

The conflict within the professional staff, and the ambiguity of the doctors' roles in this case also appears to be significant. Dr. Preston was the patient's managing physician and later on, the day of the last shock treatment, he was assigned as the patient's therapist. Yet he did not give the ECT. Although Dr. Preston had more than six years of active experience in hospital work, he had never given an ECT. Moreover, Dr. Preston was as strong a proponent as any person on the staff for "psychological treatment for the psychologically disturbed."

Dr. Preston's characteristic method of handling pressure from relatives was to make it clear that he was in control of the treatment; the relatives could take it or leave it. In this case, although he was nominally responsible for the patient, the responsibility was in good part held by Dr. Doren. Dr. Preston was aware of this and found his position quite vague.

In a later *modus vivendi* Drs. Doren and Preston had nothing to do with one another's patients. But at this point, Dr. Doren was the new medical director, was closely involved with this patient; and the responsibility for the patient was unclear. Dr. Doren gave the ECT, was supervising Dr. Preston, and seeing the patient from time to time. This was very different from the "usual" way of dealing with patients at Crest.

A nurse stated that she felt that Dr. Preston did not know "exactly what to do as far as management of the patient was concerned." "In this particular instance with Ullman what we needed was a strong figure." She added:

« There was a big difference of opinion in the management, I am sure, between Dr. Preston and Dr. Doren . . . for instance, the example of ECT. Dr. Doren wanted to give ECT pretty definitely, but he had to buck Crest to do it.

Regarding Dr. Doren's position with Ullman, she observed:

« Being a new director and not knowing that usually the managing doctor handles things without any interference on the ward (and let me clarify this—as far as we were concerned, the ideal way is for the medical director and Dr. Preston to talk this thing over, what's best for the patient, but not permeate it through the staff, until they reach a definite conclusion between themselves). . . . Of course, what Dr. Doren did at the beginning was that he would come up and sort of manage patients also. . . . This was something that we were not used to at Crest, that the doctor was managing and another doctor came in. They don't come in and just write orders. This is another line of disagreement also.

On the day prior to the beginning of shock treatment the following catalogue of events was reported in the nurses' notes: Ullman had been using a bedpan. He asked an aide for permission to use the bathroom, adding, "Maybe you can put me in a harness and take me." The aide wrote: "Was referred to Dr. Preston for an order." At lunch time he was eating with a wrist out of restraint. He had a cigarette after eating, and when he had smoked it about halfway through: "I took it away from him because I didn't think he was holding it correctly. I then held the cigarette until the patient finished it." That day the patient made many hopeless remarks, such as: "It's too late. I can't be helped. It's not any use." The aide reports: "I spoke to the patient and gave him reassurance (such as I could)." Later in the afternoon the patient was found to have stuffed one corner of a pillow into his mouth. The pillow was removed by the aide. It is noteworthy that this occurrence was later reported by some of the staff as an attempt by the patient to choke himself. In the evening, while accompanied, he had one arm out of restraints and was wearing his glasses: "Patient took glasses off and jabbed eye." Later: "He had managed to inflict two surface lacerations on the inside of his right wrist by rubbing it on the side of the bed."

After the first ECT, on his ninth day in the hospital, Ullman showed signs of confusion, asking how long he had been there, where his watch was, and so forth. As he was eating breakfast, he asked that the restraints be taken off. The aide said no, that he was almost through and he should just finish his meal. The patient said, "All right," and after a few more bites, jabbed his eye with the spoon. "I grabbed his wrist at once. He offered no resistance. 'I can't do it that way. I didn't. My eye is almost gone anyway. My sight is going.' I looked at the patient's eye and he apparently had not damaged it." Later that evening, he requested the newspaper and glasses. The aide responded: "I'm not going to give you your glasses this evening Mr. Ullman." Ullman said: "If you bring in the paper I can read without my glasses." The aide responded: "If you are interested in the news I'll bring the paper in and read the news. I don't think it would be good for you to read without your glasses." Ullman said: "Okay." This concern about eyestrain which is referred to from time to time in the notes seems inappropriate. Yet it, too, led to the patient's being dealt with as helpless.

After his second ECT the following morning, Ullman complained of feeling sore and stiff, and "also said that his throat was sore, more on the outside though, and indicated his neck." That morning he went to take a tub-bath, accompanied by a male nurse. The note states: "Patient made no attempt to put head under water." Later in the afternoon he appeared sad and depressed, and said, "I want to die." The note states: "In response to my telling him that we will do everything possible to prevent him from hurting himself, the patient said, 'Boy, don't I know it. You guys watch me like a hawk.' He seemed relieved." The aide added: "Patient has not made any self-destructive type of gestures when I have accompanied him." The themes of fear and helplessness continue even as the ECT was being given; the orientation of the aides, the nurses' reports focussed almost totally on Ullman as a self-destructive person. That evening he was given a cigarette with the admonition: "I don't want you to swallow this." The note continued:

« I let him smoke it half-way, and he kept it away from his face when not actually smoking. He did rub or massage his face—particularly around his eyes—frequently, and I felt that he might be building up to something. In view of my previous experience with the patient I wasn't taking any chances at this point. So I suggested he finish it immediately. He complied with this. He was offered the paper and attempted to read it, but was uncomfortable, and asked for his glasses. I refused, really without thinking, saying, "No, not now." The patient said, "What the hell can I do with my hands tied down?" I agreed silently with him, but I had made a decision, so felt I should stick with it.

The nurses and aides varied in their treatment of the patient. One nurse reported that the patient asked why he was allowed at one time to go to the bathroom, when previously this had not been allowed. The nurse replied that she, the nurse, was comfortable in letting him up, while some people were more comfortable with him when he was restrained. Therefore, these differences were better for the patient, better for the staff, and would be of most benefit to the patient. This was a clear communication that many of the staff were very anxious, and that restraining the patient was a consequence of staff insecurity and anxiety.

On Saturday, Ullman's eleventh day, there was no ECT. Ullman protested about the small amount of water drawn for the bath, but said he would make it do when he was told there would be no more water added. He was allowed to walk around the ward a bit, and both of his arms were out of restraints for the meal. He was allowed to wear his glasses frequently, and was up and about much more. That evening, however, when he asked to have his arms out—as he had in the afternoon during his meal—only one arm was removed. A male aide noted an interesting interchange in that evening's report:

« Lying quietly in bed at shift change. Immediately requested glasses (i.e., when I brought dinner) and was refused. Ate well and had a cig. afterward. Asked to have both arms out; only one was removed from restraints however. When I returned from dinner, I brought newspaper and asked "How do you feel about wearing your glasses?" "Fine." Read paper. Then we played three games of checkers, played a sharp game; seemed comfortable and was outgoing. True generally of whole evening. Up to bathroom at 7:30 and voided. Asked to walk in hall a bit but was refused. Later we played 2 games of casino. Pt. had both arms out of restraints at this time, handled it quite well. At the conclusion of this, as I started to re-apply restraints patient asked, "Say, will you tell me why I have to have my arms down at my side like this? No one has ever explained it." ("To keep your hands away from your face Mr. U.") "Why?" ("So that you won't hurt yourself.") "I wouldn't do that." ("It seems as though you have tried, isn't that so?") "Well, yes, but it wasn't serious." ("I would say it was quite serious.") Patient then wondered if restraints couldn't be a bit looser at night and was told that if I did that, the restraints would not serve their purpose. Patient's manner during this time was one of half-jokingness, though I felt he was serious underneath as he tested. I left room to set things in bathroom for HS* care and when I returned five minutes later was horrified to find that patient still had glasses on. (Well, I guess I slipped up, huh.) Patient smiled at me, though manner did not seem to have changed since I had left. Handled HS care quite well. Cig. at 11:20 and lights out. No self-destructive gestures. Generally, was more relaxed (and quite pleasant) than I have noted him.

It is significant that the self-mutilative gestures the patient had made—which at best could only be called halfhearted—were explicitly interpreted by the aide as "quite serious" in his remarks to Ullman. The aide was saying to the patient, "You are very sick and irresponsible; you are a person trying to hurt himself; if you think your self-destructive behavior is inconsequential, you are wrong." (Mr. Ullman reported later, "I

---

* HS refers to preparation for bedtime.

thought I was trying to kill myself.") At the same time, in leaving the patient with his glasses, the aide was participating in facilitating what, in his view, was the great danger. More of such participation occurred later on, with critical consequences.

On Monday Ullman had another ECT, the last. He was given considerably more freedom: both his hands were out of restraints; he had his glasses often, always accompanied. On the following day, when he found he was not going to have an ECT, Ullman expressed surprise. "I thought I was going to have one this morning. I don't know what to think." The following day he again expected he might be given further shock treatment. It is noteworthy that in the interviews—although these took place considerably later—many of the staff people reported that they, too, were surprised that ECT was stopped so quickly, and had no idea why.

The patient received only three electroshock treatments. When asked, in the interview, whether the staff's ambivalence was a factor in stopping ECT, Dr. Doren stated:

« I think I should say undoubtedly it was a fact that existed. The attitude toward it was certainly in the background and was certainly antagonistic toward shock. Perhaps this was a factor in stopping it at the time. But I don't think this was the major factor. The major factor was that it was not our intention to treat him with electroshock treatment. Our intention was to treat him with psychotherapy, and the shock treatment was used only as a means of implementing this, of obviating the barrier to it.

After three treatments:

« The purpose for which we gave it at that time had apparently been achieved. He was communicating and was apparently active in psychotherapy. This was the purpose of giving it, and also the staff was able to deal with him, the staff anxiety was relieved . . . now it was time to return to the treatment we hoped to use in the first place.

Dr. Preston said: "Well, he cleared very quickly after a couple of ECT's, and we gave him the third and I decided he's back in contact, let's talk. . . . We've achieved what was expected, why continue."

On the day of the last shock treatment, Ullman's thirteenth

day at Crest, the order was written: "Dr. Preston will be patient's therapist." Dr. Doren commented:

« Preston had mentioned a definite rivalry of his own brother. Then coming up to the point now with Ullman, the patient, one of the major factors in Ullman's situation was his relationship with his brother, a very intense, a very pathological one, and a very deeply involved one. By wondering how much Preston was involved with Ullman, how much of his attraction in terms of interest in the case might have had other deeper significance, I certainly had question about. . . . When we discussed the treatment of Ullman, Preston expressed a wish to treat this patient. I, knowing that it was a very difficult one, had a little hesitancy about letting Preston take it, and yet on the other hand not wanting to deprive him of the experience and responsibility if he felt capable. So I asked him once or twice—anyhow, repeated the question—are you sure you want to handle this, it's a tough one, do you think you feel comfortable with it? And he assured me that he did.

That there was some conflict between the two doctors, at least on a covert level, seemed to be perceived by other staff members. For example, one nurse stated:

« I felt that he [Dr. Doren] and Dr. Preston were at real odds over this patient almost from the very beginning. Dr. Preston was treated as if he were an intern with no brains, couldn't handle a patient—he's too important to leave to Dr. Preston's care—and Dr. Preston's resentment about this was intense. Sometimes he would say this directly to me. I don't think he communicated this directly at all to Dr. Doren, nor to anyone else in the hospital that I know about. But these two men were at loggerheads over this patient, almost from the beginning I think.

The patient began to complain a good deal about being tied down. His complaining was characterized as "Like G. I. griping" and "not bitter." On his sixteenth day, the order was written: "Patient may be out of wrist restraints alone at staff discretion except at night. May be up in lounge in evening with male staff at staff discretion." Ullman began to speak more positively at this time. He said: "All I want to do is to be able to do some-

thing that is worth while. I don't even seem to have the capability
to do anything to get started."

On the following day this order was written: "May be up
ad lib on regular S precautions and also patient may have
glasses in lounge only"—he was then permitted the use of his
glasses in the lounge whether or not he was accompanied by
an aide.

This order about Ullman's glasses had been a subject of
much discussion and conflict. The Director of Nurses said in
her interview that after shock:

« The patient seemed to be relieved of his, if I can call it,
picayune gestures about suicide, and did somewhat better,
though there was a great deal of concern about him. Dr.
Preston still felt him to be very suicidal. There was a good
deal of push from the ward staff about could the patient
be allowed to wear his glasses, that he had complained a
great deal about not being able to see. They felt guilty about
this. They weren't doing right by him when he couldn't
read or do anything. So the order was written that he could
wear his glasses in the ward lounge, unaccompanied. And
in retrospect, of course, we could all see that this put a
burden on the patient for turning in his glasses when he
left the lounge, because he was not accompanied.

Dr. Preston stated: "He was very nearsighted, and I allowed
him to have his glasses with some ambivalence. When glasses
are an issue you give them back with some reluctance."

The patient's behavior changed. He was reported as being
pleased with the new orders. He enjoyed listening to a ball
game on the radio. He did a jigsaw puzzle, slept better, was
chatty, was talking of sports, and was considerably more organized. Clearly, Ullman was feeling better. He began to think
more positively about the future and to be concerned, though
unclear, about it. At this time, the following was reported in
the nurses' notes:* On his nineteenth day he was accompanied
by a nurse at breakfast. "Nurse said that Mr. Ullman seemed
despondent. Patient asked nurse if he thought he would get
well. Nurse asked Mr. Ullman if he felt like hurting himself
today. Patient replied, 'No.'"

Note here that the patient was apparently raising positive

---

* The nurse's report was transcribed here by an aide.

questions about his future prospects. The nurse replied by reminding him of her view of the situation, in which Mr. Ullman was still a person who wanted to "hurt" himself. The impressive thing about the situation up to this point is that the patient's post-shock attitudes toward himself and the world seemed to increase in a positive direction. The orders written by the doctor also seemed to point in this direction. He had considerably more freedom. At the same time the general anxiety about his glasses—which were pertinent only to the suicide danger—remained. Thus, in spite of the patient's changed behavior and the changed orders, the staff could not rid itself of preoccupation with the danger of suicide.

A crisis illustrative of the communication of anxiety arose the following morning. At the time Ullman was served his breakfast tray, it was discovered that his glasses could not be found in the office. They were subsequently found in his bedside stand. This is all that the nurses' notes stated, but a great deal more occurred. Dr. Preston reported:

« According to the patient, the nurse stormed in to take the glasses out of the stand and acted as though a gun had been left in the stand over night. And the patient's delusional interpretation of this was, as it had been of many other things, "You've had your chance and you've muffed it." . . . He felt we were offering him opportunities and then taunting him for not having taken advantage of them. He felt this particularly about this episode in which the nurse got very upset about his having had his glasses all night . . . . It was right up his psychopathological alley; he was told, "We gave you a chance, you've had a chance." It was graphically pointed out, dramatically, because [the nurse] is a dramatic person. This is exactly the sort of fantasy this man had all the time, that it was pointed out to him that he had muffed an opportunity to kill himself. This is a fantasy he had for years. The nurse's behavior in this situation just played right up his alley, just exactly . . . . And, of course, the behavior of the night aide who had left his glasses in the stand also was right up his alley. In fact, there had been a haggle on the ward about his glasses: Should this guy have his glasses unaccompanied because he's on S? Should he have his glasses because he's so helpless without them? He was doing pretty well, fine. Don't have trouble with him, he can have his glasses. But trouble was made about the glasses, really.

That morning, after the uproar about the glasses, Ullman was in the lounge, dressed, working on a jigsaw puzzle, wearing his glasses, unaccompanied. The aide assigned to him was in the ward office. She wrote: "Patient apparently left the lounge unnoticed by me, went to his room where I found him lying half across the bed, head down. Patient had cut both wrists and throat in a suicide attempt."

The patient had used his glasses in the attempt. Dr. Preston later stated: "If his glasses had not been an item of S precautions I doubt if he would have used them."

The reactions of those involved with the case at that time varied. Some felt that Ullman was very close to death. The physicians, however, stated that the effect of the attempt was not that serious. The patient was taken to a nearby general hospital where his wounds were sewed up, and was returned to Crest the following morning by ambulance. He wore casts on his wrists and neck. These were, of course, a constant reminder to staff and other patients of his attempt. The orders written on his twenty-first day, the day after his attempt, were: "Strict S precautions. Waist restraints when not accompanied. May walk in hall accompanied. May have Demerol once if complains of pain. No cigarettes."

Some of Mr. Ullman's later reflections on this period enrich the picture:

« These people know best and they are my—you know, I'm looking to them for everything, for all my security, for all my help, for all my answers. I wasn't questioning them at the time, but I was busy trying to interpret, and every interpretation I made came out to the conclusion that they are trying to tell me I should kill myself.

What happened there was that I got to believing that everybody wanted me to kill myself and were giving me little hints, and little aids, and so on. And that is the way this business came to occur to me, people taking them away and giving them back—that they are trying to draw attention to my glasses and telling me, "Use them: you can use them for the purpose that we think you ought to use them for." And that business about the glasses in the nightstand, when the nurse came in—why did she have to tell me? She told me about it, and she seemed upset. Well, to me this meant she was upset because I hadn't used them. So that these little things that happened just kind of reinforced my distortion of things. I could fit them into this distorted pattern to the way I was seeing things.

After the shock treatment, after I got up (and I learned or heard since that this is kind of a dangerous time, when you actually have rounded the corner and are beginning to get better, which I guess I was at the time)—but at that point I had made a pretty serious commitment, I decided I am not going to play around, I'm not going to give myself away until I really get the chance. This was more conscious, more deliberate, more planned.

I started getting pretty tricky while I was still strapped down that first time, and at that point I was consciously trying to give the impression that I'm doing better so that they will let me up and so be free to do it. As I was lying there that first time, and strapped down, it seemed to me— this time with some reflection—there is no point in living, this is my fate, so what if I get temporarily better, this is what I'd come back to, and so on. So that actually, I suppose, there is several days of fairly serious thinking about it before the big one.

It was carried to such ridiculous extremes. For instance, after [the attempt] they kept me strapped in bed all the time. I would get up in the morning and dress, but then whenever I was in the room by myself they'd take my glasses, and take all paraphernalia, and strap me down again. I would lay on the top of the bed with my clothes on. There was one nurse or aide—she strapped me down and then she'd take the shoelaces right out of my shoes. Here I am strapped in bed and she takes the shoelaces out. Well, this is the same deal. I said what in the hell can I possibly do with shoelaces; and then I start thinking—and I never did come up with anything you could do with shoelaces, but I guess there is something you can do with shoelaces. She got me to thinking about it. Whatever it was you could do with them, I'm sure I couldn't have done while I was strapped in bed. But they would just carry this thing to such ridiculous extremes.

Shortly after his return he was seen by Dr. Preston; the staff noted "much moving about of his hands and arms—raising his arms to face and about his neck—twitching of his fingers." His arms were tied down with a blanket, since the restraint straps would not fit around the casts. He is reported to have had "a look of frustration and stubborn determination on his face when he realized that the nurse was going to use the blanket strips to restrain his arms (a sort of 'I will find a way anyhow expression')." Later a sheet restraint was put over the patient's chest. He was reported as "shaky, and looked very miserable." He was seen by Dr. Doren that afternoon, and later in the evening by Dr. Preston again.

The staff reactions to Ullman's suicide attempt were extreme. One nurse stated:

« At any rate, the patient did make this very serious suicidal attempt—and you know the reaction to that was something really quite fantastic. The patient did not die. The thing was handled. It was obvious from the beginning that he was not going to die, because he didn't cut any vessels which would exsanguinate him; and yet the anxiety around this man was just fantastic. It was as though the guy had really killed himself. [Anxiety on whose part?] On Dr. Doren's, Dr. Preston's, the ward staff, everybody. And it was absurd, and something with which I couldn't empathize, and didn't understand. From that time on I think there was no decrease of anxiety on the closed section.

A nurse on Ullman's ward said:

« Of course, the thing that bothered me also on suicidals—which I think in a way hinges on this problem—is what do you do with a guy once he has tried to commit suicide, and you keep him in a hospital? I'll speak staffwise for the personnel on the ward. Nobody wanted to work with him. They were afraid. And this had actually been said: "What if something happens to him while I'm working with him? I don't want that responsibility." This is what it amounted to. So as a charge nurse making out assignments it was very difficult to get anybody to work with him, because they felt they had to watch him continuously after he had attempted and almost made it. So he couldn't move. Even if he was able to move we wouldn't let him move. We wouldn't let the doctor let him move. The safest place for him was in bed with restraints on. And I went to the other extreme. If he went up to take a bath, I insisted myself on going, because I didn't want anyone else to take the responsibility. I was charge nurse; this was my responsibility; I had to take it.

The nurse went on to say that after the attempt the staff became "much more cautious."

« We've had other patients who have tried stuff, things in their mouth or around their neck, and it never seemed to bother too many people. . . . But after the attempt was made and almost succeeded, this is where the staff freezes up and nobody wants to take a chance on him then. And even the managing doctor didn't want to take a chance.

Following Ullman's suicide attempt the staff's general level of confidence took a marked drop, and the anxiety about suicide in general markedly increased.

Shortly after the suicide attempt, a decision was made to transfer the patient to another hospital. His therapist, Dr. Preston, said:

« I felt bound to the situation, but the first opportunity to get out was relieving, and when they said [Palm Clinic] I said, "Fine." I might have felt differently—but only ten days later [later than Ullman's attempt] Einston killed himself. I don't have a clear memory of this ten-day period. But one of my first feelings [immediately after the attempt] was one of reassurance, that he could make a determined attempt, but while in hospital he couldn't kill himself, so he might as well stop his threats and gestures. But Einston kills himself, and I seized the first opportunity to get out.

Dr. Doren, in a progress note written on January 15, three weeks after the attempt, described the situation with some different points of emphasis.

« Refer to copy of my letter to the referring doctor for progress report up to December 27.

Since that date the patient has been kept under very close surveillance and in restraints at all times when not attended. The patient has made no further overt suicidal attempts, although he has at times been somewhat preoccupied with his confusion as to the reason and motives involved in his behavior. In the past week or ten days the question of his being transferred to another hospital has been seriously considered. The reasons for this are several.

His suicide attempt at this hospital has had an effect upon all of the staff in such a way that an undercurrent of distrust has prevailed, in spite of the fact that overtly all of the staff has been most considerate and desirous of helping this patient. This difficulty particularly involved his psychotherapist, Dr. Preston, whose able and realistic appraisal of his own countertransference revealed a degree of distrust and even moderate antagonism since the aggressive suicidal act of the patient was felt, with justification, to have been also an attack upon Dr. Preston in terms of the transference relationship. Because of this we believe that although feelings of the staff and Dr. Preston to the patient were not so disturbing as to preclude the possibility of successful treatment, they were sufficient to introduce some impediment to the patient's progress. Our conclusion is that the odds in favor of the patient's recovery under present circumstances would be greater at [Palm] than at Crest.

It would be our first choice that the patient and his family make all arrangements for his transfer to that hospital and that Crest be totally relieved of responsibility as soon as the patient left the grounds. However, it is impossible for us to make good recommendations as to who might be employed by the family as qualified attendants for the patient on this trip. Therefore, we are making the arrangements in the best manner possible to provide for the patient's safe transfer. It is recognized that the patient is a suicidal risk, but all reasonable precautions will be taken. The following are our plans:

a. Crest will provide two experienced and well-qualified attendants.

b. They will take with them all necessary equipment, such as restraints and drugs, to be used if indicated in the assurance of the patient's security.

c. The hospital will make all plane reservations and schedules.

d. The relatives will not be on the same plane as the patient and his attendants.

e. We will notify [Palm Clinic] as to the expected time of arrival.

f. A detailed list of charges for the plane tickets and attendants' pay will be presented in the form of an itemized statement to the patient, who will pay this amount in advance.

g. It is considered that we might ask the patient and/or his relatives to sign a form releasing the hospital of responsibility for the patient after he has left the hospital grounds. However, the logical one to sign this would be the patient, but to ask him to sign this we feel would be more upsetting to him than helpful to the hospital. According to his previous pathological thinking he would very likely interpret this as an invitation to make a suicidal attempt en route to the hospital. Therefore we will not ask the patient to sign such a form.

Considering all aspects of this situation we feel that the best judgment is being used in the decision to transfer the patient and in the means of affecting this transfer. Current plans are that Mr. Ullman and his attendants will leave Sunday evening, January 20.

Similar feelings are represented in an interaction as reported in the nurses' notes. In the evening of the day following his attempt, the patient asked if he could play cards. The nurse responded: "I don't know yet. I don't have to take any chances with you Mr. Ullman." "What do you mean?" he asked. The nurse replied, "The restraints." Later on the nurse said: "Mr. Ullman I don't feel like taking your wrists out so we can't very well play cards."

The following day the patient was seen by Dr. Doren, who described the interview in a letter to the referring physician dated December 26, Ullman's twenty-third day at Crest:

« The following is the essence in meaning, of my interview with him on December 25. He said in effect that we were at fault in making him regress to the point of utter helplessness. He was most resistant to recognizing that his very behavior necessitated the progressively increased surveillance and restraint, and also the active intervention of the electric shock treatment. He described his extreme fear of becoming completely helpless, in that it would admit to his being without bodily feelings, that time would completely stand still, and that he would be totally locked in with his own horrible thoughts. This he says would be worse than suicide. I told him that I could understand his great fear, but that on the other hand I was not similarly afraid because I knew that he would be safe and cared for here in the hospital, to whatever degree would be necessary. I did not expect him to be convinced to the point of losing his dread, but I did hope that he might realize that we did not share his fear in the same way as he. I told him also that I was aware of his feeling of almost total loneliness, and that his great fear also had to do with how close he wanted someone to be to him. He showed understanding of this.

Later that evening the patient referred to his talk with Dr. Doren. A good part of the nurses' notes for that evening seem to be pertinent:

« Patient appeared very anxious. "Is Dr. Doren here? I want to talk to him! I'm afraid he . . . drew the wrong conclusion today." Patient seemed to be getting increasingly frightened. I sat down. Patient looked at me pleadingly—respirations were rapid and heavy and patient looked scared to death. ("What's the trouble, Mr. Ullman?") "I'm scared of what's going to happen." ("And what's that?") "It's so horrible I can't even talk about it." Patient was literally writhing and a grimace of agony on his face. Patient's obvious pain and anxiety made me feel I must say something. ("Nothing is going to happen to you Mr. Ullman. No one is going to hurt you—except what you try to do to yourself.") ". . . you mean I get another chance?" (as though wanting it). ("No—we'll do all we can to prevent your hurting yourself. . . . Are you scared of yourself, Mr. Ullman?") Patient breathed out heavily and said rather dully, "Yes, I guess I am." Patient was quiet and I sat with him a long while. He was restless and disturbed and seemed bewildered and afraid. Asked for water. ("I feel like tightening this up now.")—wrist restraints which have been quite restrictive all P.M. "Oh, I'm not going to do anything." ("But we don't know.") Patient just looked at me. I returned and patient drank some water. I remained with patient and he was still in obvious and pronounced pain—mentally. Suddenly looked at me and whispered pleadingly, "Nurse! Help me!" I could not answer for a few seconds. ("How do you mean?") ". . . to hang on for a couple of days —I told Dr. Doren today . . . I feel like I'm getting catatonic." (This is what I thought he said but cannot be absolutely certain.) Patient was looking painfully at ceiling. "He suggested we let it go to that point . . . but I got to thinking—maybe he meant—they'll do away with me in a couple of days . . . or something. I thought maybe they're putting poison in my food

—or taking something away they've been giving me." ("I can assure you this Mr. Ullman—nothing like that is happening. We'll be taking care of you for more than just two days.") Patient laughed bitterly, "For an eternity!" ("Is that how you feel?") "Yes." ("You sound pretty hopeless about it all.") After a long while said, "I hope you don't mind sitting with me." ("Not at all.") "It helps." An aide relieved me after awhile and I called Dr. Doren. Aide reports patient was silent for about 10 minutes then said, "Mind if I talk crazy for awhile?" Aide told patient he could talk if he cared to. "I'm damn angry with each one of you. I wish I could redirect it." This was all as I came in then. Aide felt patient sounded more intellectual than emotionally involved in this statement.

On his twenty-third day an order was written that a relative might visit Ullman for a half-hour. Accompaniment was to be available if necessary. Later that day the order was added: "May smoke accompanied if he can hold his own cigarette."

During the next day or so the patient attempted to plead, in a sense, for release. He tried to get permission to wash his own face, to have his glasses in some safe fashion ("You could tape them on!") and he was reported to have had a pleading expression on his face almost all the time, even when he was not talking. Almost daily, from this point on until his discharge, he was visited by relatives; and although he was anxious at first, the visits seemed to be rather comfortable. The pleading and questioning stare of the patient's was reported by many and interpreted. One aide noted on his twenty-fourth day: "Some point of staring at me in a questioning way. I feel a good portion of this is perhaps the patient is questioning self: how well are you protecting me, from myself?"

On that day an order was written that the patient might wear glasses accompanied if the staff member accompanying him felt comfortable. Ullman was reported to have made many requests of the aides, as if he desired to detain them. He seemed to be frightened of being left alone for any length of time.

The staff anxiety, and preoccupation with the patient as a self-destructive person was obviously constantly in the wind, while the patient seemed to be better. On his twenty-eighth day an order was written that he could be up in the lounge for games while accompanied. He played some games of Cribbage, was out of restraints and: "Did nothing that was indicative of a suicidal frame of mind." The nurses' notes stated: "He seemed concerned but not anxious when his glasses could not be found. (He was concerned, I was anxious.) Patient said that Dr. Preston had probably walked off with them; he had." The following evening* the patient seemed more comfortable. An order permitted him to have the radio on the floor next to him. He said: "They have a good staff here. It is a good place to be sick." He told a joke about schizophrenia. He admitted that he would stall the aide for as long as possible but: "Didn't mind my firm statement about when I could be there and when I couldn't."

The next day he had a tub-bath and the aide suggested that he help him wash his hair. Ullman was enthusiastic:

« Said his hair was so dirty he didn't want to sit in the tub when he washed it. He said he wanted to stand outside the tub and bend over to wash his hair. I told him that this would be okay but I really feel I should put a towline on him if he is going to do that. He chuckled a bit at this suggestion. Finally he decided to wait till the afteroon.

On his thirty-third day an aide reported: "I felt somewhat ill at ease having not spent any time with him for over three weeks. . . . Was reminded once not to fiddle with his glasses and he in an apparent nervous gesture touched glasses and his eye."

By the thirty-fifth day, Ullman was sometimes able to express direct anger appropriately at some of the things that were being done to him; and there were appropriate responses by the aides. He complained a good deal about the restraints and demanded a great deal of attention and accompaniment, but seemed to be getting better. He was speaking about his interest in teaching. On the forty-second day he seemed to be restless. He was scratching his face and his hair, and his hand seemed constantly near his face. An aide noted: "He doesn't appear particularly perturbed by the noise on the ward, which makes him about the only one who isn't." He was in restraints on and off, was having visitors, and talked of his interest in psychology before his illness.

The following day, twenty days after his suicide attempt, the patient was reported to be quiet. He had a cigarette accompanied and asked the aide, as he had done often, to check the heat register and straighten his pillows:

« I fluffed them a little. He said he still felt a lump. I felt

---

* On this day, January 1, the first actual suicide occurred. Mr. Einston killed himself while out on pass.

each pillow and as I got to the bottom one I felt a hard object. I immediately knew it to be glass fragment. I dismantled the pillow and found a section of eyeglass. I put the pillow back together and then said quietly, "There was a piece of glass. I have it now." The patient said, "Oh." I left the room and reported to the nurse who helped me strip the bed down. Nothing was found. The patient sat docilely in a chair while this was done. He said, "I had forgotten about that until aide found it. I put it in there when I did this." (indicating his throat and wrist.) He was put back into full restraints without incident and appeared comfortable.

The aide amplified on this experience:

« He asked me to straighten his pillow, or do something, and I straightened his pillow as he asked me to. He said, "There is a lump in my pillow, could you fluff it out?" and I fluffed it, and I said, "How's that?" and he said, "It still feels like there is a lump there." And somehow, in the way he said it, I got kind of suspicious, and I felt in the pillow and could feel a hard object. I was behind him. I had moved around behind him where he couldn't see me. And he was lying on his back. And I took the pillow out of the pillow case and unzipped the pillow. As a matter of fact, the zipper was on the open end of the pillow case, which it shouldn't have been. I reached down inside and found this—felt this object —which I knew by feel was half an eyeglass, and I think I probably about dropped right in my tracks. I just was really shook, and I was so shook I knew I couldn't say anything at the time. And so I took the pillow apart and kind of palmed the piece of glass, and felt around until I felt comfortable enough to say very quietly, "I found a piece of glass and I have it now." And he said, "Oh, okay." Then we took him out of bed and sat him down. I don't remember who the nurse was, but anyway we stripped his bed. (He had asked?) He had told me, he asked me to get rid of that piece of glass, and he had been laying on it for a week, I think it was a week. He must have been just anxious as hell about it.

The aide was still very upset the next morning,* and asked

---

* On January 16 (Ullman's forty-fourth day at Crest) Mr. Oakson, who had become an outpatient nine days earlier, and who was due for a therapy hour, killed himself.

the head nurse: "Who checked? God, who didn't put the eye-glass back together to see if it were all there?"

« And I couldn't imagine this. It really kind of tee'd me off, you know. And somebody else had thrown another piece away . . . and God, I was mad as hops, because they should have known it was gone, and God, you always try to see if you've got all the stuff out and . . . let's see . . . . Well, that about takes care of him, I guess. He left pretty soon.

Mr. Ullman said:

« I put that thing in that pillow at the time I first broke it. If I get stopped I'll have this piece in reserve to use later. I forgot all about the damn thing. A couple of days after I was back in Crest again, and they brought that same damn pillow in with a zipper, then I thought of it. Geez, I wonder if that thing is still there. Oh they must have found it, or this is just a pillow that looks like it, or something. I didn't give it too much thought. But about that time I had made my internal commitment the other way, that come hell or high water I'm going to live. If they want me to die here, they'll have to kill me or something, whatever it was, however I was thinking at that time. In any event, I was looking the other way at this point. And so that when they found that thing, they came and got me out of bed and tore the whole goddamn bed apart, looking for more, to see if I had anything else. . . . But anyway Preston came in the next day—I was kind of bitter about the goddamn reaction, they came in and scoured the room and tore the bed apart and all this junk—and he said, "Well, why in the hell didn't you tell us, you knew you put it in there." Well, in the first place, I really hadn't thought about it for several days; and when I did think about it— and I told Preston this—I had come to the point then where I thought it was my own goddamn business whether or not I kill myself, and it's no concern of yours, Preston and the rest of the staff, or anybody else's, it's my business. And at that point I guess I had remembered it then, and I thought maybe it was in there. I couldn't check, of course, because I'm tied down. Well, that's fine, it's there and I can make up my own mind now, and I can call the cards on whether or not I do. And that's the way I felt then—that it wasn't their business.

At breakfast on the morning of his forty-seventh and last day at Crest, Ullman was: "Probably miffed because I left him in waist restraints (per usual). He seemed pretty ill at ease during the afternoon particularly when patient Arlington was yelling and screaming." Later Ullman made out a check to pay his hospital bill, said warm thank-yous and good-byes. He seemed in good spirits, and a little excited about the trip. He said: "The world will probably look a little strange—people doing things." It was noted:

« Patient seemed to know nothing of patient Arlington's suicide [that afternoon] and circumstances were such that with this patient that he would not (radio playing loudly in his room. In the lounge, card game when other patient taken off ward.) He shaved, changed clothes and talked to Dr. Preston. . . . He sounded sincere when he said he would miss us. Discharged per taxi at 10:30 P.M., accompanied by nurses. He signed the release forms and everything.

The discharge note, by Dr. Preston (and it is noteworthy and unusual at Crest that notes on one patient were written by two physicians) described in summary Ullman's course in the hospital and in psychotherapy after his suicide attempt:

« Following repair of the lacerations and a bilateral wrist tendon repair, he was returned to the hospital on the following day. At the time he was still quite panicky and expressed a continued wish to die. Gradually his mood lifted and in spite of his continued complaint of his fear of becoming totally regressed in the use of restraint and accompaniment, which was felt to be necessary, he gradually came to some reconciliation with the immobile position into which his actions had forced him. In his psychotherapy appointments, which were carried on for a half-hour, five times a week, he spoke of his lifelong preoccupation with "going to bed" which he saw as the inevitable result of a catatonic illness which he felt himself to have. He spoke of the experiences of his psychosis with some intensity and his feeling constantly being tempted and directed to kill himself by people who presented themselves as helpful and friendly. After a time he became somewhat irritable about the services offered him by nursing personnel and thought of being demanding, although his expectation was that his wishes would be fulfilled without his asking. At times when he felt most angry he generally later had an experience of feeling better and more hopeful.

Because of the anxiety surrounding the patient in this hospital arrangements were made for his transfer to [Palm Clinic] after some consultation with the referring physician. The patient was initially somewhat dismayed by this and felt that the transfer was an admission of hopelessness. But he later indicated that he had had some idea himself of transfer to [Palm Clinic] and began to think about the transfer. As alternate moves, he considered going with his uncle but he rejected this with the knowledge that this would be a treatment which was carried on by his brother. Toward the end of his hospital stay he began to talk about his feeling of need for dependence which would lead to feelings of need for a total regression, going back to bed, as well as feelings of becoming independent, which he equated with insanity and berserk rage. However, during the last week of his hospitalization he seemed much more friendly with personnel and began to report having a return of sexual feeling for the first time in over a year. Four days before his discharge a piece of glasses lens was found hidden in the zippered pillow slip on the bed apparently having been placed there at the time of his attempt. At the discovery his projections returned and he spoke of his feeling that the glass had been left there to test him and also his feeling that he did not tell about the glass because of his determination that his living or dying was his own business. The patient was discharged to the care of two psychiatric nurses on Sunday, January 19, for transfer.

Discharge diagnosis: 000-x25, Schizophrenic reaction, acute undifferentiated type. Post-hospital treatment recommendations: continued hospitalization. Prognosis: the prognosis is guarded.

We have described the transactions surrounding Mr. Ullman while he was at Crest. The implications of this data in its more general institutional and historical context will be discussed in the final section of this report. We believe, however, that in itself the experience of Mr. Ullman offers strong support to the hypothesis that the emotional atmosphere of the milieu has significant influence on the choice of symptom manifest in mentally disturbed individuals. This hypothesis gains further and perhaps crucial support from a follow-up letter written by the Clinical

Director of Palm Clinic one year after Mr. Ullman's suicide attempt. Note that the same patient, in a different milieu, behaved very differently. The letter follows:

« I have talked to a number of people who have been concerned with Joe Ullman about our attitudes toward him and about our ways of dealing with him since he has been here. I have also talked with the patient himself about it. At the time he came here, we received advance reports from Crest which had made us almost uncertain as to whether we wanted to admit the patient here or not. In any event, we were surprised to find him, at the time of his arrival, in nowhere near as serious condition as we had anticipated. Nevertheless, in the first few weeks that he was here we kept him under very, very close supervision. In fact, for the first two or three weeks that he was here he had a special person with him twenty-four hours a day. We made it clear to him that this was on the basis of the history which we had received and that even though he did not seem so sick as to require all this supervision, we felt we would have to keep it in force until we had gotten to know him better. On the other hand, the general attitude of both his administrative physician and his therapist was from the first that he was capable of doing a great deal more than he was allowed to do and that he would probably get along quite well and improve quite quickly. This attitude certainly continued to dominate our feelings with the patient ever since he has been here.

The patient himself said that he could write volumes on the subject of what was the matter with Crest at the time that he was there. I do not personally think that it would be a good idea for you to contact him directly at this time. Although he seems to speak freely and with considerable confidence about his suicidal attempt and although he seems to have shown great improvement, we still feel that there is much underlying depression and uncertainty present which would need to be worked on for another year or two before the patient would be encouraged to get into too much from a purely descriptive point of view. I can tell you, however, about some of the things which he mentioned to me. He stated, for instance, that when he came to Crest everyone seemed to be quite worried about him and to "expect the worst." He said that they would not allow him to get a haircut for weeks after he came there. He was impressed by the fact that when he came here and stated that he wanted to get a haircut, he was taken downtown to a barber shop to get a haircut the first day that he was here. He mentioned that a number of things that were done at Crest seemed to him to be encouraging him to think of himself as more depressed and sicker than he was. He mentioned being left alone in virtual isolation for the first day and a half that he was at the hospital. He contrasted this to the fact that here he spent several hours talking with the doctors and was involved in activities with nurses and aides almost from the very minute that he arrived.

He mentioned, in addition to that, that many of the security measures adopted concerning him at Crest seemed to him to reflect a lack of logic on the part of the people there which made him feel a general lack of confidence in them. He mentioned, for instance, that his glasses were taken away from him because of fear that he might break them and use the glass to cut himself. He stated that this idea had never occurred to him and it was particularly worrisome to him because at times he was restrained in bed and would not have been able to use the glass anyway. He mentioned also having his shoe-strings taken out of his shoes as something that both puzzled him and also filled him with dismay. Although all of this sounds quite impressive and the patient assured me that he could go on for hours telling me other contrasting experiences, I do think it quite probable that at the time that he came here he was on his way out of the depths of the depression and one must take some of these statements with a "grain of salt."

Not long after he had been here, Joe actively entered into many activities here at the hospital. He became actively interested in the patient government of the hospital and became a very active worker in the committee which the patients had set up. He also became interested in the patient newspaper and became editor of it. He also entered actively into work with the drama group and had the leading role in the major play which was presented last year. He has carried on some of his interest in drama and has taken some courses. He is also now playing in a play given by the local Little Theatre Group. Not long after moving out of the hospital, Joe went to work . . . and has done very excellent work, having been complimented greatly by . . . [his boss].

In his work with his therapist Joe has done well. She has found him interesting and likeable from the beginning.

In August, 1962, one and one-half years after the above letter, Mr. Ullman (now released from the hospital) was interviewed by one of the authors. Some of his comments have been interspersed in the chapter. His progress has continued. Suicidal ideas have not returned; he stated that they had disappeared while he was still at Crest, after the attempt.

Chapter V

HARRY
EINSTON

HARRY EINSTON, A 23-YEAR-OLD COLLEGE STUDENT, was admitted to the hospital on March 6, 1959. He was brought by his parents and was admitted voluntarily. The admission note states:

« Harry is a . . . very anxious young man, who criticizes himself incessantly. He complains that his life has been a total failure, that in his 23 years he has accomplished nothing, and he will have to start again from the beginning, and he is not quite sure whether he will be able to do that or not. He has thought that he would be better off dead than in his present state, but apparently has not made any suicidal plans or attempts. He describes himself as feeling confused, unable to remember, and generally bewildered with the changes that have taken place within him. He talks as if he has experienced a recent change within himself, as he constantly refers to "how blind he was before" and how he sees himself in a new and much less satisfactory light now. In spite of his specific complaints about confusion and memory loss, there was no objective evidence of this, nor any glaring disturbance in his thought processes. Likewise, though he complains of depression, activity and speech are not retarded. . . . there seems to be a passive-aggressive quality to his constant self-criticism, in which he subtly criticizes others for failing him or for disliking him.

Einston came from a family of four, including an older sister. His mother was born and raised in the West, the oldest of a family of four children. She had a great deal of responsibility in the raising of her siblings. Her brothers and sisters have all attained considerable success in life. Mrs. Einston said of herself: "I've always been a worker . . . I've worked hard in my marriage, my house, and my community, and in my children."

Einston's father was raised in a highly authoritarian and patriarchal family. As a young man, he worked first in factories, and then started a trucking business. He maintained the business until he retired, five years before his son's entry into the hospital. After his retirement, he worked as a salesman.

The senior Einston was described by his wife as an excellent family provider, who gave Harry all sorts of athletic equipment and other luxuries. Although he never used physical force, he was a stern disciplinarian, nor was he less demanding of himself than of others. Harry's mother said, "His father is a type of person that if a thing has to be done, you don't shirk it, you do it. If there's a lawn to cut, you do it." His approach to family life was highly patriarchal; he made a clear distinction between his role and his wife's.

Harry's sister Roslyn described the father as follows:

« He just doesn't talk about himself; I just never felt that I had gotten to know him as most people would learn to know their fathers because he just isn't that way, he just doesn't open up. A good provider—everything in a material sense that you would ever want from a father, and I know he is the most loving father in the world, but he just plain doesn't express himself the way that we would have liked, probably. . . . He's not an affectionate person, I mean, as far as you know.

Of the mother, Roslyn said, "She is just the outgoing person, has all the interest." Mrs. Einston was better able to communicate with the children than their father. "Mother," said Roslyn, "was just kind of the sounding board there, because she just felt that she had to be, because Dad wasn't going to change."

Roslyn herself had been a quiet, shy girl, who "came out of it" when she went to college. She had always been the "big sister," protective of her younger brother. Harry felt that he was like her in many ways; he evidently felt a real loss when she left for college. At the time of admission, she was living by herself.

The case history stated:

« Both parents remarked that as a baby he was "always a sunny little fellow." The mother notes that they always had help in the home. When the patient was a child they had an exceptionally talented girl from the time the patient was two or three years of age until he was six. This woman was very kind and considerate and the patient was very close to her. They recall that he was thin and underweight until the age of three when he underwent a tonsillectomy, and then became a "chubby little fellow until the age of 15."

During his childhood the patient was always quiet but actively entered into neighborhood play and interaction with the other children at school. He always seemed to have many friends. Academically he did fairly well in school except for spelling and mathematics. He improved in high school and was on the honor roll and did not have difficulty during his undergraduate training at [the state university]. He was particularly interested in history and social science.

The patient began to be aware of a problem with his shyness and feeling of inadequacy during adolescence, particularly centering around his relationship with girls. He could not have a date alone but only could go in the company of a strong companion. He was interested in athletics, and never "quite made his letter." He states that he "likes bodily contact sports—football and hockey" and also prides himself on being a good swimmer. He seems to have some need to compensate in these areas and takes quite a bit of pride in his achievement here.

Since his high school days he has been interested in civil liberties and championing the underdog. He joined a few groups on the university campus, had an occasional date and developed a rather close relationship with a strong, aggressive friend. Through this relationship he was able to go to parties and dances and even [the year before his admission] take a trip to Miami. However, on his own he always feels inadequate and particularly perturbed by "not knowing what to say."

On the trip to Miami, he had sexual experiences for the first time. He also met a girl in whom he became quite interested. His sister said of this period, "In Miami he had met a girl who he liked a bit and whom he was writing to . . . they didn't know each other too well, but she was writing nice letters to him, and shortly after that . . . she wrote him and said she was engaged to someone else."

The friend, to whom the patient had been very much attached and whom he greatly admired for his aggressiveness and all-around ability, was married in the fall of 1958. Einston's feeling about his friend is indicated in his sister's comment: "Harry just—I don't know the word exactly—but he idolized him; I guess he just thought that Joe had everything, you know, the confidence and the way with women, and the grade point; I mean, the whole works." His mother said:

« Joe was very aggressive, very ambitious, and Harry tried to pattern himself so much after [him] . . . Joe was a great influence in Harry's life. When . . . he became engaged . . . I always felt this bothered Harry—all the boys were getting married. He possibly wasn't matured in this manner, he felt it was a great challenge: marriage, and obligations of marriage, and so on. He was also kidded by the boys a great deal about being pure; he wasn't promiscuous, that was another thing that they all—you know—used to kid him about. But this was something I guess that bothered him.

A year before his admission, the patient was rejected by the Army because of insomnia and sleepwalking. He took this as a blow. His sister said:

« All the guys were saying, "Oh, Einston, you're so lucky," you know, all this sort of thing to get out of it. But Harry didn't feel that way at all and yet I don't think he would say it too much because he would get razzed if he had. But he knew he needed it, he wanted to go in like nothing I've ever seen, and I mean to him I guess it was a therapy of a sort at that time, and the fact that he didn't get in bothered him. The fact that it was a rejection, number one. And it just kind of lit the match, from there everything just went downhill.

His mother commented: "That year, after his rejection from the Army, he absolutely insisted that he wasn't going to work [for the family], was going to get the job by himself because he felt that somebody was always helping him."

At the University, Harry prepared himself for teaching social sciences at the high school level. His choice was influenced by a family tradition of teaching, and by his great admiration of a social sciences professor at the University. Mrs. Einston said:

« He was very attached to Dr. McNeil, he was his idol. So
he went down there, and to major in that field [social
sciences]. And then he decided after that, he would teach—
teaching had run in the family: his sister had been a teacher,
his uncle. So there was no pushing, but this is what he wanted,
he set great goals for himself.

Harry began practice-teaching in the Fall of 1958. He had
difficulties with his critic teacher, however, who, he felt, was
extremely hard on him; and the practice-teaching assignment
ended in complete failure. Roslyn described the experiences
of this period:

« I remember his saying, "I just get up in front of the room
and I just feel all these people staring at me and I knew
I had to start talking," and I just cringe now that I think
about it, what he must have gone through up there in front
of the room. And I was helping him, typing notes, and I
remember how hard it got to be, because we had to plan
it, he had to fill out—we still have the very last one he did
at home—I had had it with some of my papers I had had at
my apartment where he had ended in a middle of a sentence,
that was when he just couldn't go on, you know, when he
was outlining this project for teaching that next day, or
whatever it was, and it was just rough trying to get him to
get a thought out so I could get them down on paper. I
just remember how difficult it was—"Now Harry, you've
got to, you just must." Here was I not knowing whether I
was doing for good or for bad, but saying "You've got to
concentrate, you'll never get it done otherwise," and he just
couldn't, he was unable.

Some of Harry's troubles with practice-teaching may have
stemmed from his ambivalence about making a career of
teaching. It was after the failure at practice-teaching, another
in a series of blows to his self-esteem, that Harry's behavior
began to deteriorate. At this time, he was living in the same
town in which his sister lived, and his parents still lived in a
nearby town. His mother recalled that during this period she
went to a Columbia hospital for a few days, and that Harry
visited her several times.

« [He] came in for breakfast one morning, all dressed up in
his Ivy League clothes, and he had his wrist watch on, and

he said to me, "Look at this, it's sort of scratched here." And I was so naive that I didn't know what it was, I just thought it was some roughness under his watch that he was showing me; and he said something about scratching it with a razor blade. And even then I didn't understand what he meant. A few days later that doubt was removed when he told us— he didn't tell them what—but that he had this tendency.

His sister reported that Harry called on her regularly for assistance in such matters as typing papers. She describes the incident through which she became aware of how disturbed he was:

« He wasn't sleeping at all, he'd come over in the morning and have breakfast with me just because he knew if he did not eat there he probably wouldn't eat, I guess. But he just didn't eat, he wasn't sleeping. . . . One night when he had to go see the critic teacher . . . he wanted to give him some extra time that he couldn't give him at school; and Harry was very upset about having to go see him, and it was a real icy, snowy night. . . . But I remember his driving over to Mr. K's that night, and on the way over, I could just tell how upset he was, and how scared he was about going, and I said to him at that time, if you want to come back here afterwards, you can, and I gave him the key to my apartment. And he came back that night, and he slept with me that night, and that's when I knew how sick he was, when he couldn't even go back to this other place. And that was, I guess it was that night, that I phoned home, and I was really afraid, I just didn't know what to do, because I knew that he was just getting so violently angry with himself and the world, that he just couldn't control himself.

Harry's mother continued:

« One day Roslyn phoned: "Mother, Harry is just so nervous and so upset, he isn't eating, and he tells me he's not sleeping." And still I didn't put my finger on it, but I went over immediately to see. He was over at the college there, and Roslyn was living in an apartment. And I could see that the boy was nervous—and came in dressed the way he always did—clothes were important to him—and said he would get up in front of the class—he'd phone me every once in awhile —and, "I just feel so nervous up there, I just feel cold and clammy. I get so scared when I'm up there," he said. "And when they ask me questions, I say to myself am I able to to tell these forty youngsters?" And he had other friends who taught high school who would say, "Oh, Harry, you just bluff your way through. It's all right." But Harry wasn't built that way, he couldn't do it, and this all took place rapidly. And then I phoned Dr. Jules in town and I said, "I'd like you to see Harry, he seems so nervous." He was so busy, he said, "That's only natural, I'll give you a few phenobarbs for him," which he did.

Dr. Jules then saw Harry in his office. He told Mrs. Einston that he thought Harry was thinking of self-destruction, and suggested he see a psychologist, Dr. Lloyd. Mrs. Einston arranged for Harry to see Dr. Lloyd, who felt that Harry could be helped. He suggested that Harry not return to the University, and referred him to a psychiatrist, Dr. Smyth. Harry had to wait two weeks for an appointment with Smyth. During this period, Harry became more and more disturbed, sleeping little, muttering to himself. Drs. Smyth and Jules jointly decided that Harry needed some hard physical work. Accordingly, Harry went to work in his uncle's warehouse.

His behavior while working in the warehouse did not improve. He avoided people, hiding himself in the warehouse, behaving, in his sister's words, "animalistically." His mother described this period:

« He'd have to get up in the morning to go to work. This is the routine which they decided, which I think was very very wrong because [although] he did work . . . when he . . . would come home . . . it wasn't our Harry. He would drive up to the house, and he would sit in the car for about ten minutes before he would decide to come in . . . and weep by the hours, just cried, all I could see was long lashes of tears falling, there was nothing anyone could say or do, and we didn't try to give him any home medication, but we knew enough, I knew enough about the thing, we didn't try to tell him, "Oh, pep yourself up," I know that was like putting a flame on a fire—oil on a fire—to say that, so we didn't do that.

During this period he saw Dr. Smyth about three times, at two-week intervals. His mother said:

« And I was never very sure that he was going to get to Dr. Smyth's, he would rebel so. He said he just couldn't understand what he was going to get out of it. He said, ."I talk and find out that I'm not getting anywhere and I just can't understand this." He saw Smyth about three times. . . . The only other thing that Smyth said he should have is psychiatry at least two or three times a week, [and] quickly to get help as soon as possible. Well, we went along with that, and then of course the family inquired and then Crest was suggested.

As Mrs. Einston indicated, the family had great difficulty in finding any kind of hope in any professional aid, shifted from physician to psychologist, from psychologist to psychiatrist, and ultimately to Crest. The hopelessness of Harry's situation and of the people around him increased with each blind alley. So that when the family, after all its tribulations, turned in hope to Crest, the burden of expectations placed upon the institution was enormous.

Harry entered the hospital on March 6, 1959. The admitting psychiatrist, Dr. Rhodes, was encouraging. His initial diagnosis was: schizophrenic reaction, latent type. His prognosis was that Harry would leave the hospital after not too long a time, once he was thoroughly involved in a psychotherapeutic relationship. The psychiatrist pointed out that the patient had "many intact assets." He based his interpretation of Harry's problems on the young man's relationship with his family.

« The central disturbance in this patient seems to be with his father and that he wants his father's approval but resents his father's rejection in the past. It seems quite definite that he must fail to injure his father and at the same time be feminine and impassive to win the father's approval and avoid dangerous competition with the father. This problem centering around being a man became most acute when he was placed in the role of an authority masculine figure during the teacher-training program and when he had to face the end of his dependent position in society as a student. His self-esteem was further lowered by being rejected by the Army, which seemed to him conclusive proof that he was not a man and could never be successful as one.

There seems to be quite possibly a more serious underlying problem with the mother, although very little evidence of this came up during the examination. It is quite possible there is a close symbiotic identification between the patient and the mother and one has rather vague impressions that the patient, as an extension of the mother, is giving the mother some gratification by his frustration of his father's wishes for him, and by pointing out to the father what a failure he has been as a father.

During the period from March to August, the pattern of Einston's experience in the hospital consisted in a series of cycles in which he communicated hopelessness to the hospital staff, which would then respond anxiously, even to the point of interpreting his behavior as suicidal whenever it was in the least ambiguous. Einston's usual response to the staff's anxiety was an increase of hopelessness.

His hopelessness was expressed in many forms. On his third day he said to an aide: "Do people ever stay here for the rest of their lives? My sister told me that Crest was a very good place before I came here. It's funny, me sending my sister a birthday card, I may never see her again." And: "I'll probably never use my automobile again. I'll never get better." The aide commented that he was "pessimistic regarding effectiveness of treatment here."

On March 10, four days after his admission, he bitterly stated: "All I do is work up sweats and take showers." On March 16 he said to an aide: "I'm going crazy, Bob. How do I talk to these people [i.e., staff and patients]? I don't seem to know what to say." On March 19, an aide wrote: "Walked very slow upon meeting several other patients and staff out walking. 'I guess it's time for walking the dogs . . . I'm only joking.'" On March 21, the aide reported: "Mumblings were of self-derogatory nature, apathetic, despondent type, for example, 'I'll be here at Crest all my life, help me.'" On the 22nd, "What's the good of it all. I'm not getting any better. I've got to get well." On April 17, "The phrase that was most often repeated was 'What shall I do, do, do, do, do,' etc."

In April, he continued to express hopelessness and anxiety to the staff. As a consequence, on April 18, his off-ground bowling trips were cancelled. On April 19, the following was reported:

« The patient had piece of broken glass in his hand and stood up and put the glass on the edge of bed. He looked quite dejected. "What's this?" "Just a scratcher." "For scratching what?" "Nothing, I've had it a long time." "What were you planning to do with it?" "Nothing. What can you do with a piece of glass?" "Looks very obvious but I don't know what your intention was." The doctor called and the patient was moved to the closed section. Protested feebly but came with me without difficulty.

The managing doctor's interpretation was pessimistic:

« Harry seemed to settle considerably after about three weeks in the hospital but during the past ten days there has been an increase in his "display" of agitation at bowling, the lodge, and in the lounge. As far as I can see, this symptom represents a combination of self-punishment and indirectly expressed hostility. It seems often that he is compelled to fail "to spite" his father and I imagine he will respond similarly to treatment. Last evening he was found playing with a piece of glass on his wrist. This seems to have resulted from my being increasingly firm and restricting in his privileges because of his symptoms. I believe his suicidal gesture is to a large degree motivated by unexpressed hostility for me as a substitute for his father.

He has been placed on full suicidal precautions because of the real but probably small danger that he might seriously injure himself but also to indicate that he will be protected by us. It is also my feeling that as a whole our original plan to move the patient fairly rapidly into activities and limited restrictions has not been successful, so a more extensive milieu experience on the closed section seems indicated. Therefore I expect him to be there for some time.

In another report of the same incident:

« That evening the patient made a suicidal gesture scraping a piece of glass across his wrists when he was observed by an aide. While it was not felt that this patient was acutely suicidal, it was felt that it would be best to manage this gesture as a suicidal threat. The patient was placed on suicidal precautions on the closed section.

Up to this point, Einston had been in the semi-open ward of the hospital. Here he had enjoyed a certain degree of freedom. As indicated, he was transferred from the semi-open to the closed ward. This was the locked ward of the hospital, in which the most disturbed patients were kept under close supervision.

If Einston had been looking to the hospital for hope, he received a disappointing response. The action of transferring him to the locked ward was not hopeful, nor was the managing doctor's negative interpretation of his behavior. It is interesting that the managing doctor attempted to give the orders to restrict Einston a positive flavor: "[Einston] must find out that he can be very sick without us being concerned or pressuring him to get well."

On April 24, while Einston was still on suicide precautions, there occurred an incident which illustrates the negative, suicidal interpretation placed on almost all of Einston's actions. He was out on a walk with an aide, when he "apparently" began looking down at "what seemed like" some broken pieces of glass.

« He seemed to be on the verge of picking them up and I called his name and we continued on. He asked the time. "We should be going up to the doctor's now." He wandered down a bit further, to pet a dog, when a car started by and Einston started to run toward it. I called him quite sharply a couple of times and he pulled up barely ten feet from the car and came back with flushed face. "Let's take a short cut back to the doctor's, it's getting late," said the aide.

The managing doctor's tendency to interpret Einston's behavior in the worst possible light is indicated in his report on this incident:

« While out exercising with one of the female aides, he walked down to the road and threw himself in front of a car, apparently in such a way that there was not too much danger of him being injured. Following this he has been confined to the ward except for the past week when he has been again allowed to go off the ward to therapy appointments. . . . These suicidal gestures could possibly be related to direct attack on his symptoms of muttering and passive resistance, first by the managing physician and second, by his therapist.

It is significant that the psychiatrist interpreted the aide's note to indicate that Einston jumped in front of the car, when the note, although ambiguous, suggests more strongly that Einston ran after a car which was going by.

On May 27, Einston at mealtime broke a spoon in half, making "two dangerously sharp edges." Asked about his reasons for this action, he replied to an aide that he was "p—— off." The physician found in the action the "implication that [the spoon] could be used as a self-destructive instrument"; and as a result, some privileges which Einston had recently regained were once more withdrawn. Einston reacted with bitterness and sarcasm to the withdrawal of these privileges.

A few days later, Einston began an action of rubbing the back of his head, a habit which was to become so severe as to cause a bald patch. His reply to an aide, who said that if he continued the action she would have to "hound" him about it, was: "Guess I'll have to keep doing it, then."

A week after this exchange, he made some superficial scratches on his wrist. He said that he had inflicted them with his comb. He spoke of his discouragement with his treatment. "Got to go to another hospital, got to go to another hospital," he said.

During the period in which these incidents occurred, between March and August, the staff was under instructions to maintain a detached attitude toward Einston. The managing doctor's March 12 directive to nurses and aides read:

« His self-derogatory remarks should not be responded to but bypassed. Marked anxiety can be handled by matter-of-fact or casual attitude giving patient support by your presence and direction of patient to activities.

Again, on May 1, the following order was written by Dr. Rhodes:

« I think it very important that all personnel continue a matter-of-fact, distant, and uninvolved attitude toward Mr. Einston. This does not exclude a show of warmth and interest in his activities and interests, but it definitely does preclude any direct or indirect expression of concern or emotional reaction to whether or not he does have symptoms and whether or not he makes progress. Thus, I see it as out of line to give any of the usual verbal signs of encouragement or praise regarding his treatment progress.

How these instructions were carried out, and the effect they had upon Einston, can be seen in the reports of this period, such as that of March 18. On this date, Einston is reported as saying to an aide, "I can't figure out what to do next. I can't talk to the people." The aide replied: "These are things to talk to your doctor about. I can't give you any answer." Einston protested, "I know, but—." Then, subsiding, he remarked he'd be willing "to trade places with that dog"; and putting back his head, he gave a dog's howl.

On May 1, he asked an aide to intercede with his doctor, to see if he could be allowed outside, as he was getting tired of being confined. "Do you suppose you could ask Dr. Rhodes? He and I aren't getting along anymore . . . or is it myself I'm not getting along with?" The aide gave the prescribed response, that Einston should talk it over with Dr. Rhodes. The patient then "mumbled something."

Of this situation, one of the aides said in retrospect:

« At times he would assert himself and become positive and clear thinking, had no trouble being decisive about his actions. And other times he would whisper and mutter—have trouble getting his words out. It was my feeling that we should handle this firmly, quite matter-of-factly. I wanted to say things to him like, "For Christ's sake, come out of it now, we're here to help you and we like you, and we are going to help you." But they were extremely passive with this kind of behavior, didn't do anything very direct. I don't know whether it would have made much difference or not. I often told the doctor what I wanted to say to him. I would report what had actually gone on and say what I really wanted to say and I never felt as though I had said the right thing. The doctor thought the things I would say were too harsh, that you cannot be that interpretive, in a sense saying, "I don't want you to interpret what he's doing."

It was manifest that this kind of response would conflict with the prescription against "expression of concern" or "verbal signs of encouragement."

During this period of limited communication with the staff, it might be assumed that Einston had been communicating with his therapist. But this was not the case. Dr. Preston, his therapist, and Einston had never established adequate communication; for long periods of the therapy sessions, the two sat in complete silence. Thus, the ward staff's referral of Einston to his therapist, each time he expressed anxiety, presented him with a bitter dilemma.

When, in May, Einston began to seem "better," he was given

permission to have his spectacles, which had been removed as part of his suicide precautions. His response showed an interest in the future: "Great, I can save my eyesight."

In August, Einston received a letter from his sister which depressed him. He commented to a nurse, "I don't know why I came here. I'm no better." When the nurse said, "You must do exactly what the doctor says to," Einston replied: "Did you ever talk to him?"

Preston, Einston's therapist, later said: "He was obviously withholding tremendously in therapy. And in the face of this I allowed his activities to expand because he was fairly appropriate about it. He looked much better, still scratching his head, but he looked much better."

In this period from March through August, while Einston's communication with the staff and the therapist declined, he continued to be able to communicate with his family.

When Einston first arrived at Crest, he corresponded regularly with his parents. On March 13, he wrote a coherent letter in which he commented: "I hope to see you very soon because things are rather lonely and I miss you a great deal."

On March 15, he had a visit from his parents which was described by the aide as follows:

« Apparently talked very sadly with parents about not being able to think. "Why am I here? I always forget what I want to say to the doctor." As the parents were leaving, his father said, "No, you talk to these people Harry, when you see them just say, 'Hi there.'" The patient replied, "But Dad, you told me that all my life and look where it's gotten me." The father said, "That's all right, son, you just talk to them—talk to that college boy, he went to your school." The patient retaliated again verbally, "mumble, mumble." The patient had also said, "They are giving me all those tests and things. It's beginning to make me feel really sick." The mother then kissed the patient goodbye and said, "I kiss your picture everyday." The patient turned away and said, "I know, I know, Mom." He then returned to his room looking very sad and anxious. He said to an aide, "It's so good to see my parents but then it isn't." This was said in a very dejected tone of voice.

On March 18, he wrote to his parents again. "It was wonderful seeing you last Friday. My condition hasn't changed very much because of my inability to foresee my next move. I saw Dr. Preston, the psychotherapist, today and I'll be seeing him three times a week."

Shortly after this letter, he received one from his mother in which she wrote: "The doctor told us you are cooperating and we know it won't be long before you are back home. We hope then that you can plan a trip."

Later that month he wrote as follows to his parents:

« Dear Folks: It's getting tougher. I can't see my way clear of this whole dilemma. My mind is gone and my inability to communicate and my general state of worry (about everything) had driven me to despair. I would like to see you but that wouldn't solve my problems, for only I could do that.

My life in a mental hospital is bleak because I'm not thinking rationally. Oh to write something in a lighter vein, but I am not able to comprehend the gist of this whole thing.

First day of spring—what a beautiful day—but they are beautiful only if they can be seen through receptive eyes.

Roslyn is wonderful—I wish her the best.

This exchange of letters occurred at the same time that he was expressing so much hopelessness directly to the staff. On March 31, his parents visited him again. The patient was walking out the door of his ward when his parents arrived:

« The patient started crying and said, "I can't stand this place. You've got to get me out." Sobbing and crying all the way down to his room. Several times while the aide passed room patient was talking in a high pitched sort of hysterical voice complaining about various things in the hospital. After 55 minutes the aide went into room and said, "Five minutes more." This was more or less ignored. After one hour the aide went to room and knocked. No answer. So aide walked in and said, "It's time now," and there was no move on the part of the visitors to leave. All the efforts on the part of the aide to get the visitors to leave were ignored. Finally, after an hour and a half the mother joined the father, who had been standing by the door ready to leave ten minutes before. Food and records were given to the patient before this aide realized she should have taken them first. Patient settled down fairly well after visit. Was invited for walk at 3:30. He conversed a lot, attempting to be friendly.

Another visit occurred in May: "Was visited by his mother from 1:15 to 1:30, afterward appeared tremulous, mumbling, hesitant, etc. Repeatedly said, 'I didn't get much chance to say anything or didn't get to say much.'"

On June 19, he was again visited by his parents. Harry was heard saying, "No, no, no" loudly, and his father left several times saying, "I'll let you know." The patient looked pale and shaken, continuously talking to himself. After this incident, he said to the nurse that he wanted to be as good as the next guy.

The general impression the hospital made upon Einston's parents is indicated in a comment made later by Einston's father:

« It's worse than a jail. First of all you've got those fellows in there walking around or the nurses with a chain here and a bunch of keys, they lock it like in jail, they rattle the keys, they unlock it, and so on. One day when we were out there, the side door in there, you could see footprints where they were kicking up against the door, I guess about as high as they could kick. You think that they would have enough sense to wipe the thing off, that the father or mother or somebody or another patient wouldn't see all that stuff.

Einston's parents felt that the attitude of the hospital staff toward them was neglectful, even antagonistic, during this period.

« Of course, I do know you're not supposed to have any contact with the person with whom—the psychiatrist with whom your child is working. But they—as you pass them, they look at you, and you know you think to yourself, I'm a human being—they would just pass and not say a word. . . . And another thing, when we would drive up, the doctors would be wandering back and forth, and they'd see me sitting there waiting for my appointment, and they'd come up, "Now what are you doing here, why you," and I said, "Doctor, I have a son here, I can wait out here." They made you feel even that the grounds were so sacred at Crest, you couldn't walk on it, I mean, they gave you that terrible feeling that you were the worst arch criminal, honestly.

The negative attitude of the hospital staff toward the parents was communicated most markedly by the social worker, Miss Simmons, who was having regular one-hour sessions every two weeks with Mrs. Einston. In August, Miss Simmons wrote a report covering her interviews with Mrs. Einston from April:

« Then she began talking of wondering if she and her husband could live long enough to help him get well. One interview was so full of death and morbidity in one form or another, including her statement that it would be easier to adjust to her son's death than to his mental illness, that I felt quite concerned about her and her ability to hold together.

Mrs. Einston herself indicated in interviews subsequently that she felt very hostile toward Miss Simmons, who, she said, made her feel extremely guilty about her role in Einston's illness. She felt that she never could develop any rapport with Miss Simmons. Mrs. Einston later said: "She'd talk down to me, as if I were a little—as if I had taken this boy and had given him this terrible affliction—only God knows where he got it—but I had given it to him. This I resent!"

Mrs. Einston's uneasiness about Crest was reinforced by her visits with Harry.

« May 30, Decoration Day, we went out there, and there were so few around, the place was so desolate, hot, that hot summer, and Harry said that the heat in there was so terrible, and there were days he wasn't allowed [out], and he told me, you know what it's like to be locked up for four and five weeks in this one room pacing back and forth. I think the place was highly, highly over-rated. I didn't expect over-stuffed furniture or anything, but there was something so— I don't know. There were old people, young people . . . he was very kind by nature, he was so troubled about this little old lady . . . you possibly know, an old lady who kept going around saying, "Oh, my God, my God, my God." He was troubled for everyone there and he kept saying, "I'm just the sickest one here, but I cannot accept therapy," that was his cry, that was all. . . . The sounds, the noise and some of the things that people say, this same woman you speak of, that we feel that was Harry, the one who, the things that were her complex, the things that she shouted about, these things he told me. These things I remember, as I say if you ever want to know more, but these things were all things that were against his very nature, because he wasn't a crude person. Unfortunately, his father can swear, Harry would have been a better swearer if he had been living today maybe, he never could swear or never could blow up or anything. And he was a gentle man by nature, he was fine and nice, and until he was ill I never heard profanity, but there was profanity there, and I remember he would ask us when we'd come over there, "Bring me something to do something to myself," and I said, "Harry, don't ask that, you know we can't."

Mrs. Einston's impressions of the hospital's negative attitude toward her heightened in June, when Dr. Preston decided to prohibit further visits from the mother. The basis for this decision was in part the belief that Einston tended to depend on his mother too much, and to regress in his visits with her. (Dr. Preston had taken on the responsibility of hospital doctor as well as therapist since Dr. Rhodes had finished his residency training and had left Crest.)

The Einston family thereupon began to try to get advice from psychiatrists outside of Crest about the merits of the hospital. Mrs. Einston visited a doctor at a state hospital of which she had heard good reports. He gave her an extremely negative evaluation of Crest. She also asked a psychiatrist friend of the family's about other hospitals. Apparently, however, Mrs. Einston did not contact any. Mrs. Einston prevailed upon another psychiatrist to visit Crest and her son, and to evaluate the treatment. The psychiatrist returned with a positive report. He reassured the parents, who then decided against moving Einston from Crest.

Einston reacted gloomily to the news that his mother's visits had been canceled. His head shaking and muttering were noticeable. He received letters from home the following day; and was heard to remark, on this day and the following one, "I'm sick, I've got to talk to someone . . . got to see someone . . . got to get well and get out." He spoke a good deal of his homesickness. A robe sent him by his mother on July 5 brought on another period of mumbling.

During the early part of August, Einston's behavior began to improve. On August 3, he wrote a warm, completely coherent letter to his sister:

« Other than that things are going pretty well (but slowly) with me here at Crest. The most important ingredient in this treatment is keeping busy and presently I've stepped up my activities. Most of the people here are pretty nice, but in my position it is hard to really appreciate exactly to what extent they are helping me.

On August 19, he sent his parents a friendly postcard in which he said he was planning to do some sight-seeing. On August 22, he sent another postcard.

« I'm enjoying the fine weather, as I'm certain you are also. I'm hoping and working to find the answers to my problems here at Crest. Progress is slow, but steady. I'm again bowling, which I enjoy very much. I'm regretful that I'm not a part of the things I have known, but in time I'm sure that situations and my life will be much more meaningful.

At about this time, Dr. Preston, in psychotherapy, had made an interpretation to him that the reason he continued to fail to make progress in treatment was his hostility to his father, who was paying for the treatment.

« The issue of withholding came up, and the issue of money came up; and I made an interpretation at this point. I recall that he sort of opened the way to an interpretation by negative things, sort of, such as "wasting my old man's money doing this"; and it was obvious that there was something in the wasting of the old man's money that was not unpleasurable. So I brought up in an interpretation the fact that this was one way of getting at the old man, in that he knew that money was very important to his father, and that this was a way of pinching him where the pinch hurt.

During this period, Einston read an article on schizophrenia in a popular magazine. A paragraph in the article stated that there was little hope for effective treatment of schizophrenic patients, and that only in modifying the conditions that led to the development of schizophrenia in susceptible persons was there any hope of mastering the illness. In other words, hope lay only in prevention. The article discouraged Einston greatly.

On August 24, the weekend following the session in which Dr. Preston had suggested to Einston that a hostile motive might underlie his reticence in therapy, Einston participated in an outing with several other patients, accompanied by staff members. Although Einston had been sarcastic and aggressive the day before the outing, he awakened with apparent enthusiasm and interest in the trip.

The outing included a trip by ferry boat. When the ferry was within several hundred yards of a peninsula, Einston left the group to buy a cup of coffee. As the ferry approached the landing, the aide realized that Einston had not rejoined the group. A search of the boat did not uncover him; and the authorities were notified.

Dr. Preston later described his feelings upon learning that Einston had disappeared:

« And it was on the weekend following the hour in which I had made this interpretation about his hostility toward his father that he jumped off the ferry. And when he turned up missing from the ferry boat ride, I sweat; I had a lot of anxious fantasies about the interpretation of hostility to the father. I had a lot of anxious thoughts and fantasies. I was sweating.

Exactly what occurred is not altogether clear. There is some indication that a woman patient challenged Einston to jump off the boat. Whether or not as a result of this challenge, he did jump from the ferry. He was an excellent swimmer, and stayed afloat for a while. Then, apparently, he was picked up by a small motor boat, which took him to a nearby island. There he went to a cabin, where he met two men. They gave him dry clothes; and he called his parents. The two men drove Einston to his rendezvous with his parents, who then drove him to their home.

On the way back, Mrs. Einston reported that Harry said he planned to drown himself. "He got in the car, and he was discouraged to the end of the world. He said, 'I tried, I thought I could drown myself.' He said that he jumped from the upper deck; and he said, 'I simply kept swallowing water, and for my life I couldn't submerge, I simply couldn't drown.'" She described what happened when they got home: "Then he said to me, 'You know, Mother, I tried to commit suicide; you know I'm liable for arrest, suicide is a legal offense.' These things bothered him. The fact that he might lose—he never, of course, was committed, so he didn't lose his citizenship—but this worried him, too."

Two aides, Mrs. Einston reported, were sent to the Einston home to bring Harry back to the hospital.

« That's what the doctor said we had to do, was send him back. He didn't say, *"You* bring him back; send him back." So . . . all that night Harry walked the floor, and said to me about four o'clock in the morning, he said, "I've got to do something, I just can't go back to that place, there's only one way out." And I knew what he meant, I was fearful because there were cars in the garage. I just didn't know which way he was going to figure out what to do, this is what he said. I said, "Harry, you mustn't, you can't do this, it isn't right, it's against God, it's against everything, you can't do it." "I can't go back to that place" . . . he was going to get his car, that was a Saturday night, you see, they came for him on Sunday. He sat—the arm my husband is leaning on there—Harry sat on the edge of that arm for about two hours straight. The boys [aides] told us to leave him alone. Mr. Einston had contacted his brother that morning, he was desperate, he didn't know what to do. This also angered Harry very much, because he knew his father had contacted his uncle; and that's the uncle he had worked for at that period; and they were all telling him, "You can get out of it, snap out of it," that critical month that he worked. Those boys sat here—about three hours, was it? Harry came out in the kitchen, I fixed a tray, the way he would when his friends were around, the social things that were nice, he'd always been used to, fix a cold drink, brought it in and talked to the boys; and finally, about five o'clock, he says, "Well, what choice have I?" and he went out in the station wagon with the boys.

The official nurses' notes report the scene in the home as follows:

«   Aides L and K to Meadsville to return patient to hospital. Arrived at parents' home approximately 2:30. Met by uncle, later joined by father in front of the house. They stated that patient did not want to and would not return. The patient could be heard inside the house yelling loudly; words however not distinguishable. Convinced parents we should like to see patient before leaving. Greeted by patient at the door on entering house. Patient shaking hands with the aides and appeared calm. Although apparently it had been necessary that parents chat with patient at length to convince him to talk to us. From approximately 2:45 until departure the patient alternately talked with aides and parents, former in living room, latter kept more or less out of sight in kitchen. The patient's appearance outwardly at least calm but in interaction with aides would become agitated, weepy and anxious whenever any other family members entered room. Quite indecisive regarding returning to hospital but at the same time receptive and amiable on three or four occasions to the point where the aide's impression was that he was ready to return. Derogatory remarks in parent's hearing when they and the patient chatted alone. Shouted insults re hospital and the hopelessness of his case.

During this period patient's conversation and verbalizations for the most part clearly understandable. Usual muttering notably absent. Expressed "I know what's wrong with me but I also know my mind and it has not changed. Will not change. Maybe people [at the hospital] thought I was better, but inside I know I wasn't." Argued futility of returning to the hospital. "I know what I'm going back to. The same old thing. Starting all over. Going back to vegetate for another six months. Well, a vegetable couldn't play volleyball. Right back where I started." Much talk re: "My problem. What good would it do to tell anybody." Seemed to really want to talk these things out with someone. Aide supported by declaring awareness of difficulty in putting thoughts into words when talking with therapist. And as a last resort that the patient should return if for no other reason than to give therapy another chance and really make an effort to talk things out with the doctor. Patient related having read an article describing his illness and stating that the chances of his getting well were nil. At times the patient seemed to be saying "I don't want to get well" at others "I want to get well but it's hopeless to try." Expressed concern re possible restriction or removal of privileges as a "punishment" for eloping and as related to what he might say in future therapy sessions.

Parents reported patient called them asking that he be picked up yesterday evening. The patient was shirtless and trousers wet when mother met patient. Of this patient related to aide only "That all problems had to come to a focal point with only one answer. I tried to do it but could not and swam to shore" [*sic*]. Parents state that the patient told them that he had dived from the top deck of ferry in suicidal attempt. The parents conveyed the idea of feeling hospital had not taken adequate security measures in taking this patient out, not properly searching and showing concern for his whereabouts or well being. Aides faced difficulty of coping with parents' misinformation, misconception and emotional outbursts, necessary to ask parents to leave us alone with patient. While the aides attempted the use of calm reasoning, friendliness and some assurance, the parents tended to use supplication, demands, pressure, threats, compromises. The aides insisted that the patient's decision to return be his own and did not leave with patient until patient did decide he felt on his own that he wanted to return.

Patient sighing heavily and fearful while shaking hands with father, uncle, and kissing mother. Parting shot while walking out: "It was nice spending a little time with you." Seemingly little real feeling in statement. Quite preoccupied during the early part of the trip back to Crest. Nervously shaking head, breathing heavily, cracking knuckles, digging at head, biting nails. This subsided to the point where patient able to carry on some casual conversation with aides. Mentioned drinking beer with father and spoke of weekend as being "quite interesting." No signs of attempt to elope during trip. Did ask twice to stop to go to BR. Accepting refusal with "I'll try to hold it." Upon approaching hospital patient restated his uncle's proposition that he try it for thirty days at Crest, and if nothing happens he could go someplace. As an afterthought added "Yeah, thirty days, free home trial." Seemed to be seeking reassurance that he could start anew. Getting out of car at the hospital asked "What if I change my mind now." "I think you've made the right decision." Arrived at hospital, to ward, approximately 6:25 P.M.

It seems evident that the ferry boat incident worked to lower the already low confidence the Einstons and Harry placed in the hospital. Prior to the incident, Harry had been shaken by the interpretation of his withholding in therapy and by the negative implication of the article he had read. Now, his mother's anxiety and ambivalence about his returning to the hospital, his father's complete rejection of the hospital, and his uncle's peculiar compromise ("thirty days free home trial") further undermined his belief in the hospital's ability to help him.

The aftermath of the ferryboat incident widened the gulf of uneasiness and suspicion between the Einston family and the hospital. Mrs. Einston insisted to the social worker, Miss Simmons, that Harry had jumped from the boat, and that his jump was a suicide attempt. But the hospital staff, including Miss Simmons, were not convinced of this. Although Dr. Preston reported later that he was anxious about Harry until he was found, the staff was not only skeptical as to whether or not a genuine suicide attempt had been made, but even as to whether or not Harry had jumped from the boat. This skepticism was communicated to Mrs. Einston, in the face of her attempts to make it understood at the hospital that the suicide attempt was real.

The evening aide reported upon Harry's behavior upon his return to the hospital.

« Came into lounge on arrival. Acknowledged greetings of patients. Said that he had enjoyed himself and had drunk beer. Seemed well controlled for awhile. But then became quite anxious and flighty. Ate very little of his dinner. Was told by nurse that he wouldn't be going off the ward, etc. Then came into the office and asked, "What's the deal?" After being told again that he wouldn't leave the ward until he sees Dr. Preston, he replied in his usual sarcastic manner, "You mean I'm going to miss my TV tonight."

The next day he was quite upset. He expressed hopelessness —"These four walls again, thirty days, what am I supposed to do, I've defeated my purpose." He would follow with glances at the aide, as if awaiting comments or reactions. During a card game, he mumbled, "My sister, my uncle told me they would help me here. Cards, cards, cards." He became increasingly angry that day. He mumbled that his uncle told him that the hospital would help him. The aide said, "Why don't you talk it over with Dr. Preston." Harry replied in a loud voice, "Who can talk to him, I can't." He remarked that Crest was a prison, and mumbled something about "being dead." Pulling down the shade in his room at bedtime, he became enraged, and began to tear at the wire screen. He subsided when the aide offered to adjust the shade for him.

On Tuesday he started looking for activities again; he was willing, he said, to work at such trivial tasks as typing menus, "Just to give me something to do." He commented that he was so sick of cards, he preferred to bang against the wall. When, in the evening, he asked if he could shower unaccompanied, and was told that he could not shower at all, he again became angry. His anger, expressed in threats and wall-pounding, persisted for some hours.

On August 29, Harry received a letter from home. It evidently upset him; he shouted, "How can they say a thing like that!" When Preston happened to pass through the hall, Harry shouted "bastard!" Later that day he told an aide how dismal and disheartening things were for him. He said he knew many people were "pulling for him," that Crest was a good place, nationally renowned, and that the type of treatment here had helped many —but it "is not for me." He went on to say that he couldn't talk; he was miserable; he didn't like the thoughts he had; nothing seemed to help; he was wasting his time and his money. He was told, in reply, that "therapy is a tough business."

On this day he wrote a letter to his parents.

«   Dear Folks:

I find it impossible to respond to psychotherapy treatment here at Crest. Talking to Dr. Preston or any doctor isn't the answer.

I have inquired about other forms of treatment, but here at Crest they don't believe in anything but *trying* to talk yourself into feeling better or different. I feel that a frontal lobotomy operation is the only answer because if I'm to re-main like a vegetable in a hospital it might as well be that form of operation or let me go to a different hospital which is run differently, and less expensive. You must act upon my request because I can't see my way clear here.

The next day, Harry asked to speak to the head nurse. He told the nurse that things weren't working out, and that he wanted another kind of treatment. His mail again disturbed him that day. He was heard to say, "How can they say it?" By Friday, he sounded somewhat more hopeful, and seemed to be trying to maintain some control of himself. The next day, in conversation with an aide, he criticized Preston severely. He pointed out that he did not communicate with Preston, while the aide kept say-ing, "Well, you tell Preston all about this." The patient said, "I can't talk to the doctor." The aide replied, "Why don't you tell the doctor about that." He expressed concern to the aide about "remaining in the hospital the rest of my life, getting along in society when I get out, explaining all this to my friends," and made comments about his worthlessness, "The only thing I can do around here that is worth while is type menus and make my bed." Later that day he said, "If this doesn't work I don't know what I'm going to do." He asked many questions about other treatment, other hospitals, other doctors, to which the aide responded: "I don't know anything about that." He then spoke of going elsewhere to get temporary relief, and later re-turning to Crest. The aide's reply was, "If you had a bad cold probably you would have a headache along with it. Would you go to the hospital to get the aspirin for your headache and then go home to straighten out the cold?"

Einston was preoccupied with essentially the same doubts and fears throughout most of September. He spoke continually of disbelief that he would ever get well in the hospital; queried others as to whether or not they didn't believe he ought to try something else—another hospital, another kind of treatment, another doctor, perhaps even quitting the hospital and trying to make a go of life outside. Again and again he repeated: "Got to get well. Be here forever. What should I do?" The response continued to be that he should talk with his doctor, to which Einston countered that he and the doctor did not talk. Einston also continued to express hopelessness at such futile, trivial occupations as card-playing and menu-typing; yet, as before, he often accepted these occupations. "I'm sick of cards, but if it will help me get well, I'll do it." He made consistent essays at finding hope in his situation, at convincing himself that something would come of his internment in the hospital; but he was unable to sustain such faith, and was overwhelmingly dominated by feelings of hopelessness. Mail and packages from home also caused Einston anxiety. He expressed warmth, love, homesickness for his family, but remarked of them that they "didn't understand."

As the end of the month drew near, his speech was less distinguishable; at times he spoke in a voice too low to hear. He began to use profanity freely, remarking on one occasion to a female nurse: "I never used to use that language. I was too good a boy." His behavior in the last week of September seemed to reach a new low. September 23: "Another interesting day tomorrow," he said. "I see the doctor. Real interesting. We sit there and look at each other. $17.50. Not a bad deal. Shit." Going into the lounge, he said by way of greeting: "Hi—hi forever." And then, as if answering himself: "Hi, forever." Later in the day, when he spoke with exaggerated sarcasm to a nurse, and she asked him: "Why don't you get that anger out in therapy, Mr. Einston?" he responded, "Who's angry?" and then, shaking his head: "I just cannot talk to him." He continued, after a bit, "I'm having a real good time kissing my dad's money away —that's what I get out of Dr. Preston, that's all. Yeah, a real good time." September 25: "Stranded in a jungle," Einston said, "thirty days trial, sure, Uncle Mark, I'll try thirty days, huh, thirty years, forever, in this place, I'll have to stand it, it's forever." Aide remarked: "You sound pretty determined about that," and Einston said, "Huh?" Einston's anger was expressed not only in sarcasm to others but also toward himself. "God damn it, I'm such an idiot, fool, fool, fool," he said angrily, referring to his decision to return to the hospital. "Bad seed, my dad's money, oh, I'm having a real good time pissing it away. He's aged a hundred years. They'll have to mortgage the place." And then, without sarcasm, but in embittered hopelessness: "My thoughts are bad. Cut my tongue out." The note continues:

« He was able to talk some of school and home, and back to: "never see my home again, nice place, never to be in it. Uncle said where there is a will there is a way. Huh." "Sounds like you've lost your will." The patient exploded in a sense, now and then getting up, exhaling, heavy grunt rather, panicky expression in eyes. Just before bath gave patient letter from mother. The patient read it quietly, cried, threw it on the table, rose up on his legs with a loud anguished cry, "We'll get together, huh, what a joke, what a laugh!" Patient has appeared most of the evening impassioned with resentment, fist clenched, mouth set grimly, eyes flashing. At times during a discourse utterly enraged, expressing this in subtle ways, at uncle, father, Dr. Preston and most openly at himself.

The notes of September 26 quoted Einston as saying, "I'm an idiot. The cure is in me, but I'm me, how can I change myself?" And then: "I guess I'd be the same anywhere, I'm still me. What will make me change? What will make me talk?" On September 27, he said that he didn't want to go home when he left Crest. His sarcasm over the next two days extended even to other patients, when they tried to express some hope. He condemned himself on the score of allowing his parents to pay his bills. "I hoped to come here and cure my dad, cure my family, cure everyone." He slammed the door at the mention of the word "game." September 28, he said, "What's the life expectancy? Sixty-nine, sixty-seven, only forty more years here, got to take advantage of everything they offer here." There was more hopeless talk about his relationship with Preston. The nurse tried to tell Einston that Preston really understood him. September 30, when the nurse was cutting his meat at mealtime (Einston was allowed only a spoon), he said he didn't want any. He hung his head and went back to his room saying, "Like a baby." He asked

Dr. Doren, the new director, to visit him. Rushing to the office, he cried to the nurse, "Come and help me, I'm sick!!"

Einston was still disturbed by letters from his home, and although it is not known what his parents told him in these letters, it *is* known that Mr. and Mrs. Einston were strongly considering removing him from Crest. They went to see Dr. Doren, the new director, who had just assumed his duties that month. He reassured them; and they were much impressed by him. They thereupon decided to leave Harry at Crest.

Harry now began to receive visits from his father, rather than his mother. This shift was the result of Dr. Doren's intervention in the treatment. He suggested to Dr. Preston that Einston be brought closer to his father, to allow him to identify more closely with a masculine figure. Doren also felt that Einston should be given more freedom and encouragement—that the restrictions that were placed on him should be lifted. Doren had several interviews with the parents, to try to encourage this closer tie with the father and greater separation from the mother. Dr. Preston accepted Doren's ideas. Preston later commented:

« Doren was very involved with Einston. It was Doren originally who formulated the thing of getting him back en rapport particularly with his father. Doren talked to him frequently. Doren talked to his parents. In effect this was the trial run on Doren's methods. This was the way he wanted to go about approaching this type of clinical problem and I was going along with it quite enthusiastically really. . . . It seemed [that the formulation was a good one]. As a matter of fact I felt a little like a chucklehead for having been so locked with this man in a clinical impasse in which he was sitting there saying, "Bastard, bastard," and I was holding him on the ward and was going to hold him on the ward for a good long time and we were going to go nowhere and I wasn't expecting much. This was Carpenter's [a consultant] formulation. This guy is very very sick and he's sicker than he looks and move very very slowly and be careful and don't let up until you get ample evidence to let up. We had the evidence that letting up was followed by indications not to let up.

But Doren's approach was considerably different. He got very interested in Einston, talked to him a lot, he was

interested in seeing him move along and Doren was more
or less supervising me. But there was a good deal of press
on Doren's part to have Einston sort of move out, and I
felt an unspoken criticism of the sort of loggerheads that
Einston and I had been at; in retrospect, loggerheads that
were peculiar to this case, and probably I should have been
sitting there looking him in the eye and saying, "Why don't
you tell me what you are thinking?" till today. But this was
hard to judge at the time. I was enthusiastic about Doren's
methods. . . .

He [Doren] was an enthusiastic participant in treatment
at that time, talking to patients and so on, and at that time
I wasn't resistant or hostile about it. Fine, let's try a new
way, wonderful; the old ways are tiresome and unrewarding
and tough, and this was a tough patient and I was really
locked in with him. . . . And Einston seemed to respond.
I began to let him go off grounds to football games in the
fall, in October. I finally let him go to a Thanksgiving Day
football game at home and go home for Thanksgiving.
Things seemed to go along okay and then he began to ask
about the possibilities of his leaving the hospital and going
to college again, getting his teaching degree. It didn't seem
unreasonable. At this time the interviews were more directed
to college and his aspirations and thinking about how he
had always before wanted to go into the family business and
then he wanted teaching, and remembrances of college days
and fraternity . . . . also, he was talking about some of the
troubles he had had, not these fantasied troubles of huge
proportion, but of troubles that had been real for him in
college. Something about his dating, something about how
his folks were involved in his choice of fraternities, and his
kind of essay of independence in joining fraternities his
folks didn't want him to belong to . . . and dating girls the
family didn't know. He began to go home some and see
old friends. Bought clothes, talked about getting his car,
and seemed to go along all right until the visit home when
he brought his car back.

As Dr. Preston suggests, following this shift to a more hopeful
therapeutic approach, there was a gradual decline in Einston's
hopeless statements on the ward and an increasing number of
comments from him about going back to school. He became

more involved in social activities at Crest, such as working on the hospital newsletter. A nurse commented later:

« There was no doubt about it in my mind. His whole tone was changed; he was much more optimistic; his whole outlook had changed. This was of course superficial, I guess, but from what we heard from him he seemed to be getting better, he looked better, he performed in all activities, he did well in groups, his relationships with other patients and staff were on a very high level. There was nothing to show that this boy actually thought about suicide any more, certainly nothing verbal on his part and nothing that we could see from his behavior.

Although Einston's bitterness continued to be evident, it was somewhat ameliorated during November. On November 3, he made some hopeless remarks about not being able to get well in the hospital, and sarcastic outbursts still occurred; but these expressions were much less frequent. He became more quiet and withdrawn rather than angry or aroused. He had an unscheduled visit from his father on November 11, which was broken up by the staff. On November 11, he attempted to annoy an aide by pretending that he heard voices and insisting that he wasn't hallucinating; at length, he decided the "voices" were the aide's crepe sole shoes squeaking. On November 12, he was moved out of the closed ward to the semi-open ward. He seemed only moderately enthusiastic at the change.

On November 14, after lunching silently with Mr. Oakson (one of the patients who later committed suicide), he made a few sarcastic remarks about people writing to him. However, he seems to have been withdrawn and observant rather than communicative in this mid-November period. The general impression of him at this time was that he seemed sad. He appeared to have struck up a slight friendship with Mr. Oakson, playing ping pong, conversing, and playing cards with him. He made some self-praising, possibly joking remarks on November 26. He appeared to be happy about his scheduled Thanksgiving trip home.

His increased expression of hopefulness is indicated in the letter he sent on November 18:

« Dear Mother and Father:
    I'm glad we had the opportunity to be together on your

anniversary. I know that there have been happier moments when we have been in each other's company, however I see no reason why we won't be able to get to be together soon, providing I get permission from Dr. Preston, and I'm quite certain that I'll be able to get that privilege.

I have made the big move to the [semi-open ward] where things are more pleasant and with time and work I hope to assure myself that things will be for the best. There is so much that I must understand about myself. I know also that there is much good in this world if only I can find and cultivate the positive aspects of my own personality.

I received your letter which expresses the hope you have and the plans which I hope to make for my eventual return to college and my completion of my education. I would find contentment in returning to the campus and continuing with my therapy here at Crest.

During December his behavior at the hospital continued to be hopeful. As noted above, he also made a number of shopping trips and visits to his home, using his own car. On such trips, however, his behavior was much worse. His anxiety off the hospital grounds is indicated in a number of ways. On December 11 he wrote to his parents about a trip he had made three days previously.

« Well, my long weekend spent at home is behind me and I must stop and evaluate its significance. I know that being home is rather trying; however, I also know that I can control my behavior in a manner befitting most of the situations which confront me. Viewing familiar sights and seeing old friends is very heartwarming. Of course controlling my anxious moments is perhaps my most difficult task and I feel that I am successfully dealing with that segment of my makeup. While at home, my conversation with my old grade school principal helped to convince and assure me that teaching is something that I earnestly want to pursue. The way I had it planned as far as my returning to school was more or less counting on resuming my studies after the first of the year. I feel that my progress has been going quite well and that my hope of being able to handle the responsibility of college work is completely possible.

He was still ambivalent, mixing hope with skepticism. His

behavior became more hopeful in the hospital, more skeptical on his visits to his family.

On the Saturday morning of December 14, he made an unexpected call on his sister. He had been given a pass by the hospital, to buy some clothes in a shopping district near his sister's home. Roslyn was very surprised to see him; although a few letters had been exchanged between them, they had not seen one another for ten months. When he came to his sister's apartment, she already had a guest, a soldier. Einston appeared to his sister to be very distraught. He told Roslyn that he didn't want to return to the hospital, but to stay in her apartment. He also said that he did not want to go on living. Roslyn anxiously talked him into going on his shopping tour, accompanied by herself and her guest. The three made an uneasy tour of clothing and book stores, Roslyn and her guest meanwhile attempting to reason Harry into returning to the hospital. Finally, they persuaded him to take a bus back to Crest.

Roslyn heard from her parents about another trip Harry made, to their home.

« Mother and Dad drove him back and they had an awful lot of trouble because he was tensing up his body, and I know that Dad almost went off the road, I don't know how many times, because his arms were flying and he didn't have any control, he was just so violently angry, and I know that Dad was afraid that they were going to crash.

The ferry boat incident; Einston's suicidal talk following it; his behavior during the visits with his sister and parents, obviously had the effect of making his parents extremely anxious about his trips. They communicated this fear to the hospital, primarily via Miss Simmons; they indicated that they had great fear about his driving home on a very dangerous highway, the most dangerous in the state. This anxiety was ignored by the hospital, because it was interpreted partly as being an expression of a death wish toward Einston, partly as being an expression of Mrs. Einston's desire to have her son remain dependent upon her.

During the Christmas season, on December 20, Harry visited his home for a weekend. His family's anxiety was so strong that any of his behavior which was ambiguous in intent was inter-

preted by his parents in the worst possible way. His sister
describes this incident:

« I can just tell you my number one fear, I mean, the things
that stick out in my mind. We had some knives on a rack
in the kitchen on the side of the sink, and I remember
Mother was hiding things, which I guess was the normal
thing to do, keep things kind of out of sight, out of mind.
I remember we put away the scissors, and we put away a
few things, but we didn't put away everything. I mean you
just couldn't, but I remember these knives were in the
kitchen and Harry was so angry; well, I mean, if you want
to know, I guess this is what this is for, I remember his going
down to the basement looking for a piece of rope which he
found and wanting to do something with that.

The interview continued:

> *Interviewer.* While there were a lot of people in the house?
> *Miss Einston.* No, just my Mother and Dad and I.
> *Interviewer.* Well, how do you know he was going for a
> piece of rope?
> *Miss Einston.* Well, he just was, there was rope down there
> and he knew there was rope down there, and he went down
> there and Dad went down afterward suspecting that he was
> going down to get something, and he did—that's what he had
> gone down to get.
> *Interviewer.* How do you know? Did he say so, or did he
> have the rope in his hand?
> *Miss Einston.* He had the rope.
> *Interviewer.* He had the rope?
> *Miss Einston.* Yes, yes, but of course nothing had happened
> then and Dad was able to bring him back upstairs. But he
> just didn't have any control over anything, and the knives
> were in the kitchen, I remember.

And his parents also describe this incident:

> *Mrs. Einston.* Well, while he was home during one of
> these later times, he went down the basement. We didn't
> know what for, but he talked as if he were looking for
> something there.
> *Mr. Einston.* Well, they're all bound to look for something.
> *Mrs. Einston.* At that time he was looking for as he called
> it a limbo, is that the word? Anyhow, he was looking.

Mr. Einston. Once they have that thing in their mind they always look for something, whether it's a piece of rope or whether it's a hose and go into the garage and . . .

Interviewer. How did you people feel at that time? Roslyn said that you were sort of half mixed up; you put some things away and couldn't put other things away.

Mrs. Einston. No, I didn't put anything away, the only thing I did put away was the set of carving knives that lay in the kitchen.

Mr. Einston. Yeah, and a bunch of razor blades had been put away.

Mrs. Einston. No, I never did.

Mr. Einston. Oh, sure.

Mrs. Einston. But he had them in his desk, I found them afterwards up in his desk. You don't hide a razor blade, because after all, if he wanted one, he went out and bought them anyhow, he bought them.

Mr. Einston. You can't go ahead and hide stuff.

Mrs. Einston. You couldn't, no; you know, he said to me one day, after being over to the hospital, you know, he says, "You can't even wish yourself dead, you can't even wish yourself dead."

Interviewer. Roslyn said you went down to the basement after him.

Mrs. Einston. Yes, made him come up.

Mr. Einston. Sure, we knew that he'll either find a clothes line rope or find this kind of rope or that kind of rope.

Interviewer. Did he have a rope in his hand when you found him?

Mrs. Einston. There was one there, a blue rope was lying there, we knew it was there; I don't know whether he had it or not. But he was always on the prowl for something.

Mr. Einston. Oh, he was just walking around looking for something, and I knew it, so that's the reason I went down.

Mrs. Einston. He said this was the only way out, that was all, he thought there was no . . . .

Mr. Einston. See, you've got to go ahead and think the same way as he's thinking then, or be two jumps ahead of him to know as to what he's got on his mind, and I was just two jumps ahead all the time to see what might come up.

His mother described the difficulty and anxiety regarding his return to Crest on Monday, December 23.

« There was a funeral [Mr. Einston] had to go to, and I was home to deal with him alone. We had the car here. That was the time he did not want to go back and Dr. Preston said, "I want him" (he had an appointment). "I want him here for this appointment at a certain time" [10:00 A.M., December 23], and I knew, the state he was in, that it was treacherous to let him on the road alone driving, and I said that, and Preston said, "I still expect him here." So [my husband] wasn't home and I couldn't get hold of him . . . I think I did finally get him, and I decided, I'm riding with him. Anything that is going to happen is going to happen, I'm going to be there so I can prevent it, so I drove back with him. And as we approached the hospital he said to me, "Mother I'm so tired, I'm so tired." And I said, "Harry, dear, you know I think it's best if I don't go back to the hospital, the doctor was so definite that you come back by yourself, maybe you'll let me off and I'll take a bus back to town, you go up alone." He said, "And face all those people myself." And I didn't know what. I was torn between my pity for this child and how the doctor would figure that I'm trying to run this boy's life; I didn't know what to do. Finally he said, "Mother, don't let me go back there and face these people."

When we got back to the hospital, Doren was going out, he was very busy, but I said I wanted to see him, so I saw him. And Preston saw Harry. And then Harry said he wanted to go back with me, his birthday was the next day or so, I forget, they said, "No, you can't go back," and he said, "Well, would you let me drive my mother down to the bus stop?" It was a pitch black night, and the taxi was five dollars and at that time I was angry and hurt and five dollars was a darn lot of money, and I figured I could take the bus; so I stood out there, it was just before Christmas and the traffic was terrible. I stood out there and I looked up at the sky, to what depth can agony be; there's this boy, I know he's worrying, I know for his sake I should have taken a taxi; I should have, to alleviate his suffering because he would not normally let me do this.

On his return to the hospital, Einston's behavior indicated that he was glad to be back. A nurse commented later: "His greeting, and his smile, and his obvious relief at being in the hospital was something that was moving."

Ullman made his attempt at suicide on the morning, December 23, the day of Einston's return. As described in the previous chapter, the hospital staff was shocked and demoralized by Ullman's attempt. There was a great loss of self-confidence and a great deal of anxiety in the air. Thus, Einston returned from the anxiety of his visit home to the anxiety of the hospital. There can be little doubt that he also learned about the cause of the staff's anxiety.

Furthermore, Einston's therapist, Dr. Preston, was particularly shocked by Ullman's attempt. Preston was the latter's therapist as well as Einston's, and his self-confidence received a blow.

Dr. Doren, in an observation about Dr. Preston's treatment of Einston, indicated his feeling that Ullman's suicide attempt generated so much anxiety in the hospital staff, and in Dr. Preston, that Einston felt the anxiety as withdrawal of support. Doren felt that Einston, feeling Preston's withdrawal, was again susceptible to the pull of his mother, which was always a factor in his problems.

Dr. Doren felt that Dr. Preston should slow the pace of the increasing freedom Einston was being given. When Dr. Doren mentioned these misgivings, Dr. Preston expressed great confidence in his own judgment, and Dr. Doren did not press the issue. Thus, for example, Einston was given permission to leave the hospital again, leaving on December 25, staying out overnight, and returning in the evening of December 26.

While Dr. Preston did not know the details of Einston's behavior at home, he was aware that the family "was making noises about not wanting him to visit home again for awhile." In retrospect he noted that, had he known these details, the patient's anxiety would have been more understandable to him. Nevertheless, around the hospital Einston's behavior was excellent. He was talking a good deal about his future plans, and seemed comfortable and happy. Preston stated that Einston had made plans to go home for New Year's Eve; he said he had a date for the occasion.

« I was direct about this: "You want to go home, and they've indicated they don't want you home. What goes on?" . . . "Well so they don't want me home . . . but I want to go out and I made these plans." It looked all right to me.

Preston was aware that during this period Einston was again withholding something, and he recalled that he made "an interpretation, based on the feeling about what was going on in the interview, that he acted as though he weren't going to inform, as though he weren't going to be a stool pigeon on what went on in the family." Preston later wondered if his feeling was not a product of Einston's withholding the details of his suicidal feelings during his visit home before Christmas.

Meanwhile, at the hospital, Einston had developed a strong friendship with Mrs. Arlington, who later committed suicide. They often were seen conversing, sometimes in such low tones that no one could hear them. Mrs. Arlington was from the same town as Einston. Some staff members feel that the two discussed suicide. There is no direct evidence about the content of their conversations.

On December 28 and 29, Harry continued to talk hopefully at the hospital about returning to college. On the 31st, after bowling in the morning, he made an elaborate departure, taking many clothes with him. He seemed to be in good spirits when he left the grounds. He appears to have driven to his uncle's home for lunch. There, he made several very melancholy remarks, including, "There's only one way out." He then left for his home. Neither Einston, the staff, nor Einston's uncle had notified Einston's parents that he was out.

The next day, the hospital called the Einston residence and asked for him. His parents were amazed and shocked that he was expected to be there. His father instigated a search by the sheriff. Einston was found hours later in his car on a country road. He had killed himself by cutting his wrists. He was found near a place where he had spent a very happy summer working in a camp.

Chapter VI

WILLIAM
OAKSON

WILLIAM OAKSON WAS ADMITTED TO CREST HOSPITAL
on September 19, 1959. In his middle fifties, Oakson was a tall,
spare, acquiline-featured man. He had traveled alone to Columbia, by plane, from his home, and arrived at the hospital
accompanied by Columbia friends. For a little more than a
year Oakson had been suffering from insomnia, depression,
multiple somatic complaints, and inability to work. His condition had not been materially improved during this period
by the administration of tranquilizing drugs, brief psychotherapy,
or ECT.

The patient had been born in Columbia, one of six siblings,
his family removing to the town in which he still lived when
he was seven years old. His father was a hardworking salesman
—"never missed a day of work"—who was respected and well-
liked, albeit rather stern; he died of a coronary at the age of 62.
Oakson's mother was in her eighties, still in good health, at the
time of Oakson's admission to Crest.

As a child Oakson had no major illnesses. He was a good
athlete and continued his athletic activity in adult life until the
time of his breakdown. From his earliest possible opportunity,
the boy Oakson worked at part-time jobs. He left high school at
16 or 17 years of age to devote himself to wage-earning, but
continued his education through evening classes and extension
courses. He attended a local college for one year, during which
time he played on the college baseball team.

At the age of 20 years, Oakson applied for and obtained a
position as maintenance man with the Apex Typewriter Company. He remained with the company for twenty-eight years,
working as a field repairman and as a salesman. In his business
life Oakson was well thought of; he was respected for his sales

ability and energy, and was regarded as a jovial, engaging person.

He met his wife at a church dance. A son, their only child, was born to them when Oakson was 26 years old. Following the boy's birth, Mrs. Oakson developed a severe chronic illness. She was told at this time that her life would be endangered by further child-bearing, nor was she able, at first, to care for her son. By the time the boy was about 4 years old, Mrs. Oakson had regained adequate health. She and her husband were very active socially; they were also active in athletics, skiing, and golfing: "They have always done every single thing together." Mrs. Oakson was described as the kind of woman who never complained, who always seemed cheerful. It was reported at the time of Oakson's illness that Mrs. Oakson recently had been chronically tired, but never mentioned her fatigue. "She just goes and sits down and then when she is rested she will get up and move around again." The Oaksons were one of the "nicest couples to be around," friends said, because there was so little friction between them. If Mrs. Oakson became angry at her husband, he would be quiet, and let her talk herself out. They "never had a real or lingering quarrel." If there was a difference of opinion, Oakson would give in to his wife—he was the kind who would "speak his piece and then keep quiet." Mrs. Oakson, it was speculated, probably made most of the decisions in their home life.

Oakson's son, Tom, was a conservative, quiet person. Father and son had always been very close. Tom had married at 25; he and his wife had one daughter. There was some tension between Oakson and his daughter-in-law, because of Oakson's feeling that Tom's affections had been usurped by her. Tom had a good job, in a large manufacturing firm. He and his family lived in a city close to his parents.

During his employment by the Apex Company, the patient spent a great deal of his time on the road. At these times, he said, his life was much "like that of any traveling salesman"; he enjoyed convivial good times; occasionally he had casual extra-marital sexual experiences. These experiences made him feel extremely guilty; he believed that their discovery would cause his wife great pain. Therefore he attempted, successfully, to conceal the details of his traveling-salesman-life and considered it separate from his ordinary existence.

Throughout his adult life Oakson had been a steady, hardworking, but also at times hard-playing, individual. He was described by friends as a "go-getter, smart as a whip." "He was a driver, there wasn't any work that was too much for him; he was on committees, he was on this, he was on that, he just always had the time of his life no matter what it was. And a good businessman."

In 1950-51, he entered into partnership in a small business with an associate of his from the Apex Company. This business shortly failed, apparently because of the partner's lack of business and organizational ability. The patient obtained some money after the dissolution of the business, and not long after bought a retail business. During his years as a small businessman Oakson was helped a great deal by his wife. She was forced to retire from her active part in his business in 1958 due to recurrent mild heart attacks.

For several years before his admission to Crest, Oakson's interest in sexual intercourse had waned. Following the onset of his wife's illness, he became frightened that intercourse would be injurious to her. He had become quite concerned over his waning sexual interest, and had spoken to his physician about the male climacteric.

Following his wife's withdrawal from activity in the business, the patient became extremely worried about the decline of business in his area. He was convinced that his business was faltering. At last, in June of 1958, he sold out rather abruptly. During the summer of 1958 he rested and thought of working; but upon attempting to work in the late summer of that year he was stricken by a "stitch" in his side and a severe pain in the right side of his chest. He was reassured that these symptoms were no cause for concern; but he developed numerous other physical complaints. About this time, upon washing a pair of gloves in carbon tetrachloride, he became convinced that he had breathed phosgene gas and might thus have contracted cancer of the lung. Also, for about a year and a half he had been contemplating a varicose vein stripping, and had become extremely concerned about pain in his legs and bulges in his popliteal spaces; he adopted postures, sitting or standing, calculated to rest his painful extremities. He had severe headaches and insomnia; pains in his chest, side, and testicles; and occasionally he complained of blurring vision. Medical tests in Pinehurst, where he lived, and in a Columbia clinic failed to determine any physical basis for these disorders; and Oakson was referred to a psychiatrist in Pinehurst with a diagnosis of depression. The psychiatrist saw Oakson as extremely depressed, and administered moderate doses of thorazine, with the admonition that it might cause jaundice. After three or four days of thorazine therapy the patient began to feel feverish and nauseated; shortly after this he became noticeably jaundiced.

Because of his constant complaints of abdominal pain he went through an exploratory operation in February of 1959. Oakson was extremely upset by the surgery and confused by the anesthetic. He awakened to find a T-tube protruding from his abdomen, which he had not reckoned with. The exploration revealed a normal gall bladder and common duct. At this time Oakson was told that the thorazine had plugged up his bile duct, resulting in jaundice. Subsequently, he was convinced that he could "forget" his fear of cancer.

After his recovery from his common duct exploration he continued to be depressed and to have multiple somatic symptoms. As a consequence, the psychiatrist subjected him to a course of eight to ten ECTs in March and April. Some loss of memory and some relief of Oakson's symptoms resulted, particularly of his depression and anxiety; but within eight to ten days following the cessation of ECT, his symptoms were again upon him. As the ECT had not produced the hoped-for results, the psychiatrist told the patient that he would have to continue to take medication and "help himself." He also said that Oakson was going through a severe "change of life"; but that he was very lucky, because at least after four or five years' time he should be himself again.

Oakson continued to see the psychiatrist and to make use of tranquilizing drugs and of sedation for his insomnia, which he felt to be severe. He worried that the ingestion of such large quantities of tranquilizing drugs might do him damage. During this period Oakson was quite concerned that he would "lose his mind," and sought constant reassurance that this would not happen. He spent the months of June, July, and August at a lakeside cabin. There he spent much of his time outdoors in vigorous physical activity, particularly in chopping wood, and felt relatively well.

Oakson was fearful that his wife's worry over him might cause her a fatal heart attack. It was partly due to this fear that he ceased attempting intercourse with her about this time. He also confessed his extra-marital sex life as a travelling salesman.

Mrs. Oakson now became quite hostile to her husband, apparently not only because of their changed sexual relationship but also because his illness made him want to lean on her and abandon the strong, protective, masculine role.

A member of the hospital staff who interviewed Mrs. Oakson later commented: "It became very clear that her comments to her husband were on the one hand often in the form of a belittling type of comment in which she treated him pretty much as an incompetent little boy, but on the other hand, were in the form of hostile demands that he be a man. From her own quotations of comments made to her by the Martins (friends of the Oaksons who lived close to Crest) and later made directly to me by Mrs. Martin, it was very clear that the Martins were well aware of the destructive tone behind Mrs. Oakson's comments to her husband and that they, on occasion, were pointing out to her what she was doing to him."

Mrs. Oakson herself, in her hospital interviews, indicated that the difficulties in her relationship with her husband had to do with the ways in which she handled her hostility or attempted to control it. She also spoke of difficulties with the sexual relationship throughout her marriage.

In early September, after the summer at the lake, Oakson returned home and made an attempt to work, taking a part-time job. Here he had difficulty in thinking clearly, numerous somatic complaints, and feelings of faintness. These limited his abilities in the new job; and in desperation, he tried consulting different physicians. It was one of these who made arrangements for hospitalization at Crest.

Oakson made the trip to Crest unaccompanied, on September 19, 1959. He appeared to be under the impression that he would be an outpatient. Mrs. Martin described his admission:

« When I met him at the plane, Tom, his son, had heard about Crest, and asked his father to go over there. William was very shocked when he got over there, because he had no idea that he was going to stay. He was quite bewildered by it. He was shaking and perspiring and nervous, but he talked all right. But I never saw such a bewildered expression on a person when he found out he was going to stay there. He didn't realize that. He thought he was just going over there to interview, he didn't know he was going over as a patient . . . [Mrs. Oakson] had had a slight heart flare-up so she couldn't come over with him. It didn't take too much to bother him; and anything that happened to her bothered him. And so it was hard for him to come over, especially by himself, because they had done everything together.

At the time of admission Oakson was extremely tense; he had facial tics. At times he betrayed hostility and altogether appeared quite desperate. "I came here of my own free will," he repeated. "I didn't know what I was getting into. I flew over by myself and didn't realize I would be locked up. I have never been so nervous in my life." He was visibly calmed, however, by his contact with the staff.

The admitting doctor, Dr. Preston, wrote:

« The life history of this man suggests a very compulsive, hardworking person whose decompensation in the face of the serious illness on the part of his wife has been if anything, intensified by the use of milieux and agents which decrease the opportunity for functioning of his compulsive defenses.

Because of his suspiciousness, disorganization, and wariness, he will need to be approached with an attitude of passive friendliness, but attempts should be made to provide as clear a picture as possible of the structure of the hospital, and a clear structuring of his milieu should be made available to him. Occupational and recreational therapy should be started as soon as possible, and these activities should be structured in a way which allows him to use them in helping restore his compulsive defense. His many bodily complaints may be listened to patiently and referred to the physician . . .

Because of the man's present feeling that both sedative and tranquilizing drugs have been harmful to him, the withdrawal from these drugs should be with some cooperation on his part. It would seem essential to have him on a drug-free regime during this evaluation period, and I feel that he will welcome the withdrawal, although superficially he may object to it. His status will be R,* diet regular, tray on ward . . .

Although Dr. Preston signed the admission note, Dr. Doren had a large hand in the admitting procedure. Dr. Doren had been at the hospital for only a few days. Dr. Preston, who in the past had handled admissions himself, said that he would not have handled the admission in the way Dr. Doren had.

---

* R status means restricted to the ward.

« This man who was so disturbed arrived by himself, unaccompanied by a responsible relative, by plane, and it really took him several days to get into the hospital . . . I think Doren saw him the first day, and there was some business of talking him into staying in the hospital, and Oakson saying, "Well, I came over by myself." The approach to this man's hospitalization wasn't as solid as I usually make—the arrangements about who is going to be responsible, and who is going to be with him, and all this kind of thing were left pretty much hanging; and we didn't get a grip on this until after a week and a half or two weeks.

Oakson commenced psychotherapy with Dr. Doren. From the time of his admission until Thanksgiving, his stay in the hospital was relatively uneventful. His agitation, depression, and delusions about his body continued to be marked; his facial expression was taut; he had numerous vague tics. By mid-November he showed considerable alleviation of the severity of his symptoms. He had become quite active in the hospital activities program and was getting along adequately with the other patients and with the staff. In general, he had a great deal of difficulty in expressing his feelings, but by mid-November, his delusions about his body had begun to decline.

The only unique feature of Mr. Oakson's first two months in the hospital came in terms of a detail of his treatment. He was the first patient for whom Dr. Doren prescribed drugs; the first patient who had been given drugs at Crest for a very long time. It is reported that when Dr. Doren ordered the sedative, one of the aides turned impulsively to him and said, "We don't do that here!" Dr. Preston describes the situation: "He was complaining about not sleeping; I wasn't giving him anything. Doren was sort of dropping around. I think this was even before he was treating [in psychotherapy] him, and he left an order for sedation because he wasn't sleeping."

Mr. Oakson became very attached to and dependent upon Dr. Doren. In this case, as in others where the two physicians were involved, Dr. Preston "got out of it as quickly as he could." "I mean, I still continued occasionally to write the orders and was in the position of a message carrier for a while, where I could be writing orders on the man—but Doren would be telling —so I withdrew."

Mr. Oakson was given a psychological test battery shortly after admission. The tests showed a rather well-endowed individual, with no evidence of organic pathology in the psychological record. He exhibited a compulsive attention to detail. There were no evidences of psychosis on the record, although the psychologist felt that there was some remote danger of a paranoid schizophrenic break.

The hospital records report:

« It would appear that this man has developed a hostile identification with his wife with whom he is in competition. It appears that his gradual decompensation began at about the time when he was forced out of the partnership that apparently meant a great deal to him. His declining physical status can only be partially attributed to his increasing years, although it must be said that he has lost many of his compulsive outlets through a necessary reduction in his athletic program.

Although the ward staff's reactions to Oakson were varied, the descriptions are consistent in that none of them viewed the patient as a suicidal type.

« Oakson was a big façade [said one staff member]. He was one you . . . hardly expect would be a suicide. He was sort of a hail-fellow-well-met guy. Had a real nice front. As far as any of this latent or hidden . . . potential in this direction: he was one of the sort that slept well all night; got up in the morning, was very cheerful; and occupied himself with watching television and reading and taking walks and chatting with his roommate. They were pretty close together, and they kidded each other and joked, and Oakson laughed a lot.

Another said:

« I don't know, he was always talking to me about the productive things that he had done—man to man conversations. Always trying to be friendly, outgoing, even when I'm sure it hurt. I felt that he was in flight from terrifically painful psychosis. He never seemed like a very angry person. But the staff were not very fond of him. But I don't recall anyone who really enjoyed working with him, or was very concerned about him.

Suicide precautions were not prescribed during his stay at the hospital.

Mrs. Oakson began to be seen by Miss Simmons. She reports as follows:

« Although throughout this time it was very much my feeling that Mrs. Oakson should be seen more frequently and on a regular basis—preferably a paying one in which she recognized that she came because of her own problem in this, not just because of her husband's—such a plan was never possible in view of Mrs. Oakson's residence at such distance from Crest, and in view of her physical condition and the financial situation.

The early interviews she seemed to use quite constructively as far as further understanding of her husband and his illness was concerned, as well as utilizing the opportunity to talk further concerning the difficulty of living with him since his illness. She also discussed her concern about the financial situation and the business problems which were currently resting on the ability of the tenant of their store property to pay his rent; her worry about the decline of business generally in Pinehurst; her anxiety concerning her husband's continued hospitalization, and what it meant to them financially.

It wasn't until perhaps the middle or latter part of November that Mrs. Oakson began to use the interviews a little less guardedly and impersonally and began to relax a bit and tell me more of herself and her own feelings concerning her husband and their past life together. Although previously there had been an apparent easy acceptance of my recognition with her that of course she had considerable feelings of disappointment and hostility toward her husband, this acceptance had probably been pretty superficial and more or less on an intellectual basis.

Mrs. Oakson also was aware of her husband's extreme concern about her. She felt that his concern was exaggerated.

During the first two months of Mr. Oakson's hospitalization, Mrs. Oakson visited him a number of times. Mrs. Martin, the family friend, later said:

« [Mrs. Oakson was reacting to her husband's hospitalization] very quietly. She took it all in good stride. She just felt that he was in good hands and she was just leaving it that way . . . Mrs. Oakson saw him once or twice before I did. I used

to take her over there and bring her back. She would stay
here at the house whenever they were in Columbia, and she
got to see him for just a few minutes . . . she felt very sad
about [the situation]; of course Mr. Oakson, he would tell
her things about the place all the time, you know, it's understandable; and those things bothered her a little bit, and later
on she got so she understood him . . . [Mr. Oakson] had an
idea that they were policing him twenty-four hours around,
you know. Well, they were to a certain extent, and—oh, the
night nurse would do this, and an orderly would do this—
you know, just little things. And oh, they—of course he had
been on Miltown when he came over there, and medication
was taken away from him, and he'd say he spent so many
days without any sleep, and they wouldn't do anything about
it; oh, just general hospital complaints that a person in his
mind would want to get out—he wanted to get out so badly.

He was allowed to visit the Martins' home in the evening a
few times just prior to Thanksgiving. On one of these visits
his wife was also present. Mrs. Martin described that occasion.

« He and Mrs. Oakson roamed around here, went out on the
dock and just walked around and talked . . . It was a very
pleasant evening; in fact, he didn't want to go back . . .
[Mrs. Oakson] just told him he had to. She was very cooperative . . . she had her own crying spells `in her own
bedroom, but she never let on around Bill that he wasn't
getting the best treatment.

Oakson began to have fears about being "shipped over" to
the state hospital. He expressed them to Dr. Doren as well as
to his wife and friends. His wife and Mrs. Martin attempted to
alleviate these fears by telling Oakson that Dr. Doren felt that
it would not be long before he was discharged. Oakson also
continued to complain about his aches and pains and of his
fears of dying of heart trouble or cancer. His wife, who felt
that his complaints put too much strain on her as a heart patient, tried to get him to limit the time for talking about his
complaints; but this was not effective. This limitation of the
amount of time he could spend talking about himself had been
attempted by his wife before he entered the hospital.

By the Thanksgiving season, Oakson had improved sufficiently
to meet his wife at the Martins' home for a four-day Thanksgiving holiday. Although Mrs. Oakson did not suffer a heart

attack during this visit, and the visit appeared to go well, Oakson stayed only a single night. Whether or not Mrs. Oakson spoke of it, she did fear the effects of undue strain upon herself; and Oakson apparently still feared and anticipated that his wife would have an attack.

The therapist noted at this time that Oakson had begun, in psychotherapy, to talk less of his physical concerns and more of anxiety and fears. It was only when he was highly anxious that the somatic preoccupation would return. This had been the case prior to the Thanksgiving visit.

After Oakson's Thanksgiving visit, he began to worry about how he was to spend Christmas. Several times during this period he expressed to the ward staff his anxiety about returning to his home for Christmas, once saying that it would be better for him to spend the holidays at the Martin home. At another time he said it might be better for him to spend the holidays with his son rather than with his wife. In therapy he spoke strongly about wanting to go home. His therapist suggested that they wait at least two weeks after Thanksgiving before seriously considering a visit home. Mr. Oakson argued more, but it seemed clear that he was very anxious. Dr. Doren also added that he doubted that Mrs. Oakson was ready for a visit with her husband at home.

Between Thanksgiving and Christmas Mr. Oakson became more aware of his dependency on his therapist. Dr. Doren reported that Mr. Oakson's conflict—a wish for a deep regression which his masculinity would not tolerate—became more evident. Mr. Oakson would alternate between speaking of his need to return home to his position in his community, and his fear of complete insanity and being put in the completely locked ward. Anxiety was high about plans for Christmas, and it was decided that he and his wife would visit with their nearby friends, the Martins, once again.

Aside from these expressions of anxiety, Oakson's hospital behavior in this period was only occasionally disturbed. The ward staff on a few occasions thought he needed to be removed to the closed ward; but in general he got along well with himself, the staff, and other patients.

Oakson spent the Christmas holidays with his wife at the Martin home. The first day everyone, including Oakson, had a pleasant time, playing games, joking, and laughing. Oakson had by this time ceased complaining about the hospital and had begun to express his liking for Dr. Doren. Nevertheless, in some of his conversations with Mrs. Martin just prior to Christmas, he had asked her to promise to take care of his wife if he were sent to a state hospital. His wife was very careful not to exert herself, stating that her doctor had told her to "take it easy" because of her cardiac condition. Mrs. Martin felt that Mrs. Oakson's behavior greatly worried her husband. Mrs. Martin told her that she was babying herself too much; but to no avail. The second day, Christmas Eve, Oakson began to be more fidgety, anxious, and withdrawn. He asked to be taken back to Crest, and on the morning of the third day, he was brought back—a full day before he had been scheduled to return.

While Oakson was at the Martins' home, Mr. Ullman had made his suicide attempt. Oakson thus returned to a much more anxious atmosphere in the hospital than the one he had left.

On his return, Mr. Oakson strongly expressed the desire to go home. Dr. Doren reported him to be far more strongly determined than he had been before, even though the wish to be dependent still remained. Dr. Doren felt that the time was right to support Mr. Oakson's desires for independence, and so a ten-day visit at home was arranged.

The first week at home seemed to go well, as far as Dr. Doren knew. Mr. Oakson felt good, slept well, and kept busy. Then, as time for return to the hospital approached, things got more difficult. Mr. Oakson became more anxious; Dr. Doren felt this to be a consequence of increased dependency desires stimulated by his thought of being in the hospital again.

During this visit home, Mr. and Mrs. Oakson spent New Year's Eve alone together. Mrs. Martin commented:

« I think it was [lonely] because Mrs. Oakson told me afterward they had talked of many things; they talked about their will. I know for the first time I had an inkling that maybe Tom and his wife preyed on his mind a little bit; because they had one child, on that New Year's Eve Bill said that he wanted to fix his money so that his daughter-in-law couldn't spend it; he said, "I'll never worry about Tom, and I want my money to go to [my granddaughter]." And so Bill wanted it and Mrs. Oakson wanted it, and that's the way they had intended to fix it . . . They talked about their will; they probably discussed everything.

Mrs. Oakson was not very optimistic about her husband during this period. Mrs. Martin said, "She was awfully upset, and after his last set-back, I think she felt that he was not being helped."

By the time Oakson returned to the hospital on January 6, Einston's suicide over the New Year holiday had been discovered. The hospital atmosphere was increasingly tense.

Oakson saw Dr. Doren for an interview on Monday, January 6. That night he stayed with the Martins, and saw Dr. Doren again on Tuesday. (We do not know how much time Oakson spent on the hospital grounds on these two days.) Dr. Doren reported that Mr. Oakson, while wishing to attempt to return home to stay, appreciated that problems might arise. Mr. Oakson had said that he would return to the hospital if things became too difficult for him. Dr. Doren was encouraged by this. Mr. Oakson and Dr. Doren then agreed that Mr. Oakson would be discharged; that he and his wife would return to Crest weekly, he to see Dr. Doren, she to see Miss Simmons; and, finally, that Mr. Oakson would be readmitted if he became too uncomfortable.

Dr. Doren supported this plan because he felt that Mr. Oakson had received maximum hospital benefit. Moreover, he felt that continued hospitalization could result in severe regression which would then make discharge from the hospital far more difficult. Dr. Doren realized that Mr. Oakson might have to be readmitted, but the possibility of Mr. Oakson making it at home seemed to be a reasonable one at that time.

Later, Dr. Doren said that one reason for this arrangement was that there was a great danger that Oakson would regress completely. The alternative to Crest, in view of the family's limited resources, would have been the state hospital so dreaded by Mr. Oakson. Evidently Dr. Doren shared Oakson's apprehension. He stated that he felt Mr. Oakson wanted the opportunity to try to get along at home but,

« If he wasn't able to make it to his satisfaction, that he didn't want to go on. So if he had come back, and we had hospitalized him, what would have been his ultimate fate is hard to say. . . . My own feeling is that he probably would have regressed and likely never come out of it.

You asked if I thought he was suicidal. I thought of the possibility of suicide with him, but foremost in my mind was the concern that if there would be psychotic action, I thought it might be more in terms of harming his wife. . . .

Dr. Doren was acutely aware of the complex relationship Oakson had with his wife. He saw her as a fine person, who was nevertheless unable to satisfy her husband's basic needs as a man. He felt that Mr. and Mrs. Oakson's relationship was characterized too much by mutual antagonism; he was too often guilty and she too often angry. He felt that there was an organic basis for Mrs. Oakson's coronary difficulty, but that, in addition, her "attacks," which made him feel both anxious and guilty, were used as a way of expressing anger.

Dr. Doren hoped that Mrs. Oakson's talks with Miss Simmons had improved the relationship enough to permit Mr. Oakson to return home. Mrs. Oakson was at best, ambivalent about Mr. Oakson's return home. Dr. Doren had told her that he wanted Mr. Oakson to become an outpatient, but her preference was that he stay in the hospital. As before, she continued to feel that her heart attacks could be precipitated by concern over Mr. Oakson's health and could be exacerbated by Mr. Oakson's constant complaints and expressions of anxiety. Mr. Oakson continued to fear that his wife might have a serious heart attack and die.

When Dr. Doren commented, later, on his decision to transfer Oakson to outpatient status, he indicated that he thought his own anxiety over the experience with Ullman and Einston influenced his treatment of Oakson during the interviews on January 6th and 7th.

« I know when he came back I was hoping he wouldn't find out about these [suicides], which is a reflection I think of my perhaps withdrawing, of my anxiety, of a little more wish to keep him away because it would be bad for him if he were to know about the suicides.

Mr. Oakson phoned Dr. Doren on the evening of Wednesday, January 8, and reported that on his arrival home the night before his wife was ill with one of her attacks, was in bed, and was "requiring" much care. She had insisted that he not call a physician, although he had wanted to call one. Mr. Oakson was upset but was eased when Dr. Doren supported his judgment and his competence to deal with the situation. In his anxiety Mr. Oakson wondered if he had left the hospital too soon. Dr.

Doren assured him that if this turned out to be true he could return.

During the next week Mr. Oakson's emotional state gravitated up and down. In his more hopeful moods, he repaired plumbing, visited with some old friends, talked of returning to work. At the same time he continued to express great fear that he would be sent to the state hospital.

On Saturday, January 11, Oakson was very upset. His wife took him out for a drive, and they lunched in a nearby town where they had once lived, long before. While eating, Oakson started talking about having cancer of the nose and mouth, commenting that it was hard for him to eat, that he would not be able to kiss his wife any longer, and so on. His wife was very frightened. She drove him home and called her son. This was the first time Mrs. Oakson had called her son in an emergency relating to his father. She asked Tom to take Oakson for a drive; while the two were out, she called Dr. Doren, describing to him her husband's severe anxiety and delusional somatic preoccupations. Dr. Doren told her that Mr. Oakson should either be brought back to the hospital or be seen by a psychiatrist near their home. He asked particularly that Mr. Oakson call him. Mr. Oakson called at noon, but Dr. Doren was not available. He returned the call but got no response, and at 7:00 P.M. he was told, on inquiring once again, that the call had been canceled. Dr. Doren then called directly and did get Mr. Oakson. He reported that Mr. Oakson was in good contact, his conversation was meaningful, he did not seem too anxious and even seemed to be in rather good spirits.

Both Oaksons were to be at Crest for therapy appointments on Thursday, January 16. On Wednesday, Mr. Oakson attempted to call Dr. Doren, but could not reach him. Dr. Doren later speculated that this might have been the last straw.

The account of the final night was given by Mrs. Martin.

« He woke up in the night time. He took a Nembutal occasionally—I think he had permission to—and he woke up in the middle of the night, and [Mrs. Oakson] heard him, and she asked him if he needed anything. He said, "Would you get up and take a walk with me?" and she said, "No." She said, "If you can't sleep, take a Nembutal, because we've got that early morning plane to catch." He was again looking in the mirror and talking about this eating away of his mouth and nose. Oakson had looked in the mirror and had said, "Can't you see it?" pointing at his nose. Mrs. Martin said Mrs. Oakson reported that she felt, at this point more helpless than she had ever before felt. He took a Nembutal and went back to bed, and she probably took a Nembutal too, I don't know—I know she had been. Anyway, she went back to sleep; and that's when he got up and went out to the garage. Mrs. Oakson thought he had gone for a walk; so she immediately got up and put on her clothes; and she started walking around the neighborhood there, and she couldn't find him. Then she called Tom, and he came over; and they circled around in their car. And then there was one place there that Bill used to go get snacks, and they went there. So they lost all this valuable time. I mean, if they had just known enough to look in the garage, it would have been all right. By the time they got back—oh, and then they fooled around . . . oh, they left a note for him, and said they were—if he came, just to stay put, and they'd be back—they were still looking for him. So then, after they got back for the second time, why Tom went out to the car, the garage . . .

The wife and son found Oakson in the garage, dead of carbon monoxide poisoning. Later, letters were found in which Oakson expressed his great fear of being put away in the state hospital, and of never getting well.

Chapter VII

VIRGINIA
ARLINGTON

in November 1959. She was transferred from the county hospital where she had been taken following a suicide attempt with barbiturates.

She had been the seventh and last child in a close-knit, upper-middle class family. Her mother was described in the hospital records as strong and dominant, overprotective, and masochistic. Her father was described as quiet, passive, and "in every way a gentleman." At the time of Virginia's birth, her father was old and deaf. He was a warm person and fond of children. When Virginia was born her oldest sibling, a girl, was 19 years old; there followed a boy, age 17; two girls, ages 15 and 11; Ed, 9 years old; and Ernest, 7 years old. The mother was depressed at the thought of yet another child at the very time when, having got Ernest off to school, she had expected to be free for a more active community life. A few days after the baby's birth, however, she resolved that such an attitude was unfair to the new baby. She wanted to give this child the benefit of the latest developments in child rearing; these were developments in permissive child rearing techniques, which her mother tried for the first time on Virginia. She had been firm and strict with all the other children.

Virginia's mother was busy with civic activities. Lillian, the 11-year-old sister, "adopted" Virginia and did most of the mothering. Virginia has always had a good relationship with her. The younger boys Ed and Ernest were in constant competition. Where Ed did everything with consummate ease, Ernest was clumsy. Ernest also took Virginia for his own. He supervised the development of many of her learning patterns—drilling her obsessively, for example, in the exact method of brushing teeth—and while he supported her in many ways, he also teased her unmercifully. She never learned to expect the attacks of teasing and was crushed anew each time.

Mrs. Arlington's mother once wrote to her:

« In the beginning everybody was crazy about you and used to spoil you. But after a couple of years when you wouldn't mind them, they scolded and so forth and used to say what a terrible child you were. I used to get after them for it, and because I felt you were not being treated right by them and that they had so little patience with you, I used to take your part and did little or no scolding myself, with the result they always said I was spoiling you, and this went on for several years.

Mrs. Arlington recalled her shock one night at the dinner table, at about the time she was 4½ years old, when her mother suddenly changed her approach and scolded her, apparently because the other siblings had said that she was spoiled. Her mother had now decided that she had made a bad mistake in siding with Virginia "because it only made the other children pick on her more." Mrs. Arlington looked back upon this table scene as a kind of calamity which never should have taken place.

Following a period of anxiety Virginia changed from an "enfant terrible" to a model child, self-sufficient, independent, never demanding, considerate, thoughtful—a good little girl who never did anything bad unless someone else made her do it. Everyone in the family adopted the mother's attitude that if Virginia blew up it was because they had not treated her right; that she was really "an awfully good girl."

Following this time, to all outward appearances Virginia was popular and a leader at school. Nevertheless, as she developed, anxiety and psychosomatic complaints were always close to the surface, especially during her adolescence. She was out of school because of unexplained anxiety for two weeks on two different occasions and was always fearful that she might faint and embarrass herself. She also suffered from frequent diarrhea and frequency of urination, as well as gastro-intestinal upsets, headaches, and general weakness. Later, while she was in college, her health improved somewhat after the discovery and treatment of a low thyroid condition, which might well have accounted for the general weakness.

In her adolescence, Virginia's father died suddenly in the

night. She developed intense anxiety with "the shakes" for the first time. She was so upset that she crawled into bed with Ed, then 25, and slept the rest of the night cuddled up to him. She was too anxious to go to the funeral, although she thought she should have gone. Later, she recalled in therapy "I was in the background after dad's funeral. Nobody paid any attention to me. I was very sad, but it was mother's great tragedy and I knew my place and stayed in it."

At about the same time Ernest, the youngest brother, went through an intensely disturbed period, in which he threatened to kill himself. Not long after this he left home for an out-of-state college.

After her father's death, Virginia maintained her busy, active social life and wound up her senior year of high school very successfully. Her anxiety was lessening; she was ill less frequently; and she was having a very good time. She participated in many boy-girl social activities. But although she was popular with girls and had many close girl friends, she knew none of the boys more than casually, and apparently was not really popular with them.

Virginia had planned to attend one of the fine women's colleges. But Ernest was so insistent that she attend his university, located at Columbia, that she gave up her original plans, "thrilled" at her big brother's interest in her. Ernest more or less paved her way into a sorority. She enjoyed college thoroughly. Again she had a close group of girl friends, including her roommate, whom Ernest met through her and married.

Virginia could no longer be so dependent upon Ernest after the marriage. She seemed to have adjusted to the marriage by idealizing her sister-in-law and thinking of the marriage as wonderful. After the marriage, she emancipated herself somewhat by going on to another, distant, school to earn her M.A. She then returned to Columbia, found an apartment, and secured a responsible job. She was in charge of nine people by the time she was 22 years old. It was reported that "she gave the impression of being an unusually mature and responsible young woman."

A year after Virginia's return to Columbia, Ernest conceived the idea of bringing their mother to Columbia so he could take care of her, and maneuvered things so that she and Virginia had to live together. Both were unhappy with this arrangement, the mother at being torn away from her home, the daughter at having to live with her mother at a time when she would have preferred to be sharing an apartment with a husband.

By this time Virginia was "going steady" with a young electronics engineering student, Tom Arlington. This development had also been brought about indirectly by Ernest. Arlington's first impression of Virginia, as mature, intelligent, and understanding, had appealed to him. However, as he came to know her better, he began to have increasing doubts. While she was eager for marriage, he procrastinated about proposing. From her point of view, although he was independent and sure of himself in other situations, he showed a disquieting passivity in the courtship.

It was at about this time that Virginia was first referred for psychiatric treatment by her family physician, in the middle of January 1952. She had suffered an acute attack of anxiety while talking with Ernest. At the time of the anxiety attack she was trying to explain to Ernest her feelings about her mother and to secure his approval for moving out of the apartment they shared. She felt unable to make this move unless she was assured of Ernest's understanding. Later her therapist wrote:

« At the point where she felt he had understood her feelings about her mother, she suddenly became flooded with anxiety and all the concomitant physical symptoms, such as racing heart, "the shakes," a tight band twisting in her head, etc. She was terribly frightened about the physical symptoms and humiliated by the loss of control, which seemed a terrible blow to her self-esteem.

Following this talk and the anxiety attack, Ernest had a long talk with Arlington, who made the long-delayed proposal the next day.

While the marriage proposal did not immediately diminish Virginia's anxiety, it did enable her to lean more heavily on Mr. Arlington for support. She decided to follow her physician's suggestion that she go to a psychiatric clinic. The records there stated:

« Examination and psychiatric work-up revealed a twenty-five-year old unmarried woman suffering from an acute anxiety attack of severe degree. Duration of the acute attack was not more than two weeks but there was evidence of a long-standing psychiatric disorder, characterized by chronic anxiety and other neurotic symptoms as well as by many schizoid characteristics. This young woman was highly intelligent and had appealing charm but she had been apprehensive, easily embarrassed, self-conscious, and easily wounded or offended from her earliest years. She was meticulous and perfectionistic in her standards, very critical of herself and others, and at the same time extremely sensitive to the opinions of others about her and suspicious that there were hidden critical implications about her in what others said or did. Her tolerance for frustration was very low, and difficulties or frustrations which would seem ordinary to a less sensitive person seemed insurmountable and intolerable to her. She suffered acutely from shame over her symptoms and had been able for many years to conceal their full extent from family and friends.

The clinic psychiatrist saw her three times—as an emergency case—helped bring the anxiety attack under control, and recommended intensive psychotherapy with one of the clinic's psychiatric social workers, whom he supervised.

This first psychotherapy experience was not successful.

« From the beginning she presented a very difficult problem in management because of the nature of her symptoms. Her sensitivity, her suspiciousness that she was being criticized, and the ease and rapidity with which unmanageable anxiety accompanied by outbursts of rage could be precipitated made it almost impossible for her to tolerate the usual procedures of treatment. It became rapidly apparent that any attempt to deal with the underlying long-standing disorder would endanger what capacity she had retained to function normally. . . . Since she became unmanageably antagonistic to the first psychiatric social worker, the psychiatrist transferred her to another member of his clinic staff, Mrs. Marcia Clift.

The plan was that "she should be handled with a very limited goal in mind, at least for a time, the goal being to try to restore the balance she had managed to maintain with reasonable success prior to the anxiety attack . . . It was therefore decided to handle her supportively with particular emphasis on helping her to objectify the symptoms about which she was frightened and humiliated."

Mrs. Clift reported:

« When I first saw Virginia I found her to be suspicious, distrustful and very prone to see the motes in her neighbor's eye to the exclusion of the one in her own . . . During the initial period of treatment with her these reactions diminished considerably, though one sensed they could appear again readily. One began to see more of the charm and sympathy of her personality, and a certain warmth and graciousness, as well as more free-flowing affect.

With Mrs. Clift a workable relationship developed.

During this period the patient spoke a good deal of her dissatisfaction with her relationship with Mr. Arlington. Nevertheless, she went ahead with her plans to marry him in October of that year. The patient responded rapidly to the supportive therapy approach, and after six months, with the therapist's concurrence, terminated treatment. Virginia felt that she was functioning normally. The therapist suggested that perhaps later when she was a little older, had accumulated some confidence in her own ability to function, and could approach therapy without the humiliation of being forced into it by her anxiety, she might consider therapy for the more long standing difficulties of which she had always been aware.

The marriage took place as planned, about the time of the termination of this initial period of therapy.

At the time of the marriage, Arlington was a student who gave promise of doing well. Although he admired Virginia, he had many doubts, nor had they been resolved when he proposed marriage. (Shortly following the marriage, Ernest left Columbia.)

Mrs. Clift later wrote:

« With the exception of one anxiety attack three weeks after her marriage to Mr. Arlington she held her ground for six months, but anxiety began to build up following her decision to stop work with the plan of having a baby in the near future, and she again asked to see me. She again responded quickly and seemed back on her feet in a month and a half, when once again she developed acute anxiety when Mr. Arlington became ill and it was discovered he had a minor heart ailment. She was seen again for four months and again managed to overcome the difficulty, this time for another four months.

The therapist reported that the focus was primarily on reality elements and realistic solutions, although she noted that during the last four months Mrs. Arlington "of her own accord cautiously began to examine the underlying reasons for her lifelong anxiety, which seemed to center around apprehension that she would be helpless and powerless in some situation and someone in charge would do the wrong thing."

« At this time, early in 1954, Mr. Arlington lost his job. Mrs. Arlington became virtually incapacitated, described herself as completely shattered, and withdrew from all outside contacts within a short period of time, having become unable to go anywhere or see anyone without uncontrollable anxiety. She was terribly embarrassed and bitterly ashamed of her reaction, but totally unable to control it. She had requested to see Mrs. Clift, and at this time the whole course of her prior treatment was evaluated and reviewed, all possible alternatives were considered, and the decision was made that her interests would best be served by continuing to see Mrs. Clift under Dr. Lyle's [the psychiatrist] direction.

Mrs. Arlington began to experience severe anxiety attacks whenever she left her apartment; consequently, she "holed up" there. Her conversations with Mrs. Clift were extremely confused and confusing, and she apparently felt that the therapist was unable to understand her even when she explained what was wrong. Mrs. Arlington pleaded with Mrs. Clift to talk with Mr. Arlington, hoping that Mrs. Clift might then understand what she, Mrs. Arlington, was trying to tell her. Mrs. Clift and Dr. Lyle both felt strongly at that time that Mrs. Arlington's inability to communicate what was wrong to Mrs. Clift was frightening her further, aggravating the anxiety and the "shattering." The basic need, both of them felt, was to prevent further disintegration of her ego.

Mrs. Clift reported:

« Since she was completely out of hand and was talking [vaguely]* of killing herself, I talked to Mr. Arlington. He felt himself to blame, since he had lost all initiative, was lethargic and unable to do any of the things she wanted him to . . . He was anxious that the marriage would break up unless he did something about it, and I referred him to Dr. Lyle for discussion of his own difficulties.

Mr. Arlington was seen for a time by Dr. Lyle, who referred

---

* This, and other bracketed material in Mrs. Clift's letters and quotations, is a correction made at Mrs. Clift's request after she carefully reviewed her notes.

him as a therapy patient back to Mrs. Clift who was treating Mrs. Arlington. The reason for this procedure was to help Mrs. Arlington organize; in hearing Mr. Arlington's views and reports, Mrs. Arlington's helplessness in communication might be obviated. Also, Mr. and Mrs. Arlington asked to be seen by the same person. However, it was not long before Mr. Arlington's therapy became his own, and both Mr. and Mrs. Arlington then were in intensive therapy with Mrs. Clift. Actually, at this time, Mr. Arlington was reported as being quite disturbed. He had lost his position and his marriage was tumultuous. Mrs. Clift wrote that "Mr. Arlington was frightened by his inability to handle the situation."

It now appeared that the course of the marriage had not been as smooth as Mrs. Arlington had indicated prior to this time. She had immediately set up obsessive-compulsive controls about everything from finances to sex. This undercut her husband to the point where he could barely function, and he was supressing violent anger whose only expression was the blocking of her plans by being "too tired" to do anything. On the one hand, she was obviously afraid of the sex relationship and was controlling it. At the same time, she was attempting to gain his approval with the same kind of obsessive-compulsive activities which would have pleased Ernest. Arlington had taken his first position. He had been promised the opportunity of working his way up to general manager, and he was over-anxious to succeed. In the evenings, he wanted to lie quietly on the davenport to think out problems which had come up during the day. Mrs. Arlington, identifying his silences with the masochistic silence into which her mother had withdrawn when she was displeased with any of the children, grew anxious. Moreover, Mrs. Arlington was always full of projects and busy-work— home redecorating, trips to points of historical interest, picture-taking and scrapbooks. She expected her husband to join enthusiastically into these activities, making suggestions and giving firm direction and support, as Ernest had done. Tom wanted to read. And so it went. For a time, Mrs. Arlington "made allowances," overlooked, and silently resented. Then she made herself deliberately passive and nonactive, to try to force him to take over Ernest's directing role. But this cut her off from the gratification she felt in her many projects. At last, violent fights began to break out, in which she lost control of herself, screamed at him, beat him, and threw things. She had always thought of herself as a kind, sympathetic, considerate, and reasonable person. The outbreak of such primitive emotions and behavior in herself frightened and humiliated her; she also felt guilty, because she secretly felt that she might be the cause of her husband's lethargy.

The period from January 1954 until approximately the middle of 1956 was a hectic one for Mrs. Arlington, although the treatment situation was a good deal less chaotic than it had been. Mrs. Arlington was incapable of getting herself to the therapist's office, either alone or accompanied. As noted earlier, all possible treatment alternatives had been considered; hospitalization was eliminated because it was felt that the rules, regulations, and restrictions would only contribute to the disintegration of Mrs. Arlington's ego, and that she would be almost impossible to treat in a hospital setting. For some months efforts were made to get Mrs. Arlington to come to Mrs. Clift's office. When these failed, Mrs. Clift decided that she should be seen at home since she was pleading for help. Thus her treatment continued on an outpatient basis, with Mrs. Clift seeing her at home. The therapist noted in a retrospective letter:

« I should say here in all fairness to Mrs. Arlington that I have never worked with a patient with such a weak ego, such intolerance of what would be to others slight frustration, and so strong a tendency to act out in everything she does. As a result I [fumbled around] a great deal in trying to find a way to work with her . . . In addition, I felt [from the beginning] she was capable of killing herself as a last resort if she were pushed too far, and I was [perhaps] more intimidated by this possibility, in retrospect, than was good for her. On the other hand, all this seemed rather incredible in so nice, dependable, responsible, and reasonable a girl, so that I had a tendency to treat her as though she was much more reasonable and sensible than she actually was at times.

As to therapy,

« [She tried to get me to push her as Ernest would have—or at least to abet her in pushing herself as she had when I first saw her.] Basically the attitude I took with her was that it made no difference to me whether she got out of the house or not, but that if she wanted to do so, I would help her find out why she could not go out without anxiety of such proportion that she was incapacitated. I would not

prod, push or tell her how to do it, and I would have nothing
to do with the thing if she prodded, pushed, or forced
herself. After a period of testing whether I really meant it,
she settled down and order began to appear out of the chaos.
During this period I deliberately let her control her own
treatment pace and whatever limits had to be set were presented in such a way that the reason for them was obviously
part of the reality situation . . . [The rationale behind
everything we did was to develop confidence in her own
perceptions and judgments, rather than to depend on Ernest
or on someone who stood for him.] Once control was in her
own hands and she was assured she would not be forced to
move faster than she felt she could, her own wish to recover
began to assert itself, and she began to inch out of her
dependency upon me . . . This period ended when she decided she was ready to come to the office for her appointments. She had by this time added one activity after another
to the things she could do naturally without anxiety, and
while she was still a long way from completely mobile, she
had worked out the essentials of why she reacted with panic
when she did. She never once slipped backward, having
taken a step. This and the fact that she could be considerate
and thoughtful with me, reduced her guilt enough that she
could work at what the basic problem was without so much
defensive activity that one could not make head or tail of
what was going on.

Mrs. Clift continued:

« [Periods in which she was positive and cooperative alternated
with outbreaks of hostility which at first seemed to occur
for no observable reason.] It then began to appear that on
these days there was something she had very much wanted
to discuss but could never get to "because you took me off
it with your old problem." The something was a violent
fight with Mr. Arlington, which she held that he provoked.
Gradually it came out that the sequence was that there had
been love-making, usually a great deal of cuddling, being
held, etc., on her part, for which she was always eager. This
had led to intercourse, for which she was also ostensibly
eager, but which she surrounded with all kinds of "proper"
rules for doing it right which must be followed carefully so
that it was a wholesome experience. She did not have an

orgasm and felt it was Mr. Arlington's fault because he didn't do it the way the book said, felt disappointed and cheated, and wanted to revert to the cuddling stage. Mr. Arlington . . . was rendered extremely anxious by her criticisms and inwardly withdrew without giving any outward signs at first. She felt further dissatisfied and by the next day was beginning to be provocative with him. He in turn withdrew further, while she demanded further caresses. Feeling spurned, she became angry, and the sequence of anger, primitive striking out, humiliation, guilt, and defense was started, followed by [projection on to me of her self-accusations. This was followed by ruminations about occurrences more remote in time which she imagined] I had been accusatory about, and thus the hostile approach out of the blue. She was further rendered guilty in the relationship with Mr. Arlington because his response was withdrawal into silence, and eventually tears of chagrin because he was so inadequate. Since he would not fight back, she felt doubly guilty . . . As they began to be able to discuss their mutual feelings, she gradually grasped a little of what was involved so far as he was concerned, and felt less personally spurned. It never was possible for her to really grasp that if she had a need, it could not always be filled immediately. As a result of the "to-do's," Mrs. Arlington insisted [in the fall, 1956] that Mr. Arlington live in a separate establishment, an arrangement which he accepted with relief, although neither of them was ready to concede that the relationship was irretrievable, each for his own reasons.

At about this same time Mrs. Arlington began to examine, in the therapeutic situation, her relationship with her husband. According to Mrs. Clift, Mrs. Arlington began, for the first time, to see her husband as a real person with needs and problems of his own; and the relationship improved, briefly. However, as she began to grasp the implications of her new understanding of Mr. Arlington, she became depressed. For as it became clear that her husband had needs of his own, she realized further that not only was he not going to meet her demands, but above all that he could not both meet her needs and satisfy his own. In her therapy hour, she said: "I saw last night that Tom can't be interested in me the way I expect him to and I cried all night. I had the feeling I had to have my feelings all by myself and I don't know what to do with them." Mrs. Clift noted that, although she was probably talking about sexual feelings, it was apparent from the context that what she really meant by "be interested" was to be like a mother who gives a small child all her attention and who meets every need as it is felt without delay. She made her first real suicide threat at this point, in November 1956. It was as though she said, "If you do not meet my needs, I must die." Mrs. Arlington had talked earlier of suicide says Mrs. Clift, "as people do . . . but it wasn't serious. This was the first time I really thought it [should be taken seriously, but I was not concerned that she would really carry through on the threat]."

At the time of this first serious suicide threat, some new elements had impinged upon Mrs. Arlington. Mr. Arlington, now holding another position, passed through a period of extreme depression. Also, Dr. Lyle, director of the clinic and supervisor of Mrs. Clift, told the staff in the first week of November 1956, that he was planning to leave in six weeks. His assistant, Dr. Daniel Johnston, was to replace him. Mrs. Clift reported, "Just suddenly out of the blue he [Lyle] told us that he was going and wanted Dan to take over his [position]." While the clinic staff liked and respected Dr. Johnston, he had neither the prestige nor the experience of Dr. Lyle; and the staff felt dependent upon the director for guidance. It was within this complex setting that Mrs. Arlington's first serious suicide threat was made.

With the change of directors and a change in supervision came a change in the supervisor's attitude about the treatment of Mrs. Arlington. Control of "acting-out" received greater emphasis. Mrs. Clift reported:

« She continued to work at increasing her mobility on her own, and I began gradually imposing limits, first on what I would do, and later, on what she could do in treatment. This of course mobilized her negative feelings, and the result was stormy . . . If limits were imposed just a little before she was ready to move, there was a storm, but she progressed much faster. If they were imposed too fast, she gave indication of shattering completely and I waited till she was more ready till it could be imposed with success.

With limit-setting, tranquilizers were used, "on the principle that she might be able to handle the pressures on her better if the degree of her anxiety were lowered." As she became better, she cut the intake of tranquilizers down to a minimum, sometimes using no medication at all until the next occasion of stress.

« She began to make progress, although this was a very slow and painstaking process with many ups and downs due again to the readiness with which unmanageable anxiety could be provoked with any pressure or disappointment . . . By the spring of 1959, she had become able to do most ordinary things without anxiety and had re-established relationships with all members of her family and with some old friends. She had developed some insight into the sources of her anxiety and seemed much more able to cope with frustration, although there was still an underlying precarious quality to her adjustment.

After much thought she decided to try working again and in July 1959, she applied for an excellent job for which she was well qualified. She became suddenly frightened and withdrew her application, however, when she learned she was the only applicant and would probably get the job. This was the first real test of her ability to assume normal responsibilities and her failure to carry through on it depressed her. When Mr. Arlington became depressed over the loss of his job in mid-August as well as over his father's death earlier in the summer, her depression deepened. We learned later that in addition her mother, not knowing about Mr. Arlington's job situation and thinking that he had inherited money from his father, cut off the funds she had been sending Mrs. Arlington to help defray their expenses.

Over Labor Day, 1959, the therapist took a five-day vacation. Upon her return, Mrs. Arlington reported that in her absence, "The bottom dropped out with Tom," presumably because he was unenthusiastic about a house in which she had hoped they might live together. The therapist reported that by the time she got back Mrs. Arlington was seriously out of control.

« The combination of disasters, as she felt them, proved more than she could sustain, and once again she shattered at the beginning of September, but this time much more rapidly, gravely, and intractably. She seemed to block every attempt to help her, was at times assaultive, violent, and irrational, and was at other times deeply depressed and convinced of her incurability.

Mrs. Clift later stated: "She became murderously angry at me [the reason again seemed inexplicable]. I began to be seriously concerned that she would kill herself for a number of reasons. The chief one was that she had again come face to face with the necessity to give up the fantasy that marriage was like having an ever-present mother who met all your needs exactly as you wanted them met." During that time Mrs. Arlington picked up an ash stand in the therapy hour "intending to [hit] me over the head." At the last minute she flung it over against the wall, and then beat Mrs. Clift with her purse.

The therapist said, speaking of the suicide danger, "I was worried about her because it seemed to me that it was beyond [my control]. Before, I felt I could always handle it. Partly this was the innocence of never having had it happen, I think. And partly a lot of it depends on your complete and utter confidence." Mrs. Clift's supervisor, Dr. Johnston, felt that Mrs. Clift was handling it wrong; "I should sort of [push] her out of this dependency and force her into doing things which I knew would create further anxiety on her part . . . I didn't have much support." There was talk about hospitalizing Mrs. Arlington but, the therapist said, "She always said she'd kill herself in a sanitarium."

Mr. and Mrs. Arlington were living together by this time. He was worried about his wife and felt he should not leave her alone very much. Mr. Arlington himself, in the middle of September, was in "a petrified anxiety state and doesn't know what to do." With the loss of another position, his feelings of inadequacy had returned. Mrs. Arlington, disturbed by her husband's state, was "attempting all sorts of symptomatic ways of trying to organize herself which made him feel more inadequate. In the meantime she would be wanting more love and all of his sexual feelings disappeared into limbo someplace."

Mrs. Clift began to be concerned about Mrs. Arlington's hostility toward her. And further: "I had the strong feeling that with just a flick of the thumb it could turn into destructiveness against herself. That as long as she were mad at me we were safe, but that if I made a move . . ."

Mrs. Arlington's actions were not reassuring. For example, she began to write a will. She "consulted every book in the library on writing wills." It was later learned that at this time Mrs. Arlington put secretly saved money into an account, in her name only, so that if she killed herself Mr. Arlington could not get it. She had been telling her husband that they would be "broke" by December; he had, of course, no knowledge that she had banked $4000. In the will she gave nothing to her husband; she left everything—including Mr. Arlington's own car—to others.

These matters were enough to make Mrs. Clift anxious; and she was further worried because "She's got fourteen sleeping pills, and while we think it is not enough [to cause death], she's so darn sensitive to drugs we're not sure."

« Nobody could find them. She won't hand them over, and this is what had me worried . . . These had been her weapon all the last four years. But she had them hidden out. Tom couldn't find them; I couldn't get her to hand them over. I didn't want to act too anxious about it, but I knew she had them.

After a careful re-examination of her detailed recorded notes, Mrs. Clift described this intense time.

« On September 24, 1959, after a great deal of thought I finally decided that the situation was beyond my control and that I could not continue to take responsibility for seeing her as an outpatient unless Dr. Johnston himself talked to her and formed an opinion independent of my reports to him of what was going on. None of the measures which had worked before had any effect, nor did anything else I tried give any promise of stopping the steady worsening of the situation. It is impossible to convey the sense of imminent danger, a sense I had never had before with her. It felt as though her reactions were building to a climax of most dramatic intensity, conveyed mainly by allusions and subtle actions all pointing to an ultimate culmination in her killing herself. I was genuinely concerned and alarmed. This in itself concerned me, since I felt there was danger of her being frightened into action if she felt she had alarmed me.

We decided to move cautiously, in order not to alarm her if possible, toward arranging an appointment with Dr. Johnston. If his opinion coincided with mine, and if talking with him did not break up the impasse, we were agreed that we had no alternative but to recommend hospitalization . . . we decided to inform Mr. Arlington that we were considering such a recommendation.

On September 26 at her regular appointment I told her

that . . . since she and I seemed unable to break the impasse, I thought she should talk to Dr. Johnston to see if that would do it. She fought the idea, but the tenor of her objections seemed to be fear that he would reject her. I suggested that she think it over and we talk about it some more . . .

At her next appointment she . . . talked about her concern about the state she was in, thought she would like a consultation with someone, but felt I should work out whatever made me so inflexible that I would not treat her as she wanted to be treated. This again started the attacking, abusive reaction, and it became difficult to maintain any coherence . . . I finally said that I knew she was deeply concerned and depressed under her anger at me, and that rather than go on being miserable it made more sense to use whatever means we could to help her. It finally came out that she was afraid to talk to him because "when I talked to him before he said he looked to the patient for the source of difficulty in therapy and didn't think it was the therapist's fault, but how the patient reacted." . . . However, once she had voiced this she decided she would discuss an appointment with him on the phone.

In the telephone call she attempted to draw Dr. Johnston into an argument about how he would conduct an interview with her. He told her he would need to see her to determine what was required and refused to be drawn into discussion of how he would talk with her. She decided to think it over and let us know later what she had decided.

Shortly afterward she telephoned me and asked mysteriously if I had dismissed her from therapy. I said I had not. She said she had other plans than to see Dr. Johnston, which I would find out soon enough. (Threatening, but the feeling of her being desperately near suicide is gone.) Since she seemed to have come to a decision of her own, I decided to do nothing until I saw how she managed the situation herself.

The following week she called me again, asking in a mysterious voice if I had dismissed her from treatment. I again said that I had not, but added that I wondered if she wished to be dismissed so that she could go to someone else. She then said triumphantly that she had figured out that Dr. Crawford must have been my analyst and she had gone to see him and had told him how terrible I was. She thought he had said that I had apparently got into a transference with her that I could not resolve and that if he weren't so busy he would see her himself . . . He had recommended she see either Dr. Smith or Dr. O'Brien. Therefore she wanted my dismissal so that she would be free to go to either one of them. I said she didn't need a dismissal from me. All she had to do to be ethically correct was to notify me that she wished to terminate. If seeing someone else seemed right to her and really made sense to her, of course I would cooperate. She seemed greatly relieved and began to talk more naturally at this point about her doubts about whether she was doing the right thing . . . There was no feeling of any suicide danger during this conversation. I felt that the crisis was over.

I learned from Dr. Johnston that she then had an interview with Dr. O'Brien, who had one free hour which he offered her. She was dubious that she could sustain the anxiety she knew would build up between hours at one time a week, and Dr. O'Brien made it clear that if she entered treatment with him he would not accept phone calls between appointments no matter what the reason. (With more frequent appointments there never had been a problem of phone calls between sessions.) She was uncertain whether to continue with him and asked for an appointment with Dr. Johnston, whom she saw October 15. After much indecision she decided to go on with Dr. O'Brien.

At midnight following her second appointment with Dr. O'Brien she called me in a state of such severe anxiety that she could hardly talk. I had never known her to be in a state like this. She was panting and her words came in gasps, "I . . . I . . . I . . ." Her anxiety was an almost tangible thing. The call put me in a dilemma. So far as I knew she was now Dr. O'Brien's patient, and I knew that for me to talk with her would undoubtedly be contrary to his philosophy of treatment. At the same time I knew that she simply would not telephone, particularly at this time of night, unless the reason were urgent. While I was debating what would be best to do she managed to gasp out that Dr. O'Brien had dismissed her. Would I please take her back? . . . When I questioned her it became clear that this was not the case. She began to realize that she had misinterpreted something he had said and that it was her own fear of going on in treatment with him which had prompted the thought that she was dismissed. "I just can't take it. I'm down to bedrock with myself. He's undone everything you've done. He's reduced me in two sessions back down to where I was before I ever saw you." As she heard herself say this she was suddenly excited. "Now I know what happened!" The anxiety started when Dr. O'Brien dismissed her explanation of what the difficulty had been and said that she was avoiding facing that she cannot live this way. She either has to be married to Tom or get a divorce from him. "I've taken it as a directive instead of something to understand—why I can't do it. I just *can't*." . . . A myriad of connections flooded into her mind and it seemed to her that the pieces were all falling into place. I stopped her, saying that I thought it would be a mistake to tell me any more if she planned to go on with Dr. O'Brien. She immediately recognized that this was true and decided that though it had upset her his approach seemed to be bearing fruit. It was now obvious to both of us that she was eager to return to him. She was sure now that she could wait until the next appointment without any further need to call him.

Late on Saturday night, October 26 [after Mrs. Arlington's third hour with Dr. O'Brien], Mr. Arlington called saying that Mrs. Arlington wanted to talk with me. He was extremely concerned, said she was incapacitated with anxiety, and that she was unable to dial to call me. She had tried to call Dr. O'Brien who had again refused to talk to her. He had been concerned enough to call Dr. O'Brien himself, to tell him he thought the situation was really serious and that someone should talk with her and appraise it, but Dr. O'Brien had also refused to talk with him. She was determined that she would not see Dr. O'Brien again and so far as both of them were concerned she was no longer his patient. Would I talk with her? I had no question in my mind that I should talk with her. Again she was in a more severe state of anxiety than I had ever known her to have. At first she could not talk at all, but after a time she quieted and a little at a time explained what had happened. There was a note of finality in her refusal to see Dr. O'Brien again, and she wanted to go on with her treatment with me.

She had struggled to work the thing out from the time of her third appointment until now, but had become more and more incapacitated until she was terribly frightened about the state she was in. She was afraid she could not stand it any more, and that she would yield to the temptation to kill herself. That was why she had asked Tom to call me. It had started again when she tried to tell Dr. O'Brien of the insight she had had. He had dismissed it again, she felt, and had said it had nothing to do with the present—that she had to decide what she was going to do in the present, whether she was going to be married or get a divorce. Since she was exhausted she finally agreed to try to get some sleep and to consider the matter more soberly in the light of day. I suggested she call me the next day at a particular time . . .

She called me at the appointed time on October 27, which was a Sunday. She was still acutely anxious and afraid she would kill herself, and started the call by pleading with me to take her back into treatment so that she would not kill herself. I said that if I saw her again it should be because it was the right thing for her, not because I was afraid she'd kill herself if I didn't. No good could come of an arrangement like that. There was a shocked pause while she considered what I had said. After a moment she said in quite a different tone of voice, "It's funny, I feel as though I were suddenly infused with energy. I think I see where I've been wrong in my thinking about treatment. Right now I think I could work entirely differently from now on. I think I understand for the first time really what you were trying to do when you set limits on me. I think I could really work at it now without fighting you every step of the way." . . . For the first time she could see a possibility that there might be a way of working out the things that made her feel so incapable of being a wife, and she was willing to set right anything that stood in the way of it, including giving Tom the sleeping tablets she had hidden in case she had to kill herself. I told her that Dr. Johnston had to make the final decision as to whether it would be best for her to see me or whether she could make more progress seeing someone else . . .

On October 28 I told Dr. Johnston in detail of the events which had occurred over the weekend. He decided to think the matter over and appraise the situation when she called. When he talked with her he said that he would like to think the whole thing over a little longer, and said he would call her back. He then talked to me again and said he had decided that it was too great a risk to take, that she might suddenly become depressed and suicidal again and that it would be better if she were in the hands of someone who could immediately hospitalize her at Crest [Dr. Johnston did not see hospital patients.] . . . He had checked with Drs. Plant and James Dale and had found that either of them had time open and could see her immediately.

Since she seemed to be put back together at this point, it was a better time to make a change than at a time when she was upset again. He also had misgivings about my seeing both her and Mr. Arlington, and thought this might be part of her difficulty in treatment, and that she should have a chance to try having someone completely her own. I thought Mr. Arlington could tolerate a change better than she at this point, but Dr. Johnston was certain this would be a mistake, and I realized that if her husband were to have to give up his therapy for her, it would only increase her guilt. He ended by saying the whole thing had been a mess and this was the only way to clear it up. My first intuitive reaction had been shock and a feeling that this was a mistake of major proportions, together with a feeling of helplessness to convey why it seemed to me wrong to do it this way. I thought I at least should call her and talk with her myself about his recommendation, but Dr. Johnston specifically requested that I not phone her as he wanted to handle it himself.

Dr. Johnston told me that he had talked with her in the afternoon and had explained that he thought she would make more rapid progress starting fresh with someone else at this point, and that he had checked around and found that both Dr. Plant and Dr. Dale had time available and could see her immediately. She asked if he refused to have me see her "because I treated Mrs. Clift so horribly," and he assured her that this had nothing to do with it, that he thought she would gain more this way. She seemed to accept his recommendation in good spirit . . .

Mrs. Clift said: "The truth of the matter was that if it had been up to me, I would have taken her back."

That evening, October 28, Mr. Arlington discussed his wife's situation during his therapy hour, after which the Arlingtons drove out to look at Crest, from the outside.

On the following morning, Tuesday—October 29, 1959—Mrs. Arlington phoned a number of psychiatrists, among them Dr. James Dale, who had previously been associated with Crest. He reported, "She described herself as very anxious and upset . . . I said, I have a cancelled hour about two hours later in the morning . . . I gave her the time and she said she didn't know whether she could get there, and generally gave a tone of sort of complaint, as though she hadn't got enough of something. But I had no idea what was going on. Didn't grasp at it, except got that overtone—that although I gave her an appointment almost immediately, somehow or other I wasn't giving her enough, although she didn't explicitly ask for any more. That was it, said goodbye. And I told her that if she wished to, she could call me back and let me know if she wanted to take that time."

Among the calls in the early morning was one to Crest. The hospital administrator answered the phone to hear Mrs. Arlington say: "Get me a psychiatrist, I'm going to kill myself." She gave her telephone number to the administrator, who ran to the conference room where a staff meeting was in process. Dr. Preston went immediately to the telephone. Mrs. Arlington answered. It was, she said, too late—"I've done it, I've done it." Dr. Preston then called the police. They found her conscious but drowsy, and rushed her to the county hospital. She arrived there in a coma.

Dr. Dale states:

« I didn't hear any more until that night. I had a call from Dan Johnston and he told me about the suicide attempt . . . and told me about what a messed up picture it was . . . what a problem she had been, and five minutes run-down of the problem she presented—and asked me if I would consider working with her, that she was comatose in the hospital, and would I consider it. So I said I would, but first I want to see the patient, and want to talk to the husband. I'd want to have the whole thing sort of okayed. I mean, I wouldn't go in and find out two days later that the patient wasn't going to work with me. I wanted to have her agree that this was satisfactory to her, but that I would put myself in the picture until she was able to make a decision in her own right, and even if she didn't decide she would want to work with me I would see it through to some treatment arrangement.

Dr. Dale talked with Mr. Arlington, who gave Dr. Dale permission to see the patient. Dr. Dale saw Mrs. Arlington on Wednesday night October 30; she had taken thirty-eight grains of Nembutal and had been comatose for more than twenty-four hours. She was not on the psychiatric ward but on the medical ward. Still groggy from the drugs, and only partly oriented, she nevertheless knew that she was in a hospital and what had brought her there. She talked freely. Dr. Dale explained that he would come to see her the next day and asked her if she wished to work with him.

« I told her she was still affected by the drugs; that the next day I would ask her to make some decision as to whether she was to work with me, so we could go ahead and schedule plans. And if not I would help her make them with someone else she was to work with. This was fine with her. She wanted to make them right away. She was sure it was all fine. I said, "Well, that's fine, but I would like you to be very sure." She was really so cockeyed and groggy. The next day she was much much calmer, and it was obvious that she decided that she would work with me.

Dr. Dale felt that he was "taking an extremely difficult case" and was a little worried about it in terms of her intense suicide drive. "But I kind of liked her . . . and I didn't feel unduly pessimistic." Dr. Dale told Mrs. Arlington that as a condition of his working with her, he would have to insist that she begin treatment in Crest hospital. She agreed to this. He also said that he could see her only if she could get to his office; and he advised Dr. Preston, upon the patient's admission to Crest, that it would be necessary that Mrs. Arlington be driven to his office, she and the driver to be accompanied by a third person. There must be "safe accompanying transportation arrangements" or "I would not be able to work with her." Dr. Dale adds: "You see, I couldn't get out [to Crest]. I just had the time in the middle of the morning and no way of traveling out at that schedule, at that moment." All of these conditions and arrangements were made known to Mr. Arlington.

Mrs. Arlington entered Crest on Friday, November 1, 1959. The admission note stated:

« [Mrs. Arlington was sent to Crest] because of Dr. Dale's feeling that in order to continue treatment with him, hospitalization during the early part of the treatment was necessary. The patient had been hospitalized on October 29, following a serious suicide attempt with barbiturates which had been taken after she had informed Crest of her intention to commit suicide. . . . [She was] a rather anxious appearing, spare, somewhat messy individual who . . . in spite of the tremendous intellectualization . . . it is quite apparent that she is intensely anxious and somewhat frightened both by the examiner and by the situation which she seems to see as one that she will have difficulty manipulating. Although quite anxious and openly concerned about her self-destructive attempts, it did not appear at the time of examination that she was significantly depressed or that she was psychotic.

She was diagnosed as a "passive-aggressive personality disorder, passive-dependent type." The note continued:

« Because of the recent and serious suicide attempt by this patient she will for the present time be on suicide precautions which will be rigidly maintained. Her psychotherapy, however, will be in Dr. Dale's office and she will be accompanied to and from these appointments, not only by a driver but by a member of the ward staff. On the ward she can be allowed gratifying activity and this may even be scheduled for her, although it is expected that she will occasionally or frequently refuse activity, although demanding it. She may make many requests, some of them anxious, testing of the situation, some of them genuine; these can all be referred to her physician, particularly those which appear to put ward personnel on the spot. Concerning these demands she can be met by a matter-of-fact attitude, although in other areas passive friendliness would seem to be appropriate. Her intellectualization and jargon-like talk about psychotherapy can be met by a rather passive matter-of-factness or referred to her psychotherapist. She will have a regular diet served on a tray in the ward, no medications at the present time, a status of R with S precautions.

This note, signed by Dr. Preston, was used on the ward as a guide for the ward staff. There seems little doubt that it set the pattern of the ward staff's response to Mrs. Arlington and influenced her total experience in the hospital. Noteworthy, in the light of that subsequent experience, were the "rigidly maintained" suicide precautions and the expectation that Mrs. Arlington would be "demanding," the demanding serving as her means of testing the situation. This sort of demanding was seen as contrary to "genuine" feelings and requests. The expectation too was that ward personnel will be put "on the spot." Ward personnel then were directed to act in a matter-of-fact way toward the patient and, should they feel uncomfortable, to refer the patient to her physician or her psychotherapist.

Although Dr. Preston's note called for strict suicide precautions, he remarked in interviews that he had never seen Mrs. Arlington as a "suicidal" person. Her suicide attempt prior to coming into the hospital he saw as a "vigorous attempt with a kicker"—the kicker being her call announcing that she had taken the drug. He noted too: "I don't think she took enough to kill herself . . . It's hard to take enough pills to kill yourself—you have got to take a tremendous amount. And she took her pills and left a kicker."* At the beginning of her stay at Crest Mrs. Arlington was distressed by the many hospital rules, which seemed to her to deal with her as if she were incapable and inadequate. The nurses' notes describe her reactions upon first coming to the ward.

« Asked in a rather shocked voice, "Will my door be locked?" She was told that it would not, that the ward was a locked ward. She talked a good deal about the ward rules and finally asked to use the bathroom. She was told that she would be accompanied and she complied, but seemed most embarrassed. She stated, "It makes a person feel like they are something they weren't."

Mrs. Arlington was reluctant to give up her cosmetics and watch; each new rule, as she encountered it, came to her as something of a shock . . . "more surprise that this is the way we handle things. Shook her head. 'It's sure a lot different here than I thought.' ['What did you think the hospital would be like?'] But couldn't reply specifically."

Mrs. Arlington was also distressed by the discovery, that day, that an acquaintance, Miriam Irwin, was a fellow-patient on the ward.

She was seen twice by Dr. Preston, once for forty-five minutes, at about 8:30 in the evening. After the visit she seemed more distressed and "the quality of her verbalizations had a type of hysteria and were rather dramatic." Throughout that evening she was wakeful and seemed very tense. She complained a good deal about the noise in a "sarcastic way." The other patients were reported as being comparatively quiet, and, at another

---

* Dr. Dale felt differently. He stated: "I think she would have died if the police hadn't gotten her to (County hospital)."

point, "optimally quiet." Noise at night, however, had always been one of Mrs. Arlington's bugaboos. Mrs. Clift had written that "[noises] made her furiously angry because she could not control them herself. 'I cannot stand to have someone else controlling what I do by making noise above me so that I cannot follow my own schedule but must follow theirs.' " She did not sleep very well that night. At four in the morning, she remarked that if the staff would stop looking in for an hour, she would not be so agitated and could get to sleep. She commented that she "hadn't known she would be treated like this."

Another patient on the ward, an old woman, regularly moaned, "God, God." Mrs. Arlington was moved—"Oh the poor soul. Can't you help her? I empathize too much." A little later, she said, "I'm frightened. I've regressed so far already. I'm afraid I'll wet the bed or something." The aide noted: "She had also used several other psychiatric words and I began to feel she was just seeing how I would react."

The following day her concern was still with the rules, and the nurses' notes state: "Talking quite disgustingly [*sic*] about all the rules around here. While in bathroom doing personal care said 'A person sure can't have his pride around here.' "

She was described as "quite obnoxious in lounge, telling patient Irwin about how awful this place was, they didn't give the proper treatment, everything was just too degrading. 'Why I'm just deteriorating into nothing in the 24 hours I've been here.' "

She asked to use the phone to call her husband, and when this was refused she noted that she "wished we'd treat her more as a human being." She was seen by Dr. Doren and seemed more comfortable after this. Later, she apologized "for the way she had acted earlier." She began to complain about feeling frightened and hopeless, saying that "she thought all these restrictions were making her all the more fearful." Throughout the day she complained that she felt she was deteriorating rapidly. That evening in her hopeless remarks there was some talk of suicide. It was noted that Mrs. Arlington felt "that all the precautions taken on ward made her think more of this [suicide] . . ." The nurse added: "I remained passive to most of the patient's comments, feeling she did not expect a response to most statements . . . Some histrionic outbursts . . . At times seemed to be attempting to arouse anxiety in staff or testing for responses of staff." On a few occasions she had been smiling and pleasant, but for the most part she appeared depressed; the "feeling that life is not worth living" was the impression suggested by her behavior.

She began the next day by dashing tumultuously into the office, where she grabbed the telephone and started dialing a number before she was checked. As the day wore on, she gave frequent grimaces and mutters of anguish. She broke a handle from a bowl and refused to give it up. During this incident and following it, Mrs. Arlington appeared frightened. She began to talk of her need to do something active and constructive, and of her desire to be "treated like a human being."

Mrs. Arlington kept questioning the aide about the aide's personal life and about treatment—"Maybe I need shock treatment. Do they do that here? Will I be hypnotized?" The aide refused to discuss either of these with the patient, referring the patient to the doctor—"Your doctor will decide the treatment for you."

There is no doubt that all this time Mrs. Arlington was pressing the staff to react to her. But the staff maintained its bland neutrality. Mrs. Arlington commented: "I can hear the staff's conversation in the office and it is reassuring to listen to them when they are laughing and being natural, even though it is about patients." Later that day she apologized for what she had done with the spoon and bowl in the morning. It was noted that she stated that the "protection" she was getting was not what she wanted. "Wanted to talk about Dr. Preston having saved her life 'for this.' And it wasn't worth it." The nurses' notes continually repeat the ward staff's method of dealing with Mrs. Arlington: "I attempted not to respond." "I sat with her saying little."

On November 4, her fourth day in the hospital, Mrs. Arlington went downtown to her therapy appointment, returning at 9:15 in the morning. She seemed a little more settled but this was not to last. The day was a difficult one for all concerned. The nurses' notes stated that at lunchtime Mrs. Arlington started gasping, wringing her hands, and sobbing.

« Nurse sat silently for a short while. Patient pulled herself together and went into the lounge. About a half hour later patient started her acting out in the lounge. Nurse took her to her room and sat down. Patient began pulling a few hairs at a time out of her head. "This is something I can do that hurts no one else. I'm not screaming or banging on walls. Everyone mistrusts me here. I operate much better in an environment of trust." Patient continued pulling out small bits of hair. She looked directly at nurse and said "I know what I'm doing, I'm perfectly rational right now." ["I know, but it seems quite ridiculous to me—pulling out your hair."] "I feel like doing it, it's a good project." Nurse left room and patient presently stopped and went again to lounge. After lunch patient played a half game of Russian Bank with nurse. Seemed to be trying to make nurse anxious, criticizing almost every play, the way she lifted the cards, etc. Patient went to her room, put up another very dramatic display of how wretched she felt, and again pulled herself together and went to the lounge for coffee. Mere presence and silence seems to help patient over these periods. "I know I won't be able to think when Dr. Preston comes up to see me. You report everything to him anyway so it won't matter." ["He'll be interested in anything you have to say."]

Patient seems to have a general attitude of hopelessness and futility as far as her illness is concerned. Makes such remarks as "please kill me, do something, etc." when in one of her frenzied states, very critical of various staff members in hospital. "I feel like shaking you, you don't show me kindness and trust." Advanced as though to carry out threat but did nothing as nurse sat there. Says she is out of control, begs to be killed or strapped down. Banged chair about the room a little and sat down on the floor. Immediately changed her attitude. "You're all so well trained, just to sit and stare." Walked into the lounge and sat down. Looked quite composed. Another similar episode occurred at shift change. Patient said she was getting worse by the hour. "I'll never get any privileges now. I've bashed everything." A rather hectic afternoon for patient.

It is clear that the Crest staff felt helpless before Mrs. Arlington, at a loss in its attempts to deal with her. Moreover, the staff now began to feel increasing dislike for her.

At the end of the very trying day just described, some new privileges were allowed Mrs. Arlington. For example, she was told that she might keep her partial dental plate, which until now she had been made to turn over nightly. The nurses' notes report:

« She looked up wide-eyed at me and burst into tears. "Oh, I hope I'll be worthy of this trust. I just don't understand. I'm so surprised." I felt that she was genuinely surprised but at the same time trying to provoke my anxiety. She brought them up several more times, saying such things as "I never would have thought of using my teeth for an instrument of death till they were taken away."

The following day additional privileges were given to her. On the 6th, she was to have walks around the grounds accompanied. On the 7th, she was to begin occupational therapy, also accompanied.

Concurrently, there was a change in the attitudes expressed by the patient. On the 5th, she stated that she felt "more encouraged since a couple of patients told her they thought they were better since their stay at Crest." Later that evening she said she felt "being here was really going to help her." She seemed more friendly and pleasant, and appeared more relaxed. She sang while in the bathtub. "She had a good evening." This mood continued. The notes reported her "remarkably relaxed and cheerful" and speaking about "what a grand day she had." The aide noted, "The behavior didn't seem high but rather she really seemed happy." By the 9th she was able to go to the bathroom unaccompanied. These days were regularly "good days."

The good days did not last. By the 10th, she was again upset and had a good deal of difficulty sleeping. At four o'clock in the morning, she began to call for someone to come to her. A nurse came into the room. Mrs. Arlington threw a hot water bottle at her; when the nurse attempted to be matter-of-fact about this attack, Mrs. Arlington struck her on the leg.

« I told her to cut it out, that she could control herself. She laughed and said, "You're angry." I couldn't help but grin and say sure. The patient said, "You have reason to be." She then grabbed my uniform and tried to rip it. (Nylon, pretty strong.) ["Why don't you cut out this nonsense."] She rambled on about being ready for state [hospital], shackles, and a gag for her mouth. I got very annoyed at this patient and left once she settled down.

She continued to be noisy that night; in the morning, she seemed very anxious. She was in her room alone after breakfast when there was "a loud noise from room."

« The patient had pulled on wire frame surrounding light bulb and had bent it, giving her easy access to light bulb. It was straightened by an aide, and another aide sat with her.

Patient kept asking for me to leave. Finally I said, "If you lay down I shall leave." The other aide sat with her. Dr. Preston was called and she kept saying "What's he going to do? Will he do anything?" The patient was told that she was back on strict S precautions. She was very angry at this. Hit window, hit ashtray and commented, "I can't control myself." She started punching and hitting the aide. There was no actual strength behind it. Aide was very matter-of-fact in telling her that she could control herself and to stop immediately. Patient did so saying, "Put me in restraints before I hurt someone or myself." ["You're not going to hurt anyone or yourself and you don't need to be in restraints."] Patient started crying and pulling at her hair. "If I had my privileges back I would be all right. I'm suicidal without them." This sounded so outlandish that aide didn't answer.

By this time she had quite a bald spot on the top of her head, where she had pulled her hair out. (Curiously, Mr. Einston had a similar "tic," which resulted in a bald spot.)

Mrs. Arlington was consistently "testing," albeit in a confused way. For example, on the 10th:

« "It doesn't seem like my behavior makes any difference to you people. When I do something or say something, do you regard it or do you just say to yourselves, she's sick." ["Our business is to regard patient's behavior."] "Well, why don't you respond; like when I'm angry, have you ever tried to get angry with a brick wall?" ["Because we don't say anything does not mean we don't regard it."] She continued by talking in her hopeless fashion, saying that if she was going to be the worst one here, why didn't they strap her down and be done with it. She was desperate inside, etc. Some of it had a threatening quality (toward hospital).

On the evening of the 10th, the patient was in the bath and "She put her head down under the water as though to drown. I very matter-of-factly pulled her head back up and told her if she didn't start washing I would let the water out. She then washed rather haphazardly and got out of tub, asking me to help her."

On the 11th, some of Mrs. Arlington's privileges were restored; she was very pleased by this.

Mrs. Arlington customarily wrote notes to herself, presumably to aid her in her therapy. These notes were scribbled with many personal and idiosyncratic abbreviations. One note, dated November 8, 1959, included the following comments about her therapy: "Sixth interview, Friday, nothing except 'What was your crossing thought?' About changing psychiatrists equals zero. Why do I need reassurance? Why anxious when someone doesn't talk?"

About the hospital she noted:

« Friday, decided what happened to me first weekend and every night in this room, like Russian technique of keeping prisoner from sleeping—he starts fantasizing plus initial fear of unknown. That's gone now and yet fantasizing occurs . . . each night so I also know that happening! Inadequate ventilation and excessive noise do make difference with me.

She also wrote:

« Things seem to build up—need release—no physical activity is a means here . . . Hard for me to live under so much security—I don't feel I need it. Too high standards. Can't help feeling of despair—capable of deep emotion . . . Too aware of feelings and surrounding . . . of other people and their feelings, etc. . . . Confinement is like cloud over me— keep thinking of myself as normal and as I usually live and do—additional and huge problem to cope with.

On November 12, there was a staff conference on Mrs. Arlington, at which two issues arose as subjects of conflict. One of these was the question of whether Mrs. Clift, Mrs. Arlington's previous therapist, ought to continue as Tom Arlington's therapist. The other issue was the conviction of the nursing staff that a patient seriously ill and on suicide precautions should not be traveling downtown to see a therapist.*

Dr. Doren was convinced that Mrs. Clift should be asked to terminate her treatment of Mr. Arlington. "My own feeling was that the situation of her husband having taken her therapist, Mrs. Clift, away from her—I felt that this was very important at some level, and I think it was something I never felt right about. It was only the conflict with Dale's feeling about it that made me delay action so long."

Dr. Dale, on his part, granted at the conference that the relationship between Mr. and Mrs. Arlington and Mrs. Clift

---

* This attitude differed from the one held at Crest in the past, as illustrated in Chapter II.

seemed undesirable, and that it might be beneficial to Mrs. Arlington should Mrs. Clift drop Tom as her patient. But Dale was quite firm in his belief that it would be inappropriate for him, as Mrs. Arlington's therapist, to meddle in the husband's treatment situation. He took the position that he was dealing with Mrs. Arlington in psychotherapy, and did not want to get involved in extratherapeutic complications. He did not oppose the hospital staff if it wished to attempt to separate Mr. Arlington and Mrs. Clift—although he cautioned that he himself would "be chary . . . to rush in and try to stop a patient and a therapist from seeing one another . . ."

Dr. Dale observed that although Dr. Doren had been concerned about this issue prior to the conference, his conviction on the subject had been "relatively mild compared to what it was later."

Dr. Doren became increasingly concerned, nor was he alone. Miss Simmons, the case worker, observed:

« I think there was a conviction in the hospital that her therapist working with the husband wasn't a healthy thing. I don't feel it was healthy, no. I think what concerned all of us was the method by which a change could be recommended if it should be. And this was the thing that got hung up . . . Bad as we all were recognizing the situation had been, with one therapist working with both of these people, and bad as we all recognized the patient's reaction must be— to being the one who was abandoned by the therapist—it was a very touchy thing to deal with. It was something I felt we at the hospital couldn't dive into without extremely careful examination and planning.

This issue was never resolved. Nor was the conflict over the question of Mrs. Arlington's traveling downtown to Dr. Dale for therapy.

At the conference, a nurse stated that "Dr. Dale seemed oblivious to the absurdity of sending downtown for appointments a patient who was on suicidal precautions." Generally, this issue of transportation was not given much credence by the professionals. Dr. Dale was much respected; it was felt that if he could only see Mrs. Arlington downtown, it was better that she travel downtown than that she be kept on the ward, where Dr. Dale would not be available to her. Preston, commenting upon this problem, said: "I felt concerned about it only in terms of the nursing staff pressure. Patients get to their appointments and get back, and there is an occasional screwup, but . . . I thought Dale was right at the time . . . he said this was the way he could take her; and if Dale felt he could treat her under these circumstances, I think he had to make it clear."

The head nurse on Mrs. Arlington's ward had a different view. "I definitely felt—as a matter of fact I think I told Dr. Preston this too—that in the first place she was too sick to go downtown . . . Also, it was difficult to get people to accompany her down there too. To accompany patients who you feel are going to elope, who are suicidal, and to take this responsibility, is a lot to ask of staff members. And there was reluctance. However, I felt very genuinely that she was too sick at that point to go down." The nurse added, however, "Having worked with Dr. Dale for a few years, I had the feeling that with this patient—as with every other patient I ever worked with with him—he knew what he was doing."

In the middle of November, following the conference, Mrs. Arlington had a stormy but significant therapy hour. At the conference, it had been agreed that Mrs. Arlington should continue in hospital. Dr. Dale reported this conclusion to her. This appears to have set off the explosion which then took place. Dr. Dale described the session as follows:

« The conference was over; the next hour with her I talked about the conference, and told her the general advice that she should stay in the hospital for a bit. She was angry about this. She didn't want to, and she raised hell about this in the office; she screamed and she shouted at me, and she didn't hit me only with words and noise, just pounded emotionally. In a way . . . this hour was one of the most intense, controlling, emotional efforts I've ever been put under by a patient. And I told her—I've forgotten the exact words—that it was up to her whether she worked with me; I was entirely prepared to continue with her; but these were the arrangements, this was a result of my own considered clinical judgment and that of a half a dozen people who put a lot of time into thinking and discussion of it; and it was a very serious and important conclusion for her. She just got so furious she picked up the ashtray on my table and she brought it down so hard that this little ashtray broke into about a hundred pieces. She jumped up to go to the phone and I said, "Sit down." And I told her right then, very forcefully—we were very involved—"Say any damn thing you like, feel any way you like, but there are limits to what you do. Under no circumstances whatsoever is there to be any harm to me or the furniture in this room." In other words, no physical assault on the furniture or on me . . . "Sit right down there."

She sat down, and she was so relieved, she cried for about ten minutes; said she knew what I meant, and she had no business doing this. She wondered if I would still work with her after what she had just done. I told her exactly what I had said about that, just as I did about any future assaultive action, that if any of them occurred, I would assume that it was a categorical statement that she was discontinuing treatment. We would have none of them, or it would be an explicit statement that she was discontinuing treatment. Oh, this was an intense and tough hour. Again she was extremely relieved and said that she knew, she realized this wasn't any whimsical conclusion that all these people reached, and that nobody was really trying to do all the things to her that she said a few minutes earlier. She was entirely geared to go along with this and continue treatment, very relieved. She was so dramatically improved in the ensuing appointments. . . . She was so relieved and so much better after this particular tense interaction—when she really saw that I was not flustered, upset, or under her control, nor was I going to kick her out. That nothing is going to be done to her, but that she wasn't going to do anything to me either, was the issue.

In the hospital, from this time on, Mrs. Arlington seemed to improve regularly, as indicated by doctors' orders. On the 14th, an order stated that she could spend an hour in the evening at the lodge accompanied. She could smoke unaccompanied. The 15th, she was allowed to eat unaccompanied; on this date also, suicide precautions were discontinued, although fifteen-minute rounds were to be continued. Gradually she was given considerable latitude to enlarge her activity independently.

This is not to say that Mrs. Arlington's course now became a smooth one. For example, on the 15th, at the time of her next appointment with Dr. Dale—the one following the stormy scene described above—she attempted to escape while being taken downtown. She continued to be sarcastic and demanding; there were repeated occasions when she threw things. Nevertheless, her behavior in the hospital was much more satisfactory than it had been at the beginning of her stay.

Mrs. Arlington was to visit with her husband for the first time on November 21. He had not seen her during her first three weeks of hospitalization, by hospital order. This arrangement had been completely agreeable to Mr. Arlington, who had felt unable to bear the burden of his wife's disturbance any longer, and had been greatly relieved upon her entering Crest. He considered the Crest staff competent and "objective"; and he was especially positive toward Dr. Preston, both because of Dr. Preston's pleasant manner with him and because of the physician's dictum that he stay out of the picture during the first period of Mrs. Arlington's hospitalization.

Actually, Mr. Arlington, while overtly overprotective of his wife at this time, had been secretly angered by her suicide attempt. His anger became conscious fury when, during this three-week period, he found out that she had hidden away four thousand dollars, with arrangements to prevent his laying hands upon it. Further, Dr. O'Brien's statement to the effect that Mrs. Arlington should decide to be definitely married or divorced caused Mr. Arlington acute conflict in considering the future with Mrs. Arlington. The seriousness of her disturbance was brought sharply home to him; he wondered, consciously, whether his wife could ever get well, and whether they could have a successful marriage. The separation period, moreover, was peaceful; he did not really want to see his wife.

As the time for their visit approached, then, Mr. Arlington was in a highly ambivalent state. The visit, unsurprisingly, was not a comfortable experience for him or for his wife. Those which followed were not better. It was characteristic of these occasions that Mrs. Arlington would demand something of her husband which he could not or would not do; she would then grow angry, begin to cry, say that she must not cry because if the Crest authorities heard of her crying her privileges would be rescinded; and go on to blame her husband for causing all these troubles. Mr. Arlington did not look forward to these visits. As often as possible, he "couldn't make" them. This caused Mrs. Arlington great distress.

Meanwhile Mrs. Arlington's privileges continued to be increased. On November 18, she was allowed to go down to the lodge in the evening, unaccompanied. A week later she went bowling; she also had leave to be on the grounds unaccompanied.

On December 3, after one month in the hospital, she moved to the semi-closed ward. On December 5, she was given "ground privileges," meaning that she was free to move around the hospital grounds and in and out of the ward as she wished. These were remarkably smooth days for her.

On December 10, she phoned her husband to ask why he was not coming to visit her. Mr. Arlington was beginning to try to free himself of the relationship with his wife; he told her he thought it better that he not come out for a while. This upset Mrs. Arlington considerably; but her husband held his ground. However, his wife seemed to him to be so disturbed by his refusal, that he called Dr. Preston to tell him what had taken place.

By December 15, Mrs. Arlington was again complaining about the hospital—the inconsistencies, the policies, the untrained staff. She observed that she was much better when she was away from the hospital, and complained that the staff assumed too much responsibility for patients. She spoke about her inability to accept hospitalization and her feeling that she could no longer stand it because she wasn't getting any place. She began to talk about going back to the closed section of the hospital and to ask to be restrained and gagged. These requests were interspersed with contrary statements to the effect that she didn't really want to go to the closed section.

On December 16, she called her husband again and asked him to help her to escape from Crest. She had a plan all worked out: he would visit her and leave their car in the parking lot with the keys in it, and she would drive away. Mr. Arlington said, "No."

On December 23, Mr. Ullman attempted suicide. The nurses' notes for the following day include the first report of a suicidal reference by Mrs. Arlington in more than a month: "Was very quiet this morning and answered bluntly in response to questions, but talked for a while about desire to commit suicide." Although Mr. Ullman and Mrs. Arlington were not on the same ward, news of his attempt may have been communicated to her by other patients, thus stimulating the suicidal remarks. On the other hand, suicidal remarks, while they may have been neglected in previous nurses' notes, were perhaps now noted and written down unfailingly as a consequence of the staff's sudden anxiety over Mr. Ullman's attempt.

Mrs. Arlington complained on the ward that her therapist

did not talk to her or respond to her. Her personal notes at this time—December 25 through 27—also include comments about therapy. She wrote: "D[ale] unreality—anger, frustration, disappointment." Other notes at this time were: "Fearing never get well seems to be a big thing . . . Money and hopelessness of it all = suicide. I knew Crest would have a reverse effect and eventually I will also mentally be in Crest or afraid of it. Necessity for all the restrictions I can't see—were unnecessary for me and most people . . . Not being understood." She noted too, "Tom is what I want—but it won't be easy probably."

On December 28, the nurses' notes read: "I found her in the parking lot talking with Mr. Einston about his car. They looked suspicious. She said, 'How did you find me?' She was missing from table tennis date with the aide. 'The grounds aren't so large,' laughed the aide. Mrs. Arlington decided to take a walk with Mr. Einston. A brief period later learned that Mrs. Arlington joked with Mr. Einston that she would like a ride." Later that day she and Mr. Einston were observed in the latter's room, talking in low voices. She was overheard saying only "I'm sorry," the rest being inaudible. When she came out, the note reports, Mrs. Arlington asked the aide, "Did you hear anything that was said?" The aide responded, "No, should I?" and Mrs. Arlington replied, "I hope you didn't." Later, she went to the lodge with Mr. Einston. Mrs. Arlington and Mr. Einston were very close at this time, just a few days before Mr. Einston's New Year's Day suicide.

Her personal notes, written on December 31, indicate that the problem of the relationship with her husband seemed to be her central area of concern:

« I want to go home but not to an empty place and I want him to improve and go elsewhere . . . waited and waited on Tom. No cooperation. Needs . . . Tom called Preston and said *I* upset *him* . . . why did Tom call? . . . Big realization I've been attempting the impossible with Tom. All the things I've seen and known and it's impossible for him to be different—he's very sick—and I'm pleading for what I wouldn't have to with any other person. Sapped up syrup. "People are no damn good" . . . "Looking down on women."

I take blame for having taken so much and gone into the marriage—but I didn't have enough knowledge to understand then. I don't think he's sane! He! Beat down by it all. I used to wish he'd die. I can't keep crying here like this or huffing and puffing.

At this time she was feeling very anxious. She noted:

« Crest has terrible effect on me—as I was afraid—too much enforced idleness—I can't stand it. Too many blocks. Things too late. Friday night. House. Too long here. Suicide: I don't think I can take it.* Constant tension now, unreality—I don't understand it; used to be periods of reality and freedom from tension . . . Anxiety now where I can hardly breathe. These two things I never had constantly before. Premenstrual too probably.

Again, writing of her husband and quoting past statements of his:

« Tom—"*I* can't take it, have to stay away for a few *weeks*"=?. Famous last words, if he's so responsible for me now—why didn't he help in the last week—with getting a doctor, Crest, etc. "You'll probably make better adjustment to society than me." "Repeated situation." "That's it."

By January 4, [Einston's suicide had occurred on January 1] at the beginning of her third month in the hospital, Mrs. Arlington's notes suggest that she was feeling considerably better.

« Whole world has opened up for me—and I knew I'd get well and could go and do. After a bit, I was okay. Tom's visit. Learned he told Preston re me last time and how upset he was. He wasn't upset re suicide feeling . . . In other words, his own reaction, and he hadn't heard at all how many times I said how good I felt with him. And Preston didn't ask me how (I had let off steam to him) visit had gone. So I got held back for Tom's subjective reaction. Conflict: disappointment in Tom for interpreting his problem to Preston as a reaction to me, because what I asked didn't warrant his getting thrown for three days. Also disappointment that he isn't making more rapid and real progress. I do want a marriage with him and do want him to get at his problems—and it becomes so frustrating and throwing for me—to be so under Preston's control—and to be thrown by

---

* This fragment relates to a statement her husband had made, to the effect that he "didn't think he could take" the anxiety of worrying about her suicide threats.

Tom here. My job as I see it is to learn to live with him without getting affected by his problem. (As with people here.) And not expect him to be other than he is and not ask him to do anything; big order. But to get Preston's management of me in there predicated by Tom's own problem, I don't know how I can do it . . . Part of my reaction is feeling insecure re Tom's love, etc., wondering whether I can keep my own goals in mind, etc., and how real the problem is. But at least I'm not too far gone this time, not to maintain some sensibility . . . This isn't an impossible marriage I hope. I don't feel I want to decide no while in Crest. Attitude—looking forward to, and I'm going to get well no matter what and "roll with the punches." Hold self together for treatment. "Just so your visits are comfortable for you."

The last of the patient's personal notes, written on January 4, said: "Dale is helping me!"

On January 4, Mrs. Arlington was visited by her husband. The nurses' notes stated: "Seemed more cheerful than usual. Appeared to enjoy walk. Did not pry with personal questions nor bemoan her fate at Crest." This mood continued throughout the day. In the evening it was noted: "No critical or sarcastic comments, not even implied."

The following day, January 5, she continued to be amicable. She was not on the ward after lunch at 12:30. Then: "Missing after this time. Attempted to contact husband—no luck. Still missing at shift change, at 4:30."

Shortly after 4:30, Mrs. Arlington called the hospital. She talked with one of the nurses, saying that she was with her husband. The nurses' notes state: "Dr. Preston and Doren were notified that she had called. The patient later, about 8:30, called the hospital and wanted to talk with Dr. Doren and this message was relayed. But as of 11:00 P.M. patient had not returned to the hospital."

Upon her escape from the hospital, Mrs. Arlington had gone directly to her husband. Mr. Arlington found her "hysterical." He reported that Mrs. Arlington was desperate to get out of Crest, that she felt she would go mad there. She told her husband that everyone was treating her like a criminal. Mr. Arlington's compassion was stirred by his wife's pathetic condition. He felt that she was in too dangerous a state to be out of the hospital and thought that he could talk her into returning there voluntarily. Meanwhile, however, Mrs. Arlington had telephoned

Ernest, her brother, who notified Dr. Dale. Dr. Dale called the police. When the police arrived at Mr. Arlington's apartment, Mr. Arlington sent them away, saying that he would get his wife back to the hospital. While at her husband's apartment, Mrs. Arlington made gestures of killing herself by putting a wash cloth around a hanger and trying to pull at her throat.

On the afternoon of January 6, the following day, Mrs. Arlington returned to Crest. The nurses' notes report:

« [Returned] with her husband around 3:30 and went to the reception room. Dr. Preston and Dr. Doren were not immediately available to see her. She left the reception room and went running down the hill. Her husband went after her with his car. [Two nurses] went to help bring her back. They did so and patient returned to the reception room. Wouldn't leave without husband. [Nurse] gave husband permission to come to the ward with her. They waited in patient's room until Dr. Doren arrived at 4:00. Much wailing by patient heard from room while he was there. [Mrs. Arlington] left room and asked to leave ward. Refused. Finally returned to room. Husband ducked out through the office.

Mrs. Arlington's privileges were considerably reduced. However, as she seemed to organize well, they were quickly returned.

On January 7, the patient was reported as being pleasant and having a good evening. On the following morning, she became distressed because it seemed to her that the aide was not preparing to leave the hospital in time to get to her therapy appointment. When the aide went to the patient's room to tell her that they were ready to leave, she "was sitting on her bed crying." The party started off as usual: Mrs. Arlington, a driver, and an accompanying aide. "She was very quiet on the way down." Then, in a busy and heavily trafficked section of town, as the car was beginning to slow for a light:

« Like a flash, patient opened the car door and jumped from the car. I called to patient and tried to get hold of her but I couldn't. When she jumped from car she fell in a sitting position and within seconds was on her feet, dashing across three lanes of traffic which stopped for her. I saw patient reach the sidewalk and then lost sight of her. There was nothing more I could do, so I phoned the hospital.

It was 9:30 A.M. when Mrs. Arlington escaped from the car.

In a short while, she telephoned the hospital from her husband's apartment. She was "frightened, anxious, and making suicidal threats." The hospital immediately notified the city police. The police were told that Mrs. Arlington was a dangerously suicidal woman, and were requested to pick her up and return her to Crest or to the county hospital. About half an hour later the police telephoned the hospital to report that nothing had been done because such a matter was the responsibility of the County Sheriff's office. The hospital called the Sheriff's office. When about an hour later, the call was returned, the Sheriff's office responded that a case of this kind was not within its authority but would have to be handled by the city police. By this time Mrs. Arlington had fled from the apartment. She had called the hospital a number of times, but each time had refused to say where she was. The hospital staff became somewhat frantic. Later, Dr. Preston stated:

« I was anxious in terms of the failure of response of the police. I was furious. I figured if we could get things in gear—and this was the thing that made me anxious really—I figured she was doing a little bit of what she'd been doing before, and she was leaving a paper trail as wide as highway 66, but the thing that I was concerned about was that this was the sort of thing that results in accidental suicides where the trail is left and nobody gets there. It was infuriating! I mean, this woman I felt was capable of making a dangerous gesture which, if properly responded to, was not going to be fatal. But improperly responded to, it was dangerous because she played around at this level.

The thing that made me anxious was that the police were not responding appropriately to what we were telling them that they had to do. She was leaving a trail a mile wide; and her husband was involved; and everybody was involved. But everybody was passing the buck. The sheriff was supposed to be there and didn't get there, and we find out an hour later that he didn't get there. Well, this was dangerous, but I didn't feel that intrinsically the gesture was dangerous . . . [Doren] thought that she had killed herself. I was irritated and angry, telling the police you must do something; but I felt very comfortable that this woman was leaving a trail a mile wide. We would find her and get her back in the hospital. She was making gestures all over the place.

Mrs. Arlington fled from the hospital to her husband, hoping that he would give her some assurance that they could work things out together. She felt that she would then have something to look forward to. But Mr. Arlington could give no such assurance, because he did not believe that they would, in fact, be able to work things out. He felt extremely guilty about his inability to give his wife a basis for hope in the marriage.

The nurses' notes next read:

« The patient arrived about 5:15 P.M. with husband. Office called saying the husband needed help getting his wife to the door . . . Patient was curled up in front seat saying "I don't want to go up there again. It doesn't do me any good. I'm worse since I came here. I want to see Dr. Preston." . . . She continued crying and histrionics.

This time she was taken back to the closed section. "Watch taken, clothes checked for sharps, etc." She was accompanied to the bathroom. Later that evening she spoke of having walked great distances that day. " 'I couldn't get in anywhere.' . . . Stated she was expected to control herself. 'At times I can't— my mind just seems to go.' . . . In the tub while being accompanied she said, 'Now if I could just feel like this all the time— I feel fine now—sometimes I feel like two different people.' " She was again put on suicide precautions. There was great concern about the patient at this time, unquestionably accentuated by the general anxiety in the hospital about the danger of suicide.

One of the consequences of Mrs. Arlington's second elopement was that Dr. Dale terminated treatment. Dr. Dale felt that he had made it very clear to Mrs. Arlington that he could only see her at his office, and that if it were impossible for her to come to his office—that is, if she made it impossible—the therapy would be automatically terminated. Dr. Dale did not go to Crest to see Mrs. Arlington personally, and tell her explicitly that he was terminating his treatment of her. He later noted:

« I thought a great deal about this, and the only reason I could see in coming out [to tell her personally] was some guilt about it. I really didn't feel guilty, and I thought about it. Somebody—I don't know who it was—asked me if I was going to in a way that suggested that I should. That made me think that perhaps I should. I thought it over again, and it had been very clear between her and myself—no room for misunderstanding. So I thought, well, there's no call for going out except if I'm agitated enough about this happening, except if I feel I've done something to her; but I didn't have any such feeling . . . I do remember giving this much thought and finally deciding that I had to assume that she had paid no attention to what I said, and communication between us meant nothing. To come out and see her would just imply that I didn't mean what I said before.

The view at the hospital was quite different. One aide later asked: "Is it too much to ask the doctor in town to please come out and see your patient? Maybe you can give her a little support and help her out a little bit more than we are apparently able to help her." A nurse stated: "I was concerned when Dr. Dale stopped seeing her. I think this really made the staff wonder what was going to happen to this woman, and I'm sure she did too . . . I heard several aides mention that they wondered why in the world he'd take such drastic steps." Another nurse noted: "The effect on the ward staff of Dr. Dale refusing to see this patient was really something that rocked them."

Dr. Preston was also displeased. He pointed out that if Mrs. Arlington were in any other hospital, Dr. Dale's responsibility would continue. Since she was at Crest, Dale had the option of terminating his treatment of her, knowing that some treatment would continue at Crest. He noted: "This means we are responsible for her over-all treatment. And I think this allowed Dale to move out more freely."

Upon her return to the hospital and its closed section, on S precautions, Virginia Arlington continued to be extremely agitated. The nurses' notes record that on the night of January 9, crying and moaning, she called out, "Kill me, let me die, let me die, I can't do it." She called for Dr. Doren, who saw her, and Dr. Preston, who also saw her at this time. On the 10th, she declared: "I'm insane." She asked an aide to hug her. The aide said, "I'm an aide." The patient asked, "I'm a what?" "You're a patient," the aide replied. It was on this day that she was told by one of the nursing staff, that she would no longer be going to her appointment with Dr. Dale. This information was very upsetting to her. Also, on the 10th, according to the nurses' notes:

« The patient stated "I have something important to tell you later." Saw the patient 15 minutes later. "Did Dr. Doren tell you I cut myself?" ["No."] "Well I did." ["Where?"] "On my ankles and hips." I took the patient to her room and she had a fairly deep laceration on the left instep of ankle. No bleeding and covered with piece of towel. Treated patient. The patient began to talk a lot about suicide, she wouldn't say how she cut herself and then she made sort of a game out of all this.

The staff reacted with considerable anxiety to Mrs. Arlington's self-inflicted cut. As Mrs. Arlington continued to be agitated and extremely noisy, a tranquilizer, Thorazine, was ordered after 11.00 P.M. This was the first time a drug had been ordered for this patient.* Until now, she had received only aspirin, for headaches and premenstrual pain. The Thorazine was not administered until the 12th, when orders were given that it might be used any time during the day. All this time Mrs. Arlington had continued to be very disturbed, sobbing such imprecations as "Don't keep me alive" and "You've got to do something."

On the evening of the 11th, Mrs. Arlington asked: "Do doctors think I'm putting on an act?" The nurse answered, "No, I think they are more understanding than that." The patient said, "Well, I guess I'm pretty hard to take, but it's even harder for me to take myself. I know how it sounds and how it looks." At this time she was reported as appearing anxious, fretful, and tense. The nurse commented: "I felt all this was subdued in quality and none of it to be histrionic."

Dr. Dale's termination of treatment left the hospital with no clear therapy plan for Mrs. Arlington. While Dr. Preston was her hospital physician, she was seen also by Dr. Doren. She called a great deal for Dr. Doren, saying that she couldn't stand Dr. Preston. The physicians and ward staff alike felt helpless about Mrs. Arlington's future. Dr. Preston stated: "We were stuck with the termination of psychotherapy, and there was no alternative to offer really . . . I didn't know what to do. Doren suggested a vacation from therapy. We had no real alternative to offer, and yet we still had the responsibility. . . . Nobody wanted to treat her."

The professional staff felt that another conference was necessary. Dr. Doren still felt strongly that a major difficulty lay in Mr. Arlington's continuing treatment with Mrs. Arlington's former therapist, Mrs. Clift. Mrs. Clift and her supervisor, Dr. Johnston,

---

* Dr. Dale later stated: "I stood four-square against the use of drugs."

were both invited to come to the conference. This conference, scheduled for January 22, never took place.

The ward staff was getting very anxious about what was happening with the patient. A nurse noted that she was "just drifting," abandoned by most of the ward staff. Another ward staff member observed:

« There was such an element of self-destruction there in her whole affect . . . but why wasn't ECT indicated in a patient like this, to help her through the panic period—which they had done with Ullman—to help her through with this? I don't know whether this would have helped at all, but it would have been something. Because nothing was being done really in a physical way to help this patient. In a psychological way, either, for that matter.

It was within the context of the general feeling of helplessness about Mrs. Arlington's treatment that drugs were prescribed to be used "if she got noisy and out of hand." One nurse stated that she had "a reluctance to give drugs because of the indoctrination of Crest."

« Sure we've tried to use personnel—which I still believe in —but there were very few personnel who could be with this woman—who wanted to be—who could be, without their getting real angry with her because of the type of behavior that she showed. . . . I think the staff was pretty uncomfortable working with panic patients because there is nothing you can do as far as their feelings are concerned.

Unfortunately, the difficulty in treating Mrs. Arlington was exacerbated by the staff's general dislike of this patient. One aide noted, "She just infuriated me." Another stated that Mrs. Arlington was effective in "putting a dagger in somebody and just twisting it."

« Saying, "You're really no good, you don't know how to treat me, you're not sympathetic, you're not doing everything you can for me." And there was nothing you could do for her. You couldn't satisfy her. . . . And she would be so hysterical to the point of it seemed like overacting. It often seemed like acting for attention.

A recreational therapist commented:

« I think we all felt that she was so hostile and angry that people didn't know that she was suffering—that mostly what was going on with her was an acting-out kind of thing. I think almost everyone treated her in this way. You had to, to some extent, because you couldn't let this woman manipulate, which is what she tried to do.

Dr. Preston's feelings toward Mrs. Arlington were no more positive than those of most of the staff. The ward staff was disturbed by the professional staff's attitude toward Mrs. Arlington. Moreover, they were confused about whether she was sick or not sick, suicidal or not suicidal. One nurse said:

« The therapist abandoned her and then . . . Dr. Preston, I didn't feel, ever really conveyed to the staff the seriousness of her suicidal gestures and talk. She did a tremendous amount of talk about suicide, over and over and over again. Some of it we took seriously, some of it we didn't seem to. It seemed at no point did we ever begin to make her comfortable in the hospital situation. . . . her obnoxious personality got in our way of seeing her as a very sick and a very desperate and a very lonely person.

Another noted: "I've always felt that she had asked for help and didn't receive what she needed." Another nurse, commenting that she had liked Mrs. Arlington, said that she saw the patient as histrionic, but also felt that her sufferings were genuine. The director of nurses commented:

« The whole time I had the feeling that nobody really knew how sick this woman was. They talked about her histrionics and her meanness and her acting out and how disagreeable she was . . . I felt compelled to say to the staff that this woman was sick, hurt, in pain, anxious—these kinds of things. . . . I don't think anybody really believed this. . . . I don't think Preston did, and I don't know whether Doren did or not . . . She was treated as if this was a completely histrionic type acting.

On the question of Mrs. Arlington's suicidal intentions, one aide noted: "I really figured that when she hopped out of the car in the middle of all this traffic, and didn't manage to get herself hit, and she had been home, she had plenty of opportunity. I thought this woman is obviously bluffing, she never will go through with it. But that didn't make any difference as far . . . well, if I was accompanying her in town—I did it a couple of times—I was on the edge of the seat of the car, tense and ready to grab her all the time. This must have helped her a lot." Another aide did not feel that Mrs. Arlington was suicidal in general, but, "I felt that she was more suicidal at these times when she was as scared as she was, when she was screaming to get away from whatever it was that was in her."

Dr. Preston stated: "I had not felt anxious about her killing herself, particularly in the hospital. Here's a woman who does it in the middle of Yankee Stadium at home plate. . . . I felt that she played, as you say, Russian roulette, and she counted on an appropriate response to a gesture."

On the 14th, the patient was acutely disturbed. She was given some Thorazine, which did not seem to help. On the 16th, Compazine was ordered but not used. This was the day of Mr. Oakson's suicide.

Mrs. Arlington at this time was writing her husband pathetic letters, pleading with him to come and see her even if he hated her.

Shortly after midnight, on Sunday, January 19, Mrs. Arlington was again acutely disturbed. The nurses' notes read:

« Awake at shift change [midnight]. To office at 1:00. Asked to be accompanied with cig. Said she couldn't sleep. Complained of male aide's heavy walking and [patient] getting up to bathroom. Wanted to know if there was any gossip. Patient asked if we "had heard any more about Einston." ["Mrs. Arlington, you know we don't talk about other patients."] "Is he all right, is he in another hospital?" ["Why don't you ask Dr. Preston about it."] "Josie, tell me the truth, did he kill himself?" At this point patient had me over a barrel, I didn't want to say no and she wanted a direct question [*sic*]. She kept probing and wouldn't accept anything but the direct answer. I finally said, yes. "I knew it. How?" ["I don't know."] "There is no hope for me now." Was a bit shook up but controlled herself pretty well. Wanted to see Dr. Preston. Was told it was too late to call but insisted. Wanted me to sit with her. Kept calling me back each time. I told her to try and rest but said she couldn't.

Came to office and wanted to know what Dr. Preston said. Kept saying to nurse, "What did he say? . . . what did he say? Answer me. What did he say? Did you call him? Damn it, did you call him? Josie says you don't lie around here, what did he say?" Came to office and said, "I want the truth,

what did he say? I want to be helped, I want to talk to him."
Kept screaming, "I am asking a civil question, why do you
goad me?" Aide Don had to help her out of the office.
Screamed at him to get out. Kept calling for me. I went in
and patient settled down very quickly. Talk was quite rational considering she had just been screaming. "All I want
to know is if she called Dr. Preston. A yes or no. Why doesn't
she tell me?" ["She's head nurse and I don't question her."]
"She doesn't have a good judgment. Why does she do this?"
I told her she should try and relax a bit and get some rest.
"I can't rest until I know if she called. If she doesn't tell
me, I'll scream again." Asked for hot milk, nurse brought
it in, and she again asked about Dr. Preston. Nurse said she
had talked to him. Patient was not satisfied with this answer.

The ward nurse phoned Dr. Preston at about 2:00 in the
morning. He reported:

« She [Mrs. Arlington] blackmailed Josie into telling her
what she already knew [about Einston], and then she sort
of went off the deep end and screamed and moaned. They
called me. "I want you to do something," she's screaming,
saying we've got to give her something and telling me what
to give her. . . . There was an order that when she really
raised hell, she got Thorazine. She was insisting on it, and
I was not going to give it. . . . I didn't see any reason to pro-
long an argument over things that were in my area of judgment. . . . I said we give Compazine when we feel the situation is intolerable; and *we're* going to give Compazine; and
we don't give Compazine just because *she* screams you've got
to give the Compazine. We decide.

But despite this firm stand at the time, Dr. Preston felt in retrospect that "[I was] awfully offhand. I should have been more
concerned. . . . I handled that in an awfully unanxious way."
Nevertheless, Dr. Preston was not altogether convinced that his
way of handling the problem was therapeutically incorrect. That
day, a Sunday, Dr. Preston was out of town, and Dr. Doren was
on call at the hospital.

The nurses' notes for January 19 continue:

« I sat with her and she again calmed down. Said she never
asked for company but wanted me tonight. Said she never
knew I was such a nice person. By 4:00 I told her to try and

rest. "I'm afraid I'll start screaming." ["I'll be close by."]
—[*Josie*]

At 4:15 patient came out of room and walked to end of
hall. Was told to go back to room. Headed for office when
she spied aide and asked him if he would accompany her. I
[Don] had told her that she would have no further accompaniment tonight and that she was to remain in her room. She
had been calling continually for aide Josie and now wanted
to know her whereabouts. Unable to go to room herself so I
physically helped her as I had previously done.

She offered some resistance and when we got to room she
alternately sat on bed and cried and then jumped up, shouting for me to leave and demanding to see aide Josie. She
attempted to struggle with me and to barge out of room.
"You have no kindness. Do you enjoy being cruel? Get out.
Josie! Come in here and help me!"

As she attempted to hit me I grasped both of her wrists
and sat her firmly down on the bed. ["Stop it!! No one is
coming in here now. I am not leaving until I feel that you
are able to stay in your room."] Histrionics would subside
momentarily and then, "You have been goading me all evening. Now, get out!" Again attempted to rush out as she
yelled for Josie.

Aide [John] then helped me remove her furniture when
I informed her that the door would be locked. Histrionics
reached greatest intensity at this time. I talked to her alone in
room prior to locking the door. First screamed that this was
cruel, animal and unfair. Then pleaded with me not to lock
the door, saying that she had been defying us all evening but
that she could control herself now.

["Your door will be locked for the rest of the shift at least.
Then we'll see how you are doing. This is not cruel. It is
kind. This is how I must help you at this particular time;
since you are unable to control yourself, we will help you."]

Door was locked. Shouting continued for next five minutes
though it gradually diminished in intensity. Was taken to
bathroom by nurse, with whom she pleaded to unlock the
door. Shortly she calmly called for me. Asked me to sit down
next to her on bed. ["I'll stand."] (She asked me to do this
once before and once during the earlier struggle, she had put
her arms around me and had attempted to cling tightly to

me.) Then, she said in a warm clear voice, "Don, I must talk to you about this, about what you are doing." ["Yes."] "In the first place, locking the door is unnecessary; and secondly, if you know the nature of my diagnosis you would realize that this is the worst thing you could do. Being in a room like this will drive me insane." ["Locking your door was obviously necessary. I am doing what I believe is right."] "But others who know me don't do this." ["I don't know about others. I do what I think is best. Perhaps you can't accept this right now but I am sure of what I do."] Quietly pleaded as I left the room and then began to shout histrionically, e.g., "When I first met you I thought you were such a nice boy. I didn't know you were so cruel; you don't know what you are doing," etc. Shouted sporadically afterward, mostly for Dr. Preston. Made a few requests, for water, hot water bottle, etc. Also, a few more attempts to manipulate regarding door. Was quiet from 6:30 to 7:30, and then some more histrionics.—[*Don*]

Sitting by locked door yelling for Don to open it. He checked and told her to go back to bed. After he locked door she yelled she had to go to bathroom. When I got there she had already a puddle of urine on the floor. "You are too late." She held my hands tight and said "Where have you been? Look what Don's done to me. Please open the door." ["The door will stay closed for now."] "Why, why? Get Dr. Doren." Pleaded for door to be left open. But quieted down when again refused. Said she was going to pass out. —[*Josie*]

Prior to this she had been laying on bed yelling "Don't do it, Don. Jerry [the nurse in charge], Dr. Preston." Seemed greatly excited when I opened the door. I found her huddled against it, on the floor, attempting to get out of room. Had also clawed at the door. I am sure that she urinated on the floor, since a nurse came as soon as she said that she had to go to the bathroom. Has continually tried to make us feel guilty over our treatment of her. Generally seemed greatly benefited by the application of controls.—[*Don*]

Mrs. Arlington looked tired and worn out after last night's ordeal. She picked at her breakfast and would not eat the rest until Jerry would come in and see her. She was busy and by the time she did go in her food was cold and so she ate little more. While I sat with her before and after her tray she had many remarks to offer: "I thought that Don was such a sweet boy and now I know that he is cruel. He showed no kindness or understanding last night. He has a sickness of his own. Did you know about Einston?" ["Yes."] "It's a good thing I didn't know about it before. I still have some of the clear thinking and feeling. Yesterday was my best day. If Don was to stay with a family which had lost a relative, they would kill him. Did Don do charting?" ["Yes."] "Would you be interested if I did my own charting?" ["No."] "Why?" ["What would be the object?"] "A complete understanding of the situation," said with a note of finality. During one-sided conversation patient trembled intermittently. The trembling appeared willful. Before I left her room she asked that I be sure to have Dr. Doren see her "before he gets away." Also asked that I set the table up in her room. It was removed last night. She was mad at "that damn Don" because he put away her half-finished puzzle when he took the table. About 10:30 patient began yelling again periodically. She called for Dr. Doren though I told her that he wasn't in. Said things about Einston. "I thought he would live," said many times. "I told him to hang on. What torture he must have gone through. I can just see him shaking his head." "Please help me, Jerry." said over and over again.

During the morning the director of nurses talked with Mrs. Arlington. She stated: "I've never seen anybody so frantic, I just never had seen this, not even in a psychotic patient, and she could control herself for a little bit and then would be gone again."

Dr. Doren visited her at about 12:30. He described his conversation with Mrs. Arlington:

« I talked to her on this Sunday; I was making rounds. She was quite upset and anxious, insistent on talking, and no amount of talking would relieve her. In talking with her on this, nothing would satisfy her, and there was no getting to her. I talked with her for about—one time for a few minutes —and before I left the ward she wanted to talk again, and I found that she was very distraught. I talked to her again for about forty minutes. There was no getting there. It was a block in communication. She was pouring out her hopelessness—pleading for electric shock or amytol or anything. I then went down the hall to see someone else again, before I left the ward. Came back and she was crawling on the floor; she was throwing herself up against the door; she was saying, in essence, "do something," in such a way that it was just like tearing with claws at everybody who was within hearing range.

The ward staff was thrown off balance, were ineffective in dealing with this. I couldn't talk with her. . . . She was tearing them [the ward staff] to ribbons. In my talking with her there is one point that came up, that I asked her if she felt she might be responsible for this [Einston's suicide]. She didn't answer directly; and I think she might have said no, and so on. But belabored the point that Harry was her hope . . . that this happened to Harry, and she was looking to him as someone who could make it—and this happened to Harry, this shattered everything. My own feeling was that she did have a feeling that she had contributed to this in some way, probably not as much as she felt, but in some way, that she felt she had. My asking her this—trying to bring it into the open—was not taken up by her. In retrospect, thought maybe I should have made a bigger effort to reassure her. But I question whether this would have done any good.

Dr. Doren added, "Because everyone was disabled at this point in terms of dealing with her effectively, I ordered them to give her Compazine intramuscularly; she was given this, not repeated. I put her on suicide precautions."

The nurses' notes continued:

« When he [Doren] left she followed him to the office. When I asked her to go back to her room she said she wanted to go to the bathroom. After that she stood at the office door again and so was assisted to her room. Patient yelling, grew more violent. The necessary steps were taken: furniture was removed from room. In a short while patient was given injection. After a few minutes she began asking for another injection. Did not do much good as she strongly fought against its effect. She was given a second and then put in waist restraint. [This was the first time that restraint straps were used on Mrs. Arlington during her hospitalization.]

Dr. Doren later noted that "Jerry put her in restraints, and before I left the ward she asked about wrist restraints and so on.

I told her to use whatever was necessary. She put her in waist restraints and wondered herself at the time, whether she should put her in wrists; and of course felt terrible later for not doing so." Jerry, the head nurse on the ward, noted later: "Of course, what made me feel so guilty about it is that I also thought that she should be in full restraints, but I didn't do it. I just put her in waist restraint, thinking that would be sufficient, also thinking that with fifteen-minute rounds being made, if it later proved necessary they could put her in full restraints."

The nurses' notes continue:

« Continued histrionics most of afternoon. "Jerry, help me. Help my mind. Help my soul. Oh, my God, Help. Don't let me live. Somebody kill me." Intermittent, short-lived, calms. About 3:30 more quietly moaned that she had wet the bed; when aide and I went in to change it she said that it wasn't necessary, that it wasn't that wet. We insisted on slipping on a double sheet, to which she did not protest. Was quiet while we did this. Then, as we left the room she began yelling for help. This lasted only a minute or so, and she quieted for a time. A few more comparatively quiet outbursts which ebbed by SC [shift change time, when the head nurses on the wards report what has occurred during their shift at a conference with the oncoming shift of ward staff].—[*Sally*]

The head nurse was off the ward; the aide who was responsible for the fifteen-minute rounds on Mrs. Arlington was a relatively new employee. The rounds were made. The aide, Sally, later said, "I was her aide and I didn't go in and check on her. I looked through the window to see if she was okay." A senior aide on the ward at the time later recalled that Mrs. Arlington "made a funny noise . . ."

« A noise which she had made hundreds and hundreds of times when I worked night shift, when I worked day shift—no matter what shift—and we'd go check on her; she'd be breathing funny. Sally was taking care of her, and Sally and I were sitting there in the office talking about Mrs. Arlington. Just about that time I said how much I disliked her, that somehow this woman really got me, and that I honestly wondered if she shouldn't have ECT. It seemed to me that what we were doing wasn't working; what else could we do for her? I also felt that if anybody could help her, Dr. Dale could, regardless of whether she went down there or not. If she got out of treatment with him, I honestly felt, "What's left for this woman but dying, really?" So anyway, she made this funny noise, and Sally went in to look at her; and Sally said she was just lying still. I said something about, was she facing the window or facing the door? I was concerned about her committing suicide at that time. And Sally, just having come back, said—I think she said she was facing the door. And I at that moment thought [to myself]: "You really ought to go take a look yourself." And I didn't.

The nurses' notes conclude:

« Patient found with piece of sheet tied twice around her neck on SC rounds. Lights were out and at first glance patient appeared to be sleeping. Artificial resp. started by nurse. There was no pulse. Coramine intramuscularly by nurse. Oxygen by mask. Artificial resp. throughout. Coramine intravenously by nurse. Adrenaline intracardially by Dr. Doren. Patient pronounced expired at 5:45 by Dr. Doren.

Chapter VIII

MIRIAM
IRWIN

MRS. MIRIAM IRWIN, IN HER MIDDLE THIRTIES, WAS admitted to Crest Hospital on October 28, 1959, having been transferred from a general hospital in a nearby city. She had been placed there following a suicide attempt with barbiturates in late September. Immediately prior to her transfer to Crest, and while discharge from the general hospital was being contemplated, she made another suicide attempt by leaping from a partition in the bathroom, incurring a back injury with compression fractures, and scalp lacerations. Her psychiatrist felt that "a long-term intensive environmental treatment program would be required for this patient in a hospital setting which offered more security than was available to her."

Mrs. Irwin's father, an immigrant, was a successful businessman. He had married late, in his early 40's. His wife, a small, attractive woman was almost fifteen years his junior. Mrs. Irwin, the patient, was the third of three children, all girls, born to this couple. The eldest girl was five years her senior, the next girl three years older than she.

Mrs. Irwin was not a planned-for nor a desired child. Her mother had not wanted any more children, while her father wanted a son. Mrs. Irwin's analyst later noted:

« She, being a third daughter, was, she felt at least, a *persona non grata*. As a matter of fact, her father composed a poem that she remembered quite well and frequently quoted, which went something about "We had hoped a son to see, but you, you see, are a joy to be." Well, this whole poem, I may have quoted it incorrectly, but the essence is correct, seems to form the nuclear difficulty of her whole life, in a sense that she was not what her parents wanted.

Very little is known about the patient's very early childhood. The birth was considered a normal one. Sometime between the ages of 4 and 6, she had an illness lasting perhaps a year. At about the same time, her father "had a nervous breakdown"—probably a severe depression. He was withdrawn, depressed, vague, and unable to work for a period of almost a year. This disturbance was dealt with at home, without professional help. Following the lifting of the depression, the father was able to return to work and to establish a new and successful business, which he operated until his death.

In the home, the parental roles were clear: Father ran the business; Mother ran the home and the children. From the point of view of the children, Father didn't punish, criticize, or permit; he went to work; he read the paper when he returned home; he didn't play with the children.

Mrs. Irwin's father died when she was in her late teens. She had no memory of this period whatever, never recaptured what she went through in that time.

The patient was successful and quick in school. It is reported that her mother demanded excellence of her; through this avenue, the patient could receive recognition from her mother. Her analyst stated: "She missed Phi Beta Kappa by 100th of a point, and did it practically purposefully, and was always testing her mother in this way. 'If I do something a little less than excellent, will you notice me?'" She went to four universities, finally graduating with a major in English. Following graduation, she worked for a time. Nevertheless, as her sister noted, she:

« Relied on Mother much too much, even when she was much older . . . [she] never grew out of her very childish attitude toward Mother. When she was [away] working, now that she had graduated from college and was on her own, she would call up if she got into a jam . . . and Mother would sit here and worry about it. And in the meantime, of course, the next letter would come saying "[Everything] is fine, everything is just glorious."

During this period she took a long boat trip with her mother. She met a much older man, a man of about 50 years, with whom she had intercourse. Her analyst stated: "This was her first intercourse and she always remembered it as singularly delightful. And it later was interpreted to her that this was really her reuniting with her father, which seemed to be the case."

Shortly afterward, at 22, Mrs. Irwin married. This marriage lasted approximately one year. It was terminated by Mrs. Irwin because of her unwillingness to participate in sexual practices desired by her husband. After a messy and disturbing dissolution of the marriage, followed by divorce, Mrs. Irwin moved to a distant state. She was successful and happy in her work as an executive secretary. She made friends easily and was happy and busy.

Four years later, Mrs. Irwin married again. Her husband was a professional man, a widower with a young daughter. His wife had died when the child was less than one year old. Mr. Irwin's first wife had left a large amount of money to the baby, with a bank rather than the father as trustee. Mr. Irwin idolized his daughter, told her much about her mother, and began to feel that she needed a real mother. Mrs. Irwin, a woman who appeared to be strong and came from the right social milieu, seemed a good choice.

At the time of the marriage, the daughter, Mary, was 6 years old. Mary's wealth, which partially supported her father, dominated the family and was a significant problem in the new marriage. But there were others as well. Mrs. Irwin had many rigidities: for example, everyone had to be in bed by 8 P.M. and could not watch any television programs. This was, in part, an attempt to limit Mary's television viewing, which Mrs. Irwin felt had been excessive. She had many rituals around the sexual act. Her husband's life was changed, but he complied with his wife's wishes. Mary, at 6, was not totally happy with this new woman who kept stealing her father's time. She and Mrs. Irwin locked horns from the beginning. Mrs. Irwin tried desperately to be a good mother to Mary, but Mary rejected her. Mrs. Irwin decided that it was necessary to get rid of all the reminders of Mary's real mother. They moved from the family house, put away pictures, got rid of familiar servants. The effect upon Mary of these changes was so devastating that the family had to seek psychiatric treatment for her.

In the spring of 1953, after a spontaneous abortion, Mrs. Irwin began to brood, obsessed with the idea that she was in some unknown way responsible for the loss of her baby. She realized that this was not actually the case, but continued to brood over it. In the summer of that year, she made an attempt at suicide. She was then seen by a psychiatrist.

Mrs. Irwin's mother related the immediate circumstances of the first suicide attempt as they had been given her by Miriam's next-oldest sister. The two girls, the mother said, were very close.

« The two girls and their husbands were together and, as I heard after—my other daughter told me—they seemed to be particularly jolly that night. They were having a good time, the four of them together, and all of a sudden Miriam disappeared and went down to the lavatory downstairs, locked the door and took a lot of pills. Then they took her right down to the hospital.

Mrs. Irwin then had a series of ECT on an ambulatory basis. This was followed by carbon dioxide therapy with "some interviews." Apparently she improved a bit, but became dissatisfied with her progress and consulted another psychiatrist. This psychiatrist referred her for psychoanalysis.

Her analysis with Dr. Carpenter began in January 1954, and lasted until September 1957. At that time, her complaints were anxiety, a general feeling of discontent, and periods of depression. She stated that she had always been an anxious, introspective person, but that her difficulties had become markedly more severe after the spontaneous abortion. The analyst later stated in an interview: "I thought, while she presented a severe character problem, that she was analyzable. And the initial psychological tests supported this."

The psychologist summarized the test results as follows:

« Patient was ingratiating, charming, even rather sparkling at times in a way that belies the diagnostic findings in the test battery. However, this was felt by the examiner to be a "front." In general, she was cooperative, fairly spontaneous, displayed a rather keen sense of humor, and her affect was appropriate at all times. Although not dramatically demonstrated, she seemed at times defensive and anxious. Again the impression was that she had to ingratiate herself with men as a defense against her hostile feelings.

Less than a month after beginning analysis, and without noticeable warning, she made another suicidal gesture by taking a dozen Dramamine tablets and an unknown quantity of potassium permanganate. She immediately told her husband. Her analyst reported:

« I got a call one Sunday morning about 5:30 from her husband telling me what had happened, and he was quite alarmed.

I said, "Well, you know it would take me forty-five minutes to an hour to get out there, so you'd better get a physician there and have him call me." He did, and the doctor called me and said this was nothing serious. I talked to her by phone that day and told her that I thought both she and her husband should come in the next day. I don't know just why I did this, but I thought in part because he was quite alarmed and quite threatened by this whole thing, and at this point her treatment depended on him. They both came in, and she appeared to me to be much more at ease than she had been before. I told them together about what type of therapy we were embarking on, and if this sort of behavior was something that she couldn't control, we'd have to think of something else. She was quite certain that this was something she could control quite well, and really this had been a way of getting some attention. Attention from whom? I presume me, in the short time that she had seen me. But I said I would continue on tomorrow, and from there on her therapy proceeded for about three years-plus, with no sign of an attempt.

Mrs. Irwin's analyst reported that about three months after the termination of her analysis, in January 1958:

« Mrs. Irwin saw me in one interview and stated that her marital problems had increased, that she was seriously considering a divorce, and seemed to want my approval for this action . . . she said she realized it was her decision but found much difficulty in making it. She appeared troubled but not notably anxious or depressed. Of considerable importance at this time was the fact that she had just recently had another spontaneous abortion. While she was most regretful about this, it was quite obvious that she was handling it more comfortably than before.

In June 1958, she again returned . . . Her productions were almost totally concerned with her "intolerable marital situation." Hour after hour she recited the details of her marital life, including the relationship with her step-daughter . . . With very little activity on my part, the patient did become more relaxed and finally reached the decision to seek a divorce. I told her that such action could not be taken while in therapy and she concluded that she would terminate . . . I suggested that she might want more work with another analyst [out of the state] where she planned to live after her divorce. She said that perhaps she would, but circumstances would dictate her actions in that direction. She asked for the name of an analyst I would recommend and I gave her several . . . During this second period with me the patient was again tested. In main, the report stated that the patient was "warding off a severe depression," that there was a possibility of impulsive behavior, and that the Rorschach showed evidence of a potentially severe disturbance erupting. I talked to the testing psychologist because these elements were not in the clinical picture. He stated that he saw no evidence of a schizophrenic disorder and that the test results were in many aspects "most puzzling."

The tests of October 1958, were summarized by the psychologist as follows:

« It appears that Mrs. Irwin is struggling to ward off a severe depression. The suicidal tendencies elicited in the tests together with some potential for impulsive affective expression suggest that a suicidal risk is present. The loose and autistic ideation which occurs on the Rorschach reflect a weakening of her ego and exists in relation to the depression. She is unable to express aggression outwardly, except in very subtle, indirect ways. Rather, the bulk of the hostility is turned inward in self-blame and self-depreciation. Partly she relies on the isolation mechanism to keep the intensity of her depressive feeling from reaching consciousness.

Following termination of her treatment in October, the patient left her husband and filed for divorce. She planned to remain in her mother's home until the divorce was final, at which time she would move out of the state to obtain work, and possibly to continue treatment with an analyst in that area. Her divorce was delayed because the lawyer whom she originally consulted died while arranging divorce proceedings; the divorce did not become final until September 15, 1959. During the time between her separation and the actual final date of the divorce, the patient took courses in secretarial work but did not work. Her mother reported: "When she came home she was thin and she didn't look well, but in a month she was singing around the house and was just as lively as she could be, she was just as happy. And then she decided she was going to go away; she wanted to go away on a trip, so I arranged for her and her sister to go." Mrs. Irwin and her oldest sister, whose husband had died, went on a luxury cruise and tour. Mrs. Irwin genuinely enjoyed the trip. Her divorce was in process, and she talked with her sister about it. The sister stated:

« She wanted out, but she just wanted out. I mean, nothing is ever black or white, you know; and I know it; but she didn't know it—everything was just terrible, and there was no saving grace in the thing at all, and everything was his fault—I mean, what I would call an unrealistic attitude, that sort of thing. But then I thought perhaps if she were out of it that it would settle her down.

The sister reported that upon their return she noticed that Mrs. Irwin was drinking "pretty heavily" and was upset at small things. She added:

« She was very good at concealing things. I mean, she had a very light attitude that I think took an awful lot of people in; and unless you happened to see her—for instance, we'd be out on the porch talking, and she would be quite upset. But if someone came to visit, there was absolutely no sign of anything, and you couldn't see it.

At the same time, Mrs. Irwin was full of plans for the future, when her divorce should be final. She wrote her analyst that she was feeling fine. The analyst reported:

« I got a Christmas card from her while she was on a cruise, very delightful Christmas card, saying she was really having the best time that she had had in her adult life, making lots of friends and very happy and pleased with things. This was Christmas, 1958. Her divorce was proceeding normally. In the midst of her divorce proceedings, which had been settled financially, her attorney died very suddenly, and practically starting the whole damn thing over again. As I understand it, when it was taken up again with a new attorney, her husband had decided against the settlement that had been agreed on, and it had to be reopened again. Apparently, from this point on, she went downhill.

Mrs. Irwin's husband had entered therapy in January 1959. He had been totally unprepared for his wife's actual filing for divorce. He did not want a divorce and was willing to do anything to get his wife to come back. He felt that she might return if he went into treatment. His daughter, Mary, recommenced treatment at the same time.

While the divorce proceedings were going forward, Mr. and Mrs. Irwin sent messages back and forth through mutual friends. Mrs. Irwin was then living with her mother in a nearby city. In one message Mrs. Irwin hinted that the messenger friend might tell Mr. Irwin that she was feeling wonderful—never better. The friend did, adding that Mrs. Irwin looked wonderful and was in excellent spirits. Finally, in August, one of these messages indicated that Mrs. Irwin felt that if Mr. Irwin and Mary, both in therapy, got straightened out she might consider a reconciliation. Mr. Irwin, who had undergone some change under therapy, messaged back that he was no longer interested. The atmosphere of the divorce proceedings changed suddenly. Mrs. Irwin increased and stiffened her demands; Mr. Irwin fought the changes. This resulted in further delay of the divorce settlement. From the time of the change in the divorce atmosphere, Mrs. Irwin began to be more upset.

During a visit in June 1959, Mrs. Irwin had seen her analyst for one hour. At that time, the analyst reported, she "was rather anxious and tense, but seemed to be in pretty good charge of things that were going on, and said that she thought she'd feel a lot better when the divorce was over, and that it had been a long-drawn-out affair."

He later wrote:

« Mrs. Irwin phoned me the day after Labor Day saying that she had been rather anxious and would like an appointment. Accordingly, I saw her on September 5 in the office, at which time she said she had become increasingly anxious in the past two months and also had been having rather distressing feelings of "hopelessness." This latter was attached to "most everything" and in addition, she felt increasingly less able to "cope with even simple things." During our interview it became clear that her present difficulties arose shortly after a maternal aunt had arrived in [her home town] to visit the patient and her mother for an extended time. Apparently much of the mother's time was taken up with both entertaining and bickering with the aunt. From past history I know that this particular aunt had been seen by the patient as extremely demanding.

Mrs. Irwin said that until the onset of her recent anxiety "I have felt better in the six to eight preceding months than at any time I can remember." . . . Her sleep had been poor and she worried about that. She appeared anxious and her facies showed what I thought to be a moderate amount of depression. There was no psychomotor retardation or any of the other signs associated with depression. There was, as always, no sign of a formal thought disorder, and as a matter of fact, no indication whatever of a psychosis.

We discussed her situation at some length in a superficial manner, and she volunteered that she thought she would feel better when her aunt's visit terminated (within a week) and when the final divorce decree was granted. She told me she hoped to leave [town] soon and I suggested that if her anxieties continued, she might want to consult a psychiatrist there. At her request I prescribed fifty 400 mg. tablets of Miltown, hopefully to help her over the current situation. She was to phone me to let me know of her progress.

She did phone me on the evening of September 9. She said she was feeling no better, perhaps worse, and I suggested she phone Dr. Rhodes [in her home town] for an appointment, which she readily accepted and agreed to.

At this time the divorce was not yet final. Mrs. Irwin began to see Dr. Rhodes. She had begun to experience a total and intense return of all her old symptoms; she viewed her previous recovery as a sham and a mockery and felt distrustful of psychiatry. She was very disturbed and depressed. Her mother reported, "When she went for treatment I had to take her. She wasn't even able to drive."

Dr. Rhodes stated:

« I was going to see her for a period of as long as it took for her to get settled down and on her way. So I started seeing her, I think three times a week, and saw her about two weeks, maybe three weeks, and felt that she was pretty angry at Dr. Carpenter for not taking her back, for kicking her out or something like this, I never did get down to exactly what it was, and she seemed to be fairly self-defeating in her attitude, in that she didn't feel she could do anything, she wasn't able to leave home, she wasn't able to get out on her own again. But then part of it was that she still didn't have her final settlement with her divorce, and there was a lot of money involved, and so she was tied to this area for the time being anyway.

Mrs. Irwin's sister drove her to Columbia on the day of the

divorce hearing, September 15. ". . . and she was terribly upset that day. She was afraid that the fact that she was upset would show . . . and she wouldn't give the correct answers. And I spent the whole way over reassuring her." On the drive over, too, Mrs. Irwin discussed suicide "philosophically." The sister stated:

« Well, you know there are really no logical answers to a—not suicide, you know. You can talk about it; people don't do it unless they are very upset, but logically you can just lay it on the line, there is just no reason to live . . . unless you want to. And to sit and argue with somebody about this all the way over, and all the way back; and that sort of thing is—well, I just didn't know what to say to her . . . [She said] she wasn't of any use to anyone; and she underrated herself; and what good was she to anyone; and people who loved her would be better off without her, and that sort of thing. I gave her an argument, that's all I could do. And, you know, it's that same feeling, as through a fog—you repeat and repeat the same argument, but it's just like talking to a child; they go right back to the same thing.

Mrs. Irwin's sister was made particularly uncomfortable by this discussion in the automobile because Mrs. Irwin was in therapy. She noted, "Psychiatrists have always said, 'Don't talk to them, you're an amateur at this sort of stuff.'"

An evening or two after the divorce, Mrs. Irwin's mother became very concerned about her.

« I thought she seemed so terribly depressed, and I called up Dr. Rhodes, and I told him. I said, "I'm worried about Miriam; I don't like the way she acts." He said, "Don't worry one bit, she's all right, just leave her to me." . . . I heard her up about four in the morning, and I didn't think anything about it—she went to the bathroom and back again. And then my other daughter and her son came up for some reason or other, I forget what, about 11:00. First I thought she hadn't slept well, because I heard her up. So I said, "I'm beginning to get worried." [My daughter] said, "That's just nonsense." But I said, "Well, we better go in." . . . We got her up to the hospital. They had to work on her for hours to bring her back. She evidently had taken an awful lot.

Dr. Rhodes had been pleased with Mrs. Irwin's progress. He had known of her suicide attempt early in the analysis, but "gathered that it wasn't very serious. So I wasn't concerned about her suiciding.

"She didn't give me any warning that I was aware of. I just got a call from her mother one day saying that she had taken too much sleeping medicine. So she was in the hospital. And it was a very severe attempt, because she almost died; we were just able to pull her through."

Dr. Rhodes was seriously concerned about Mrs. Irwin. He kept her in the hospital for a period, trying to decide whether further hospitalization was necessary as a precautionary measure. He did not feel she would make another suicide attempt; on the other hand, she did show occasional schizophrenic symptoms. At the time, he thought they might have been due to barbiturate intoxication, although later he revised this opinion. She had hallucinations briefly, but they disappeared quickly, and once Mrs. Irwin was free of the effects of the barbiturates she was described by Dr. Rhodes as appearing extremely well. The decision about continued hospitalization was a difficult one; on the one hand, the suicide attempt had been serious; on the other, the patient showed no overt clinical manifestations of illness.

After some struggle with this problem, he concluded that the patient should continue in the hospital for a period of some weeks. When Mrs. Irwin learned of this decision, she became extremely agitated. She felt trapped, she said; she believed she would never get out. She now made another suicide attempt. She climbed to the top of a partition between the bathroom and bathtub, and jumped into the bathtub head-first, seriously injuring her back and lacerating her scalp. After this "bizarre" behavior, Dr. Rhodes says, he was "concerned, and felt she was suicidal, and that she was going to kill herself . . . I decided that she had to be in a hospital for a good long stretch. And it was either state hospital or a private hospital. I felt that with her funds she could well afford private treatment; and I felt that Crest would probably be the only place I could think of where she could conveniently go. But I felt that if I were to keep her out here, she was going to kill herself."

Mrs. Irwin arrived at Crest in an ambulance on Monday, October 28, 1959. She was described as follows:

« The patient is a small, anxious appearing, rather neat person who seems to move well in spite of a large back brace. She speaks quickly and easily, although complaining of hesitation and inability to speak well. There is no evidence of hallucinations at this time, but the patient does complain of a bodily estrangement which results in her feeling that she looks as though she is full of hate and cannot smile or be warm because it appears phony to other people. She shows no gross thought disorder and her thoughts appear to center on her preoccupation with worthlessness, uselessness, and anger, both at psychiatry and herself.

Affectively she is depressed, with an affect appropriate to the material discussed, and although at times she feels flat, when [she is] comfortable in an interview situation, can appear spontaneous and even somewhat vivacious, although maintaining throughout a moderate level of depression. She is convinced of her worthlessness, of her inability to do as well as anyone else, and of the worthlessness of the "good part of her" which she feels has now disappeared.

The diagnosis was "reactive depression in an hysterical character." The admission note, advising the ward staff, stated:

« The need of this patient for a structured schedule is somewhat limited first of all by the necessity for scrupulously carried out suicidal precautions, and by the orthopedic disability which she presents. However, a compulsively scheduled group of activities which can be carried on for the most part in a sedentary manner, but which will include menial activities, should be presented to the patient, and it should be administered with an attitude of kind firmness with the emphasis on the kindness. Attempts at manipulation or complaints should be met matter-of-factly and it will be necessary to temper this matter-of-factness with warmth but without overindulgence.

Exercises have been prescribed for her which may be carried out on the ward, and she should keep her brace in place during the day, although she may be without it at night. Sleeplessness should be dealt with by accompaniment and warm refreshment, as there will be no sedative medication presented. She will have a regular diet given on the ward . . . Status will be R with strict S precautions at the present time.

Mrs. Irwin's family was much in favor of her coming to Crest. Her sister said, "I had heard from various sources that it was a wonderful hospital." On the day of admission the case worker reported that Mrs. Irwin's mother:

« was obviously relieved that her daughter was here at Crest. She told of being quite concerned about the care in the [earlier] hospital because, although her daughter was supposedly on precautions, she would find such things as knitting needles in her hospital room. Although she denied any feeling of disappointment in the psychiatric care, it was obvious as she told of having notified the psychiatrist that she was quite concerned about her daughter's condition prior to the suicidal attempt and he had not taken her concern seriously.

My feeling concerning this woman's reaction to the present hospitalization is that she is anxious that Crest take her daughter completely off her hands. She will go along with whatever Crest recommends, and she really wants to be involved just as little as possible.

Later the mother stated:

« Crest was the best place, we had always heard this . . . and of course Harry Einston was there by that time and I think we had no question about it. In fact, before that night, she said to me, "Mother, I need help," and I said, "Yes, I know you do Miriam." I said "I'm afraid I can't do it, I mean we'll do everything we can for you." And she said to me then, "Maybe I ought to go to Crest." And I said, "Well, we'll wait and see. If you think that you should, we'll do that." We had always heard it was the best place.

Mrs. Irwin herself had discussed Crest with the Einstons.

Later, after seeing her daughter in the hospital, the mother added:

« I didn't like the physical set-up of the place. I had heard of these places in the East that were like hotels you know, that patients wandered into a reading room or into another room; and I was terribly disappointed at the physical set-up of the place. I can see where people would feel terribly confined, locked in a little place like that . . . And yet it wouldn't occur to me to have her anywhere else, because then I wouldn't have the opportunity of getting to see her. But I felt that, really, it was a terrible place.

In the hospital Mrs. Irwin quickly and intensely began to express feelings of extreme hopelessness. She was soon to be in a state of acute psychosis.

On her first day, according to the nurses' notes, Mrs. Irwin was "shocked and surprised about having to be accompanied to the bathroom. She seems a little embarrassed over this." She also stated: "It seems sort of a waste of time to be in the hospital all day when only one hour of it was used for therapy."

Clearly, one of her early concerns was how one gets along in a hospital. On her second day she said: "I'm afraid I'm not going to be a very good patient, I don't have much character and I guess that is what you need." Later, she rather dramatically turned to the nurse and said, "I cannot go on here." Still later, "I'm just beginning to realize what a terrible person I am. Maybe if I had known it when I was little I would have done something about it, that is, if you can by yourself. I just can't take it." But the patient seemed to stop this vein of conversation most easily when the nurse listened interestedly without comment.

Over the next few days Mrs. Irwin began to try to understand the new world of the hospital. She began to ask about personnel, and to question staff directly. During the next few days, the nurses' notes report recurrent themes:

« Seemed most embarrassed about using the toilet in my presence. "This is really the last indignity isn't it?" ["It is necessary that you be accompanied, Mrs. Irwin."] "I know I look terrible and that my eyes are changing. It's amazing the people around here don't even want to stay around me. They leave as soon as they can. They act so uncomfortable. I talked to doctor tonight but he doesn't act like he believes me. What's going to become of me? I don't want any of the day people to go to the bathroom with me. I hope I can hold out until you come back. What is going to happen to me?" Said she overheard the staff talking about her.

While doing a puzzle she asked "Don't you think this is sort of useless? Do you think it is valuable?" ["Yes, Mrs. Irwin, I think it is. You can talk to Dr. Preston about it."] "I don't want to complain because I know everyone is down on me. I don't blame them because I'm such a hateful person. I don't know where to start reorganizing myself. The psychiatrist says I like things I don't think I like and vice versa . . . How do you go about changing the role you've got yourself into? I know no one likes me around here and that's because I always look so gloomy and no one could like me." ["Mrs. Irwin, these are things I can't help you with by talking about

them. You should tell these things to Dr. Preston."] "I do,
but he says that's because that is the way I feel about myself."
I met this with silence and shortly she made a remark about
the dinner and didn't attempt to talk about herself anymore.

One thing that is noteworthy is the difficulty of the aides and
nurses in dealing with a woman like Mrs. Irwin. When she spoke
about herself—with the intensity of feeling one can see above—
they pushed her off to the doctor. One nurse later stated:

« I remember her saying over and over again to me, and her
restating, "I can't get well." . . . She used to try to put me in
the role of a therapist which made it very difficult for me. I
had to keep telling her, "Look, I am a nurse, I am not a
therapist." . . . I'd really have to hold fast [not to assume the
role of therapist] and it was very difficult to do, not to really
start talking to this gal, because she was pretty good in talking about her childhood and everything else; I really had to
toe the mark with her in keeping in my role as a nurse. I'm
not a therapist, I wasn't kidding myself, but I knew that to
help her as part of the team was to be with her, support her,
protect her, and at least try in my nursing role to do what I
was capable of doing.

The staff had little choice about subjecting Mrs. Irwin to
certain indignities; after all, she had tried to kill herself in the
bathroom of another hospital.

A friend of Mrs. Irwin's, Mrs. Arlington, had been admitted to
Crest on November 1. When they met one another at the hospital, Mrs. Arlington asked, "Have you seen the doctors much
yet?" Mrs. Irwin replied, "Yes." Mrs. Arlington: "Was it fruitful?" "Not so far," was the reply. The discussion stopped when
Mrs. Irwin noticed the presence of a staff person.

Mr. Einston, another acquaintance, was also a patient on the
same ward.

By November 5, her eighth day: "Oh, I'm so sick, everyone
thinking I'm so awful. Are we going to go through this again?
Am I going to stay here? Perhaps I should find a place where
the situation is better." And, the following day, the nurses' notes
reported: "Her attitude seems to be pervaded by a general air
of hopelessness."

The case history, written after she had been in the hospital
ten days, noted:

« Strong illusions of hearing and auditory hallucinations. The content of these hallucinations and illusions always had to do with critical statements made concerning her appearance or unworthiness. As example, she felt that she overheard the nursing staff say, "She certainly looks like a moron." And she reported overhearing conversations frequently which were comments on her hopelessness and her unacceptability. During these conversations she felt that she heard herself frequently referred to as "shit-face." She reported that her body felt strange to her, distorted and ugly, and that her face in the mirror appeared to be hateful and unable to smile, and that her feelings were those of a beast.

Mrs. Irwin was diagnosed as "schizophrenic reaction, schizo-affective type." The prognosis was "guarded." "It was recommended that the patient continue her hospitalization and that cautious, individual psychotherapy carried on by an experienced therapist be undertaken, with also a continued contact with Dr. Carpenter on a less structured basis." Dr. Carpenter, Mrs. Irwin's ex-analyst, was a consultant to Crest Hospital. Actually, Dr. Carpenter saw Mrs. Irwin only once, on her ninth day in the hospital. He reported:

« Dr. Doren thought I should see her, and I thought I'd like to. And she was very glad to see me, told me that she was terribly frightened; and she was. The content of her talk was not psychotic; she kept glancing around as if she might be looking for something, or responding to something that wasn't there. She told me that she would very much like to see me again; and I told her that I would very likely not be out to Crest very much, and that in all likelihood she would be seeing someone else out there, which she seemed to accept. But terribly fearful; awfully apprehensive.

I didn't have a good feeling about her when I saw her— I mean I had the feeling—I think I told Doren afterward, "God, you know this is a person I have never seen before, really. I see her in body and face, but the picture she presents to me is so fogged from anything I've seen in her before." Let's say I had a feeling that I had failed in some way, and told Doren that I thought within the limits of my ability that she really, as far as I could judge, she had pretty damn good treatment. But what had happened remained a mystery, I told him. It was as if some untapped portion in this woman's personality had been tapped. And it hadn't presented itself to me; or if it had, I hadn't seen it.

Much later, in retrospect, Dr. Carpenter said, "I can't think of this woman really as schizophrenic."

Saturday, November 9, her twelfth day, was a difficult one. The morning went fairly easily; then:

« After lunch patient seemed more uneasy with aide in room for cigs, etc. One time she asked, "Would it be all right if I had a cig alone?" ["No, Mrs. Irwin you are to be accompanied with cigs."] After two hands of gin rummy she said "We can quit after the next hand." ["What do you mean, Mrs. Irwin, your card time has just begun—or would you prefer crossword puzzle?"] "No, it's not that, but most people don't find me fun or interesting to be with." ["I'm quite comfortable, Mrs. Irwin."] She seemed uneasy, however, so thereafter aide suggested she might play solitaire for remainder of period. This she accepted. Patient completed her jigsaw today and selected another from stock to start on after shift change. Asked three times during P.M. if Dr. Preston would be in again today. Was told that it was unlikely before Sunday.

Patient was standing near her doorway, looking rather bewildered. Had only drunk tea from her supper tray. ["Aren't you hungry tonight?"] She didn't answer, said, "Can't they donate my body to medical science?" ["Why do you say a thing like that?"] Patient didn't answer, wandered slowly down hall.

Patient attempted to escape at 5:45. [Male] aide opened back door for myself and [another] patient to come in—patient lunged out and vigorously fought both me and aide to get away. Wrapped legs about porch rails attempting to crawl under. Seemed desperate to get away and had to be, after a few minutes struggle, half carried back to room. Accompanied patient awhile. She was very calm, facial expression completely changed from usual nervous smiling—a very calm, serious look: "I failed—just like I've failed at everything." Bit later said, "It was crazy just like everything I do. I just can't fathom the time." After awhile I left—patient called in few minutes. Hesitantly asked for cig. As soon as I was in room patient asked expectantly, "Am I going to be sent away?" ["No."] "Am I going to stay here?" ["Yes."] Nodded affirmatively—said nothing more—seemed to be thinking very seriously. . . .

[Later that day] patient said, "It's very sinful to have wasted your life away." ["I don't think anybody's done that."] "I have—don't you think so?" ["No, I don't think so."] Asked if she were going to stay here forever. ["I hardly thing that."] During reading time, patient has had to be prompted several times, and each time patient would respond with "I really can't do it, it doesn't mean anything to me." Or with "Do I really have to?" ["It's on your schedule, you should try, Mrs. Irwin."] Patient has shivered a couple of times, but has not asked to have windows closed—but upon inquiry she has accepted extra sweater, blanket during rest time, window closing, etc.

Accompanied patient with refreshments. Said nothing while smoking. Seemed comfortable enough though we were not talking. I remained after she put cigarette out. Got up suddenly and began wringing hands. "Oh, I'm so frightened— I didn't realize I was this bad." ["What are you frightened of—or do you know?"] "Yes, I know." Sat down abruptly. "My face—it didn't use to look like this—it looks so mean." ["It may seem like this to you, but it doesn't look mean to us."] "Everybody's calling me a son of a bitch—it's no wonder." ["I haven't heard anyone say that."] "You haven't?" ["Certainly not."] "My, what a profound training you people have. They call me shit face and everything like that." ["It must be terrible to feel that way about yourself, but we don't think of you that way."] Long silence.

Patient jumped up and started wringing hands together. "What are they going to do if they don't lock my door?" Followed this with vague half ideas of what awful things "they" might do to her with frequent referrals to "tonight— after I'm in bed." Assured patient the hospital was for protection, nothing was going to change . . . Seemed somewhat relieved. Thanked me. Patient's manner throughout was tense, rather "unreal," masklike facial expressions, agitated and a deadly serious, doomed outlook.

Accompanied patient at card game. (Game interrupted many times by patient's getting up and pacing.) Has again expressed several times concern about what "they're going to do to me." Also mentioned that she heard "them" talking about shackles in the lounge. A couple of times she mentioned that people were calling her a bitch; once while she was talking about this she stopped abruptly, "There—see. They just said it again." ["I didn't hear anything like that."] "Well, you must have special ears—depressed or something." [Another patient] walked down the hall in an unruly, noisy way and patient said, "I always step back when she passes. I'm sure I upset her." She has also commented that "no one wants to be with me." And followed this by saying how differently I acted in the hall than when I'm in her room; patient said that people turn their heads away when they see her. Patient asked aide if she was going to have to stay here "always." ["No, I don't think that."]

The notes for the rest of that night indicated that Mrs. Irwin was able to change into her night clothes without too much difficulty, but then began to show mounting anxiety. Her panic became so great that she was afraid to go to the bathroom. Mrs. Irwin was offered her night care in her room, which she appreciated. From 10:30 to midnight, her anxiety increased; she showed "doomed outlook—rather flat but at same time tense frightened manner." At first unable to leave her room, she finally began to walk through the hall and was afraid to re-enter her room. At midnight Dr. Preston called and ordered waist restraint for Mrs. Irwin. She entered her room hesitantly. The aide explained that the waist belt had been ordered because Dr. Preston thought she might feel better if she wore it for the night. Patient went into the belt easily, asking, "Besides the shackles? Will they put the shackles on later?" Nevertheless, the notes indicated, Mrs. Irwin seemed somewhat relieved by this definite action.

She remained awake that night, panicky, delusional, hallucinating. Her back brace was removed and the nurse wrote, "I checked her brace for sharps in the office and decided it was definitely a good idea to have the brace off." About 4:30 A.M., Mrs. Irwin asked, "Is your mother alive? How would you feel if you'd just heard someone say that your mother had been killed?" She needed much reassurance and thereafter, the note read, "I was fairly direct with her re trying not to listen to the 'voices' etc." " 'But I don't ordinarily hear voices!' "

The next day: "It's a long time, won't make it, got to go, my family broken up, family turned out all wrong, it's hard to believe it's real. Death is stalking all around me ever since I came so close to death taking pills. I've changed. I look like death." Mrs. Irwin continued to be preoccupied with her delusions and hallucinations: her mother was dead, she would be tortured, etc.

She was constipated and was refusing food. Formal psychotherapy appointments with Dr. Doren began on November 13, her sixteenth day in the hospital. Dr. Doren saw her initially four times a week and then five times a week consistently. Until February 5, no psychotherapy progress notes were written, though from that time on the notes were very detailed.

At the end of her third week Mrs. Irwin was permitted to go for an accompanied outside walk for fifteen minutes. She remained out only for ten minutes, saying she didn't "look like herself" and did not want to see people. The nurse reported "a moment's panic" while they were headed toward the road, but in general felt that the walk went well.

There were smatterings of suicide talk. Mrs. Irwin and Mrs. Arlington talked together of suicide, although the details of the conversations are not known. On her thirtieth day in the hospital the nurses' notes stated that Mrs. Irwin "requested that I tell Dr. Doren that she had left a suicide note for her mother. Dr. Rhodes probably has it now."

The following day was Thanksgiving. A female aide reported:

« I said that we could go out at 2:00 for a walk despite the very strong feeling that there was something weird about patient's affect at the time. I asked charge nurse to look out the window from time to time. Aide feels that she really goofed in taking patient out at all. However, out we went. Mrs. Irwin wanted to walk down the road a way. ["No, we'll stay on the grounds."] Goof number 2, she should have been returned to the ward at this time. Patient attempted to jump off ledge of embankment* across from the volleyball court. It took all my strength to keep her from doing so. I felt her intent was serious. When it became obvious that my grip on her was strong enough to prevent her from jumping, Mrs. Irwin stopped trying. I called to the nurse who was on the court and we walked back with the patient to the ward. I had told the patient that I was not going to allow her to harm herself. "Oh, please, please let me." ["No."] Later she said she was scared, couldn't return to ward for fear of what was going to happen to her. Pretty shook up once back on ward, needed constant accompaniment.

That night, the report was very detailed and revealing:

---

* The embankment was a 45 degree slope covered with wild growth, rocky, and quite rough. It sloped down to the road.

« "Dr. Doren said a hopeless case doesn't have to have shackles unless they want them." Called herself a hopeless case and said she didn't want them . . . Said, "I'm not a masochist." Repeated these phrases many times. I asked if by shackles she meant restraints. She said no, she meant the shackles she could hear clinking at times. Repeated many times that she didn't want them. I told her she couldn't have them even if she wanted them as we have no such thing, but only the leather straps. I told her I thought she should have a leather strap around her waist tonight as she seemed so upset. Patient said the leather straps don't bother her, "It's those shackles." We placed patient in waist restraint, patient both verbally and physically resisted, mostly using stalling techniques, saying that she was afraid while in restraints, "they" would come and put her in shackles. Patient wanted to go to the bathroom but I told her I'd get her a bedpan. I left her and we were startled to see her walk down the hall—had slipped out of the waist belt which I had thought was tight enough. Said she might as well use the toilet now she was up. I agreed and we laughed. I stayed with the patient and she voided a good amount. Back to her room and we again placed her in waist restraint with her again resisting, pleading to stall for various reasons, smiling and laughing at times as if enjoying the presence of two female and one male staff member. I called Dr. Preston, after advising aide to stay with patient, and he gave okay for ankle restraints if needed, but suggested accompaniment might do. I decided to try specialing her. However patient slipped out of waist belt by squirming it over her chest and shoulders and managed to stand up in bed with aide hanging on to her. Four of us got her into a lying down position with much difficulty and I was concerned for her back condition and she really put up a fight. Got her back into waist and into one ankle restraint I had brought with me on hearing the racket. Aide stayed with patient and I went to office and was getting a wrist restraint when I heard more trouble and patient was again slipping out, but we got her in more easily and put the wrist restraint on. So the patient was then in waist belt, right ankle cuff, left wrist cuff. We then continued to special patient. She then openly told us her auditory hallucinations, hearing Dr. Preston's voice threatening to cut her up in ribbons, and little pieces and put her eyes out. ["We're not going to let anything happen to you."] By 4 A.M. the patient was talking less often and lying back in bed more frequently and seemed to be really fighting sleep. We continued to accompany her. By 4:40 A.M. patient was asleep so we left her except for rounds and locked her door.

The next morning while eating breakfast the following occurred: "I took patient's tray down at shift change. Told her at this time that I would remove restraints. She said, 'Oh that's all right, I'm almost out anyway.' And with this she gave a few twists and out she was."

After this battle, the delusions and hallucinations eased somewhat, coming back sporadically. She was still anxious and preoccupied. On December 8, her forty-first day in the hospital, after comments about a "mind reading machine," she asked: "How many sleeping pills would be considered fatal?" The nurses' notes continued, "Was also seen to be peering through window of patient Ullman's door after dinner. Accompanying patient just after this, asked her why she wanted to look in—she said she couldn't understand the bare room, 'It frightens me.' Assured patient that Mr. Ullman wanted it that way." [Mrs. Irwin was referring to the fact that Ullman's bed had been removed that day.]

On December 10, a nurse wrote:

« Mrs. Irwin seems to present almost the same type of resistance that patient Einston used to, though I don't like to compare; or perhaps she just leaves one with the same feeling of helplessness in her muteness regarding her problems, her rather passive, seemingly obstinate refusal of an activity, the distance she puts between herself and myself or any staff person combined with her need to have me in the room . . . the latter did not occur tonight however.

Mrs. Irwin was again eating irregularly, and was generally acutely indecisive. She rarely left her room, complaining that she was not comfortable in the lounge with other patients. She was often "very frightened" and "kept referring to 'something' that was 'going to happen.' " Her delusions had changed somewhat—she felt she "should be tortured or whatever they're going to do but I don't want it." She spoke of being "castrated." For example, on December 18, her fifty-first day:

« Accepted offer of cig and coffee but did not touch coffee or smoke cig. "I want both things very much but I'm afraid of the castration that comes after." Patient seems very frightened, keeps referring to "terrible thing," "I can't do it." Did not eat any lunch. Asking for almost continuous accompaniment.

She began to make "escape" attempts. Thus on the 20th:

« Mrs. Irwin made a dash for the back door and attempted to push it open. (We had not yet locked it.) Patient's try seemed very much in earnest—she kept repeating that she was frightened and had to get out. Taken back to room by nurse—she told nurse that she was afraid of being tortured—that she heard voices—especially those of three male staff members.

She expressed concern that the male personnel would attack her sexually.

On the 22nd she was seen looking through the glass doorpane of patient Ullman's room, next to hers. When told not to, she said, "I just wondered if there was anyone there." The following day, the day of Mr. Ullman's suicide attempt:

« Patient told that Dr. Doren might be delayed for her appointment—that a patient had hurt himself—was going to the hospital, but that he was going to be all right. "Oh, a patient in the cottage?" ["No, on this ward."] Mrs. Irwin had observed Dr. Preston coming out of Mr. Ullman's room . . . Expressed some delusional thinking in late P.M.—saying she didn't want to be turned into "that kind of a thing." Referred to room next door as the "hatch." Many furtive glances out the window.

Later, in speaking of Ullman's attempt and the atmosphere of the ward, Dr. Doren noted that everyone was obviously anxious, and that the other patients knew that an emergency existed. He specifically recalled that Mrs. Irwin was keenly alert at that time. He felt sure that she felt the tension in the atmosphere, since the whole situation was heavily charged with anxiety. Mrs. Irwin's delusional material was concerned, to a considerable extent, with what was going on in the next room.

On the 24th:

« Patient Einston passed and asked Mrs. Irwin if her mother was visiting today, telling her he had been home for the weekend, etc. Mrs. Irwin handled her end of the conversation well. Wanted to speak to Mr. Einston as we were leaving the cottage but returned with me to the ward when told to.

On the 26th, she was to see her mother for a half-hour visit, for the first time since she entered the hospital.

« ["I see you're having company today."] "You mean my mother?" ["Yes."] "I wish I could believe I'd still be here when she comes." ["You will be."] "Do you really think so?" ["Yes."] Patient did not really seem convinced that she wouldn't be here. . . . Patient greeted mother and sister with warm embrace and seemed most pleased to see them. Down to office 20 minutes later and called to me. "Does my mother know?" ["What?"] "You know, about the terrible thing that's going to happen to me." ["Never mind that now, Mrs. Irwin, enjoy your visit while your relatives are here."] "Shall I tell her about those things?" ["No."] "My mother is so hopeful though." ["We are too."] "Really?" ["Yes."] Said she wanted to go home with mother. "May I go with them today?" ["No."] Visit terminated a few minutes after this. Patient wanted to come down to door, but was not permitted to do this.

Later, Mrs. Irwin suddenly looked up and said, "Oh God, I'm going to that room now." The aide replied, "No, you know you're not going anywhere." "Yes, to the room next door." The following day, "Well, I guess today is the day everyone's been waiting for." "Today is no different from any other day," replied the aide. The note continued: "Asked me if Mr. Ullman was in 'research.' ['What?'] 'Oh never mind, that's a silly question.' "

Mrs. Irwin continued to be actively delusional. Her talk was most often about "the horrible things, the castration," that were going to be visited upon her because she was so "bad." This was a period of acute anxiety around the hospital. Mr. Einston, Mr. Oakson, and Mrs. Arlington killed themselves on January 1, 16, and 19, respectively. On the 19th, Mrs. Irwin's eighty-third day at Crest, the following was reported:

« Much peering out of room, disturbed by amount of activity centering around patient Arlington's room. Declined dinner tray and stuck pretty much to room. . . . Many inquisitive looks from doorway . . . Door was locked once when police came [about Mrs. Arlington]. Patient accepted this with no comment or questions but was upset and anxious . . . At one point did say, "I don't know what's going on."

Although Dr. Doren was the patient's psychotherapist and Dr. Preston the managing physician, from December 31, Dr. Doren wrote the hospital orders on Mrs. Irwin, orders usually lying in the province of the managing physician. (It was not until February 13 that Dr. Doren was formally designated Mrs. Irwin's managing doctor.) Dr. Doren's orders were both general and specific. On the 31st of December an order stated that Mrs. Irwin was to stick closely to her basic schedule, although the schedule could be modified or supplemented if the patient appeared to be too preoccupied or was not using her scheduled activity in an effective therapeutic way. He suggested to the staff that they make available to Mrs. Irwin the opportunity to do tasks like scouring tubs or woodwork.

On January 3 he noted that Mrs. Irwin was particularly anxious in the morning and that waist restraints, or more, could be used if the patient became too impulsive or the staff became too uncomfortable about the patient's behavior. If such measures did not ease Mrs. Irwin, then Compazine could be given.

On January 11, Dr. Doren again reported increased anxiety and indicated that the staff should watch for self-injurious, impulsive behavior.

Increased anxiety, this time combined with fantasies of destruction to herself brought about by others, was reported on January 21. Dr. Doren warned the staff to be on guard for impulsive behavior from Mrs. Irwin.

We have spoken in other contexts of the conflicts between the two physicians; Mrs. Irwin got caught in the same crossfire. Dr. Preston later noted:

« My relationship with Irwin was not a real one because I had no power, and so I got out. And I got out because I was uncomfortable, and got out because I felt I was adding nothing to her treatment except my name on the order book; and this is confusing to the ward staff.

Moreover, drugs—frowned upon by Crest staff—were often used in Mrs. Irwin's treatment program. The character of the orders written by Dr. Doren also became a subject of concern. A nurse stated:

« There was a lot of mix-up around her ward management; so

far as the milieu was concerned, this had pretty much been abandoned to the nursing staff; there wasn't active direction from Dr. Doren about the patient's ward activities. The people would get concerned about what was happening with her and what should she be doing. When they would ask Dr. Doren, or make a suggestion, well, this was fine if she could do this and so on.

But I think where the north wing staff really felt a lack was in not having a milieu structure for these patients; and I think particularly of Irwin and O'Toole [another female patient] for instance. I think this involved Ullman, but in a different way, and also Mrs. Arlington. But having the milieu so fluid and boundless and empty . . . and nobody really could step in and say, "We'll write down, or this is what will be done with this patient." [Problems were dealt with] expediently.

Mrs. Irwin's course continued with little change. On February 4, however, the nurses' notes stated:

« Patient went down to watch volleyball at 2:00, accompanied by nurse and myself. After game she asked to shoot a few baskets. Did this and after a few minutes started running toward embankment behind court. Nurse and I were almost on top of her, but could not prevent her from diving, head first, over ledge. Sustained a small cut under nose and chin and a swollen lip. Attempt to dart in front of an oncoming car, but was held. Very resistive to returning to ward, saying she was afraid of what would happen to her. With the help of RT, patient was returned to the ward. I accompanied her upon returning her to her room—her talk was both of a delusional and realistic sort. Seen by Dr. Doren at 3:30.

For the rest of that day, Mrs. Irwin's behavior became more and more disturbed. Several times nurses and aides found her twisting bandages, apparently attempting to get at her brassiere or slip straps, and, at one point, twisting her nylons around her neck. Her manner seemed, to the nurses, to be hasty, furtive, frightened, but certainly determined. After the gesture with the stockings, an injection of Compazine was administered, and Mrs. Irwin was put into waist and wrist restraints. Her opposition to the wrist restraint was particularly strong, and her delusional talk returned—"Now I know something is going to happen to me." Her talk was hopeless—of being in the hospital forever, of having ruined her life but not understanding what went wrong. Two more doses of tranquilizer were administered that night; the patient became "cooperative," although still fearful.

Following this day the staff's anxiety in dealing with Mrs. Irwin increased markedly. A head nurse stated that quite a number of aides, "very good aides in my opinion, who can work pretty much with anybody, any patient," had been very upset by "the attempted suicide." One of the aides who was so mentioned agreed.

« I felt that she was a highly suicidal person. How much of this had to do with what had happened, and the rest of the suicides, I don't know. How much had directly to do with her, I'm not so sure. But my feeling about it was that this was a woman who would kill herself if she was given this much chance . . . I never felt right with her off the ward unless [a male] was with us in the back; and that I didn't mind doing. I strenuously objected to her being taken down to the lodge, to the RT building, to the volleyball court, any of these places that were open. Everytime I was out with her, practically, she would attempt to leave.

This aide noted that she refused to go out with the patient and made her feelings known; "I also told Mrs. Irwin."

Another highly experienced aide stated:

« I remember the day she jumped off the hill down here, and then a few days later somebody was out walking with her; and I said, well, I wouldn't take her out for a walk. I would refuse to take her out for a walk. I wouldn't have. Because I felt she wasn't any more different; and you didn't know what to expect; and I wouldn't take the chance of taking her out.

Following the ledge jumping incident Dr. Doren began to write notes. He wrote psychotherapy progress notes regularly, noting in detail the content and direction of each psychotherapy session. First, however, he wrote an Attitude and Management note, designed to advise and guide the ward staff in treating Mrs. Irwin in the hospital. This note also summarized the patient's course in the hospital and in psychotherapy, stating first that while Mrs. Irwin had been on suicide precautions since her admission, until February 4 she had made no active suicidal attempt.

Dr. Doren pointed out that Mrs. Irwin's delusions—and her hallucinations—of horrible destructive acts to be performed on her were externalizations of her hostility, which he saw as her basic pathology. Physiological difficulties were also part of the symptom picture, mainly in the oral realm, including constipation and refusal to eat.

Dr. Doren saw the basic conflict of the patient as her highly ambivalent relationship to her mother. Mrs. Irwin's hostile feelings, or, for that matter, any negative feelings toward her mother tended to be denied and her attempt to shut them off from herself was very important in the patient's difficulty at this time. Mrs. Irwin insisted on seeing her mother only as good and kind and herself as bad and selfish. Sexual as well as hostile feelings were felt to be bad and were suppressed or repressed and replaced by her feeling herself bad, as one who had done bad things to her mother and thus deserved retribution. When these feelings were not projected, Dr. Doren felt, they were turned into self-destructive impulses related to suicide.

In continuing to tell the nursing staff his view of the Irwin situation and, as Dr. Doren later stated, to help the staff get to know him and his views better, he described something of his design for the therapy. He felt that therapy was to offer reference points in reality so that Mrs. Irwin could learn to distinguish between the real and the unreal. The major sources of this learning process were interpersonal relationships with all the persons in the hospital, but with her psychotherapist in particular. Dr. Doren predicted that as Mrs. Irwin began to see herself more realistically, anxiety and delusional confusion would increase. He noted that over the past weeks she had gained increasing knowledge of her feelings in relation to her mother; she realized they were not solely loving feelings but included anger and even hatred. This realization had been very disturbing, and had resulted in increased fear, anxiety, and self-depreciation. Her essential fear was that her mother would become aware of her feelings and would reject and hate her.

Dr. Doren then returned, in this Attitude and Management note, to the factors preceding the ledge jumping incident. He noted that on February 3, the day before the incident, the patient was taken to watch a volleyball game in an attempt to get her out of her pathological obsessions by getting her off the closed ward for a little while. This break seemed to be useful to the patient. On the 4th, in psychotherapy, she discussed her past suicide attempt and, according to Dr. Doren, she tied this to her feelings of hostility for her mother. Mrs. Irwin is reported to have said that she would have killed her mother had she not tried to kill herself by taking pills. It was following this intensely disturbing realization that she attempted to jump over the embankment.

After being returned to the ward she was given Compazine and Thorazine and was put in restraints because she still seemed bent on suicide.

At the time this note was written, on February 5, Mrs. Irwin was protesting against the restraints, but not violently. She was still delusional and was probably hallucinating. Emotionally, Dr. Doren felt, she was like a sick little child who, while complaining against dependency, was by no means strongly opposed to it.

Dr. Doren indicated that a change in the treatment approach was necessary. The new aim would be to help Mrs. Irwin have an experience where she could be dependent, even helpless, while finding such feelings neither dangerous nor bad. The essential psychotherapeutic goals would, of course, remain that of enabling her to clearly see reality.

On the ward Mrs. Irwin should be treated, he stated, as if she were a sick little child. While the staff should do the necessary things for her, she should not be forced into total helplessness. Like a child she should be permitted to do what she could for herself, within reason. The therapeutic personnel should be helpful and considerate but not overdo it. Thus, Mrs. Irwin should be able to get some dependent gratification while not being prevented from being independent. It was, of course, impossible to define specifically what should or should not be done for the patient in every situation. Staff action would vary with the patient and with the feelings of the staff member himself.

The note ended, on the same theme as its beginning, stating that full suicide precautions would be continued.

On February 7, Dr. Doren wrote the first of many very detailed psychotherapy progress notes. The major theme in these notes centered on Mrs. Irwin's fear of her positive feelings for Dr. Doren, sexual feelings as well as those wishing to be close to him as a protecting father. Mrs. Irwin, he interpreted, seemed to see such feelings as hostile toward her mother, as related to stealing her father from her mother, and leading to rejection, hate, and retribution from the mother. A second, related theme centered around Mrs. Irwin's difficulty in trusting Dr. Doren. Constantly she would report herself as believing Dr. Doren's concern for her to be real only at times, while at other times she would feel vulnerable, alone, and threatened. Dr. Doren felt this to be a consequence of her early experiences with her parents. The patient had developed into someone who could not be certain of what others really felt, or how one should behave in relation to others. Also, one had to be fearful of retribution for uncertain and vaguely defined fantasy evils.

Mrs. Irwin regularly asked Dr. Doren for permission to see her mother. Dr. Doren felt that there was considerable delusional overtone behind the requests at first, but gradually Mrs. Irwin seemed more realistic. Mrs. Irwin's mother did visit her and Dr. Doren talked with the mother after the visit. The mother reported that the visit went well except that Mrs. Irwin seemed to have to tell her that she was hopeless and a terrible person, that horrible things would happen to her while she was in the hospital, and that her mother should not spend money on treatment and the hospital. The patient, Dr. Doren noted, seemed to be freer in her ability to tell her concerns to her mother. He added that he did not believe these feelings had, at this point, much strength of conviction behind them.

Beginning on Monday, February 17, Mrs. Irwin was allowed to be out of restraints and to sit up in bed while she was accompanied.

On the ward, during this period when Mrs. Irwin was in restraints, two themes dominated her interaction with the staff: her feeling of hopelessness; and her conviction that the ward staff could not respond in any real way to her needs. (This theme was not absent in the psychotherapy sessions. For example, on February 14 she asked Dr. Doren if it were possible for her to get well. He was not able to give her the guarantee he felt she demanded, but told her he was realistically optimistic.) She talked about being in the hospital forever; she wondered aloud whether people ever recovered from mental illness. "I swear I'm getting worse since I've been here," she would say. "Does anyone ever get worse?" And, "Will I ever get out of this mess?" At the same time, the nurses' notes reported her starting to talk to an aide about her problems, cutting herself short, and saying, "I guess you'll just say I should talk to Dr. Doren." According to the notes, "Questions were referred to her therapist, at which Mrs. Irwin smiled." Once the patient asked if people got hurt here. The aide responded, "You know what I'll say." Mrs. Irwin said, "I know."

At this point Mrs. Irwin had been hospitalized for about three and a half months. She was out of restraints part of the time during this mid-February period. Dr. Doren saw her as much more concerned about and interested in her personal appearance and reported Mrs. Irwin as tending to define her identity by her surroundings. He felt this was a general tendency of Mrs. Irwin's. If, she felt, she had other clothes to wear, she would be well in a magical way; if she weren't in a hospital or if she were married, her state would be considerably different. The magical connotation, Dr. Doren noted, was obvious, and Mrs. Irwin recognized it as soon as it was suggested to her. Dr. Doren indicated this as a marked dissociation which, while not unusual in psychosis, in Mrs. Irwin had to be related to the suicidal risk. That is, she so denied the illness affect, so dissociated her "self" from it, that when it was expressed it exploded with suddenness in the form of a suicide attempt.

On February 25, in her therapy hour, Mrs. Irwin mentioned for the first time that she had left that Dr. Carpenter saw her only one time at the hospital because he felt that she was hopeless and, therefore, he was no longer interested. Mrs. Irwin next told of a dream of a boyfriend who had once proposed marriage and she had refused. Following this she wondered whether she could get out of the hospital before her ex-husband remarried, and whether it would be possible for the two of them to get together again. She then asked Dr. Doren if he truly wished her to be well. Following this there was a silence and Mrs. Irwin then spoke of her suicide attempt with pills. She was particularly concerned about having taken them in her mother's house.

A few days later, on the 28th of February, Mrs. Irwin again found herself involved with the problems of marriage, again wondering if it were at all possible that her ex-husband might have her back. She was often concerned about the emptiness of her life, saying that had she gotten into the hospital before her divorce, she would have had a place and person to whom to return. Dr. Doren shared her concern about the void which might await her, a person of such limited maturity. It was for this reason among others, that he tried to integrate the mother into the situation in order that Mrs. Irwin should not be without ties when she left the hospital. To live by herself, Dr. Doren felt, would have been impossible.

We know that at least twice during her hospitalization at Crest, Mrs. Irwin was in contact with her ex-husband. Shortly before Christmas, he sent her a book with a casual note. Mrs. Irwin responded, in early January, with a thank-you note which began "Dearest George and Mary" and ended "Love, Miriam." Mr. Irwin was drawn by the "Dearest" and the "Love"; he considered writing to his ex-wife again, and offering to see her, if she wanted to see him. Finally, he decided against this course, feeling that matters were too complicated. But Mrs. Irwin had real hopes. Shortly after Valentine's Day, although she had not heard from her ex-husband again, we know that she sent him an elaborate box of candy.

By this time, however, Mr. Irwin no longer felt attracted to her. He did not want to hurt her, or make her feel completely abandoned; but his feelings about her were no longer ambivalent: he now felt quite uninterested in any further relationship with her.

On March 7, Dr. Doren reported that Mrs. Irwin was improved. For example, she was without delusions and hallucinations. Her mother and sister had visited on the 28th of February; the visit was reported as having gone especially well. Since then, however, Mrs. Irwin had suffered with increased anxiety, characteristically expressed as hopelessness. Mrs. Irwin continued to talk of her hope that her ex-husband might take her back. This time her talk was described as having a somewhat desperate quality.

During that week Mrs. Irwin's mother had been on vacation and it was felt that part of the increased anxiety was related to her mother's absence. Dr. Doren noted that in spite of the increased anxiety there was no regression, although he felt that he would not be surprised if she should become regressed at this time because the material that she was dealing with in the therapeutic situation was, to his mind, rather stressful.

During March and April, Mrs. Irwin's fifth and sixth months in the hospital, she showed significant improvement. Her privileges were gradually increased. She was allowed in the bathroom unaccompanied, and had increased time off the ward. Socializing opportunities were increased; and she was now seeing Dr. Doren in his office. On the ward, her mood changed considerably. Although from time to time she expressed feelings of hopelessness, they decreased; sometimes, in fact, she seemed positively hopeful.

On March 9, the patient's one hundred thirty-second day in the hospital, another patient called out from her room: "Mrs. Irwin, did you know Harry Einston?" "Yes." "He committed suicide on February 5. I just got the news. Isn't that awful?" "Patient Irwin got sort of a horrified look on her face and said, 'Oh, that's terrible. It can't be true. She wouldn't say that if it weren't true, would she?' " The other patient tried to carry on the conversation; and the nurse said, "Don't respond, Mrs. Irwin." "No, I didn't mean to in the first place." Later, Mrs. Irwin started talking of her bad appearance and her lack of spontaneity. She expressed the conviction that she would never get well.

On the whole, however, Mrs. Irwin's course seemed to improve. She spoke of feeling better. "I'm eating real good. I'm not as crazy as I was." "She said she remembers only too well the things that she used to be afraid of, and some of them 'are very embarrassing to me' "; "Explained that the feelings she has now are far more frightening than previous fears because they are on a reality basis"; "When I first met you I wasn't eating. That was when I was afraid"; "I'm not delusional now."

The mother's hospital visits continued with regularity. Mrs. Irwin's sister was also a frequent visitor. The sister says that Mrs. Irwin kept these visits "light." She felt at times that Mrs. Irwin attempted to maintain this "light" tone in order that her mother not be hurt. She described these sessions as follows:

« I think she asked questions about people and friends, and what we were doing, and what she was doing. But also, again, we had that feeling—here she is in a hospital, under treatment, and that it's not—I mean, that you can destroy the treatment by saying or doing anything that's really not in your . . . I had the feeling that this was the same sort of a deal, that you've got to save it up for your doctor, otherwise you don't have anything.

The sister had the impression that Mrs. Irwin did not believe she was going to get well. "We talked that over and over too." She added: "I don't remember if she ever really discussed that she was going to get out, or going to get better, or what she was going to do then, or anything." The sister felt she must try to convince her mother that the hospital treatment was going well.

« The only thing I could do was to give her some hope; so

naturally, every time we'd go over, I'd point out all the
better things, and any doubt that I had I certainly would
keep to myself. And mother is fairly easy to bamboozle that
way, and—well, I have a will to believe, you know . . . And
that one incident, with that red mark on Miriam's neck—I
never did find out what happened with that, nor mother
either; and mother didn't even notice it . . .

The mother and sister saw Mrs. Irwin while she was in restraints.
The sister said that the use of the restraints was never explained
to her—"they made a very light thing of it." She continued:
"I just don't like restraints . . . I mean, it hurts you to see it;
and no matter how much someone reassures you this is for their
own good, and they know it, still, I think it's barbaric."
The mother's impressions were similar to those of the sister.

« [Miriam] didn't talk very much about [Crest]. We talked
about an hour. We talked about everything and everybody;
and she did mention once—one of these aides that came in
brought some refreshments or something—and she told us
this particular one was so very nice, she liked her very much.
. . . Of course, you know she was devoted to Dr. Doren, so
much that she—Oh I guess they were all under the impression
that she had practically fallen in love with him, you see . . .
She just thought he was very nice, and I did too.

In her talks with Dr. Doren, the mother said, he did not advise
her about her own relationship with Miriam. "We discussed her
condition, more than anything, most of the time."
The mother noted that Mrs. Irwin never talked about her
future while she was in the hospital. For the most part, she
discussed family. Or "I would ask something about, is she enjoying her meals; or how has she been sleeping. But more generalities."
For all the "generalities" and "lightness," however, the visits
were not entirely without shadows or portents. One day, the
mother told Mrs. Irwin that an old friend of hers planned to
visit her soon at the hospital. Subsequently: "Miriam wrote
[this friend] for pills—asked her to get her some sleeping pills."
The mother concluded, "So probably it [suicide] was on her
mind a lot more than she said or spoke of."
The mother insisted, as did the sister, that Mrs. Irwin consistently kept up a good front. "She wouldn't show—you see

what I mean? She never—you could never tell. I mean, she was cheerful and all."

Yet Mrs. Irwin did share her delusions with her mother during the early part of her stay in the hospital. "She told me at first she just thought she was in a death house there. She meant that her life was going to be taken—she was going to be killed. That's why she wouldn't eat. She said that she felt—she told me afterward that she felt like these prisoners, if they eat a good meal, that's the end, so she wouldn't eat. That's why she didn't eat." The mother said she felt all along that Mrs. Irwin wasn't improving. "I just had the feeling that she wouldn't have gotten well."

In the middle of April, a new factor entered Mrs. Irwin's case, a factor felt to be of great importance in influencing her choice of suicide. This was the public announcement of Dr. Doren's engagement to be married. His honeymoon, plus professional commitments, required that he take a lengthy trip. As has been reported, Mrs. Irwin had been obviously improving. By mid-April she felt herself to be on a plateau and began to talk of leaving the hospital. On April 14, "I must get out of here." On April 15, on the ward, she talked about signing out of the hospital against medical advice (AMA). On April 16, while near tears, she spoke of feeling worse rather than better, and felt she might as well leave the hospital. On April 17 she talked of wanting to leave Crest.

Dr. Doren noted that the announcement of his engagement and pending absence was made in a newspaper on April 20, a Sunday. That day he had been at the hospital and Mrs. Irwin asked to see him; she said almost nothing, preferring to wait for her hour the following day. However, she was about a half-hour late for her therapy appointment, having been indecisive as to whether she wanted to get there at all. On her arrival, which followed Dr. Doren's message that he would see her in her room, she stated that she assumed that she was angry about his coming departure, and jealous about his engagement. Dr. Doren reported Mrs. Irwin as being rather agitated, with a tremor in both hands and legs. She spoke of anger, but she did not express it emotionally.

The following day the same theme was raised and Dr. Doren felt that it was possible during that hour to interpret to Mrs. Irwin that her feelings seemed to be almost on the level of reacting to him as a mother who was deserting her without any concern about her special needs and her special sensitivity to rejection. It was during this or the previous hour, Dr. Doren reported, that it was possible to elicit from Mrs. Irwin strong feelings toward suicide. Dr. Doren was concerned that in reaction to her feelings of rejection, Mrs. Irwin might consider suicide. He noted that while suicide had been talked of frequently, this was the first time that it was discussed where the feeling was current. Previously, discussions had concerned attempts made in the past, or feelings about suicide in the past. Dr. Doren believed that the meaning of this expression at this time was a hostile, destructive feeling toward the mother which was so intense as to be too dangerous for Mrs. Irwin to feel or recognize in any direct way. Rather, she talked about the hostility indirectly; she would leave the hospital and be a sick little child whom mother would care for. Mother would suffer under this, and mother would deserve the suffering. It was in this context too that Mrs. Irwin noted that her mother seemed to offer her the most tender loving care when she had been ill.

In this hour, Mrs. Irwin threatened Dr. Doren, saying that she was going to write a signed request for discharge; she could then get out of the hospital, remain sick and stay in her mother's care.

Mrs. Irwin's behavior on the ward was similarly disturbed. On the 20th, her expressions were pervaded by feelings of hopelessness. On April 21, she spoke of suicide for the first time in some time, adding that the thought was so terrifying that she could not go through with it. Also, "Asked if there was an intellectual reason why it was wrong to commit suicide. Stated that with the divorce there was nothing worthwhile to return to." On April 26, she said she was frightened about not getting well but noted, "I think I feel so bad" because of Dr. Doren's engagement.

On April 30, Mrs. Irwin had written a letter to Dr. Doren requesting that she be released from the hospital. She was aware that, since she was uncommitted, according to the law she could not be held more than ten days from the date of that notice, till May 9. Dr. Doren interpreted the presentation of this letter as if Mrs. Irwin was trying to put him in the position of her mother, that is, by making him helpless. Dr. Doren reported that Mrs. Irwin rejoined, saying that committing suicide wouldn't have the power in this situation because Dr. Doren would not react in the same way as her mother, and would not suffer similar anguish from a suicide attempt.

On May 5, in her psychotherapy hour, Mrs. Irwin said that she was not getting well, that she couldn't get well, and that all she wanted to be was a baby and let her mother take care of her. She had a plan; she was going to look healthy at home for a short while so that her mother would feel comfortable about her. Then she would suddenly disappear. Dr. Doren saw this threat of disappearance as meaning that she would kill herself. He told Mrs. Irwin that she seemed to want to put him in a position of helplessness so that she could commit suicide. In that sort of situation he would almost be an accomplice, or perhaps even the responsible one, because of his lack of action. He added that it seemed that she was trying very hard to get him to feel severe disturbance and mental anguish.

On May 8, Mrs. Irwin picked up her written request to leave from Dr. Doren's desk, where he had left it. This revoked the request and the legal requirements to release her. Dr. Doren had pointed out her irrationality, and recommended strongly that she not leave the hospital. He said that in her best interests he would have to recommend commitment if she insisted on leaving. There was relief that she picked up the request.

Dr. Doren consistently interpreted Mrs. Irwin's behavior and feelings during this time as part of an unresolved oedipal conflict being played out in the therapeutic situation. Thus, on May 12, when Mrs. Irwin was angry at his missing an hour, he interpreted her anger, to her, as transference feelings stemming from her relationship with her father. On the following day the patient quickly spoke of suicide and Dr. Doren interpreted that the relationship of closeness to the father was symbolically equal to suicide, since it meant loss of mother.

On the ward during early and middle May, Mrs. Irwin, tense and acutely anxious, began asking for shock treatment. She talked intensely about her desire to get well and her fear that she wouldn't. By about the 19th there was a shift in her condition, manifested by her playing the role of a small child. "I feel childish, so why shouldn't I act childish? Can't we act the way we feel around here? Isn't this a place of free expression?" Expressions of hopelessness were absent. She was planning to go out with her family on her birthday, May 25; she expressed the feeling that this trip would give her a new outlook on life.

The bravely begun birthday trip was to be an anguish for all concerned. Mrs. Irwin greeted her mother and sister with the announcement that she had permission to take a plane out of the state to visit a friend for the weekend. The sister reported:

« When we came in she was just blooming; she was all dressed and set to go, you know. And it was her birthday; and I had the children with me, and Mother. It was a very hot, sunny day. And . . . at first—of course somebody tells you something, and you just figure that they wouldn't let her go out if everything wasn't all set. And as soon as we started to go toward downtown—I don't know what we were going to do—I started having doubts. But I couldn't get hold of Mother—Miriam was with her every second—to try to tell her, until we got to the airport.

The mother said:

« I was so naive; I never had her lie to me, and I guess I just didn't stop to think. And she told me—when I phoned her that day she said, "Well, I have some wonderful news to give you when you come over." And she told me that Dr. Doren said—she phoned this friend of her's—how she made this whole story up I don't know—in his presence; and they were going to meet her, and just for the weekend; and then she could come back again—he thought it would be better than visiting at the house here, because there are too many memories, he thought. And I just drank it all in and took her to the airport. It was her birthday, you see, and I had sent her a check for $1000. Well, we got into the car and she tells me that she has this $1000, and she'd like to change it somewhere. I still—when I look back, I know I was naive.

We did stop off at one of the hotels where they knew her. Well, it was a Sunday; and they felt that they couldn't open the vault. At any rate, she couldn't change it, and we went out to the airport. So my daughter called me aside and said, "Mother, don't you think we should check with Crest?" And I said, "You're right"—I don't know why, it seemed so silly, this whole thing, why I was taken in like this—"I think you better phone." So she came back from the phone, shakes her head no. Then I had to get busy; and so I told Miriam I inquired, and that that plane was canceled that she was going to take—(we had phoned, you see, from the hotel where she was trying to change the check)—that that plane was canceled; one wouldn't go out until 12:00 that night, and this was about 2:00 in the afternoon. So no use sitting around— I know, that we better go back, and we'd go out and have an early dinner somewhere. And she wanted to stay in the airport, but we finally talked her out of it. So we went to this restaurant up near the [hospital]. She wondered—she said, "Why are we going back in the same direction?"

The trip back, as described by the sister, was a horror:

« [Miriam pleaded] "I don't want to go back. Don't take me back to that place"—on and on like that. She struggled in the car. We stopped at a red light or something; and she started to go for the handle of the door, but I knew Mother was sitting there and had hold of her.

The sister concluded with a helpless understatement. "It was," she said, "a bad day."

After this abortive elopement attempt, Mrs. Irwin began to talk a good deal about shock treatment; she also made a number of weak suicide attempts. Her behavior became childlike. On the ward she carried on a great deal with Sue, an active, disturbed adolescent, indulging in such pranks as, for example, hiding under Sue's bed. Once, when asked about this sort of behavior, she said: "I don't know. I guess I'm just a copy-cat. I want to be one of the group. I know I shouldn't do these things." On May 28: "She said she had a big problem as to whether to get shock treatment or not. Said doctor was leaving choice up to her and asked me several times what I thought. ['I think you should follow your doctor's advice'.] 'He doesn't want me to.'"

On the first day of June, beginning her eighth month in the hospital, she was still talking about shock treatment. In the evening the patient was noticed standing on a chair in the dark in her room. She assured the nurse that nothing was wrong. The following morning, she was found standing on a chair with a stocking tied around her neck. When the aide asked for it Mrs. Irwin said, "No, just leave me alone. Everything is all right. It doesn't work anyway." On June 3, she had a cord from her pajamas in bed with her. On the 4th, she was discovered to have hidden part of an emery board, as well as the very sharp broken half of an electrical cord outlet cover. She noted that she had seen another patient do this and, "I got the idea. I shouldn't imitate other people so much."

On the following day the patient stated, "Although I think of it a lot I really don't want to get shock treatment." On the same day, Mrs. Irwin was at the Occupational Therapy shop with an aide, who was to accompany her. At about 10:30 A.M., while the aide was cleaning some leather with oxalic acid, Mrs. Irwin grabbed it and drank it. The aide brought the patient to the ward immediately. Dr. Doren was called and notified of the emergency situation. He said that he would come immediately; and, unable to prescribe a specific antidote at that moment, directed that the patient be given milk of magnesia. A pump was set up and Dr. Doren arrived. The head nurse of the ward said: "At that moment I was pretty angry, because if it had been a real poisonous acid the seconds would have been valuable; but he didn't come up right away."

Dr. Doren went in to see Mrs. Irwin take the emetic. The nurse asked why he didn't want to use a tube. Dr. Doren explained that if the acid were very corrosive, the tube might cut and break the patient's esophogus. Dr. Doren stayed with the patient for approximately forty minutes. Finally, it was ascertained that the acid was very highly diluted. Dr. Doren nevertheless wanted the proper emetic given; according to the nurse, he "had told the staff to force her to take it and this was it." The patient kept "playing games." The director of nurses had been off grounds for a time after lunch. Upon returning, she found that her assistant "was frantic."

« They were trying to give Mrs. Irwin an emetic and they couldn't get it down, and they didn't know what to do. And I said, "Stop it—this is ridiculous. An emetic will do her no good at this minute." I got up on the ward and people were spinning . . . Here she was at 2:30 and they were still trying to give her an emetic. Craziest thing I ever heard of.

The question of the extent of Dr. Doren's concern over the danger of Mrs. Irwin's committing suicide was disturbing to the ward staff, giving rise to confusion and complaint. It should be noted that Mrs. Irwin was always on suicide precautions, although there were modifications from time to time. The staff was therefore somewhat bewildered when, as a nurse stated; "Even after [she took] the acid, he [Doren] didn't put her on real S precautions." She added:

« I asked him about it. We were watching her, as we do everybody, but he didn't put her on any suicide precaution. Be-

cause the staff was wondering about this too—attempted suicide—why wasn't this woman put on suicide precautions? Well
he didn't feel we would have to—that she wasn't that much
of a suicidal risk—this type of stuff. But we still, in spite of
this, kept a real watch on her.

Another nurse said:

« Mrs. Irwin continued to make suicidal gestures. First one
thing, then another—the stocking, and the coat hanger, and
the things in the bed—one after another. And as I went
through the notes about every two to two-and-one-half weeks,
there would be one of these episodes; and it would be reported, and people would wonder, and they would ask Dr.
Doren. Then it came up directly after she took this oxalic acid
in the Occupational Therapy shop; and I asked him, "How
serious are these attempts at suicide of Mrs. Irwin's?" And
his answer to me was, "I don't think that she really wants
to kill herself."

Others stated: "The staff felt she was suicidal." "I always felt
that Mrs. Irwin was quite suicidal." "From the minute she
came into the hospital, I was uneasy about her. I had the feeling
here was a woman who was really determined to kill herself;
and that in one way or another she just might do it, eventually."
"She was pretty determined. I never felt very sure about what
she was going to do next. . . . I was far more uneasy with her
than I am with practically any patient on the ward, because
I wasn't sure."
An aide noted:

« I didn't feel she was an intense suicidal risk. I did feel that
she definitely was a suicidal risk, and I've noticed that so
many people that have been working here longer than I, did
not really—they didn't seem to feel she had much of a chance
to get well. But I, being here the time that I have, I always
just assumed that she would be well someday. I don't know
why there is such a difference.

Another aide stated:

« You just didn't realize how sick Mrs. Irwin was, because she
could turn her sickness on and off. Her mother would come
to visit, and man, she would brighten up, and you know

put on a big front; then, when all that was gone, she could be herself again—she would just fall apart.

Dr. Doren said, "She was never taken off suicidal precautions. They were modified . . . There was never any statement that she was not suicidal. She was always suicidal."

On June 12, Dr. Doren wrote his second "Attitude and Management Note," the first since February 5. These written guides to the ward staff had been, of course, augmented by discussions of the patient at conferences and informally.

Dr. Doren immediately noted that the previous Attitude and Management note, which suggested that Mrs. Irwin be treated like a sick little child, need changing as the situation had changed very considerably. He emphasized that the announcement of his engagement was a very significant narcissistic blow to Mrs. Irwin, that since that had occurred she had felt hurt and angry. Dr. Doren described at length the varying levels of Mrs. Irwin's disturbance; these concerned the relation of her feelings to her mother, her father, and the transference. He pointed out that it was important to avoid a number of dangers in dealing with Mrs. Irwin: first, the tendency to deal with her like a nasty little willful child (one must remember, he noted, she is a sick adult and significantly suicidal); second, the tendency to be manipulated by Mrs. Irwin and put into a position of total ineffectiveness, in which she could essentially dictate how she was to be treated and yet place all the responsibility on the therapeutic personnel.

He felt that the patient should be helped in her own desire to recover and to take the responsibility in making judgments; that excessive fantasying should be limited; that she should not be dictated to, but dealt with by way of firm suggestion, with kindness and consideration.

Dr. Doren noted that he would have his last appointment with Mrs. Irwin on the 20th of June and then he would be away for a lengthy period. He emphasized that Mrs. Irwin was going to feel rejected and abandoned even though they had spent weeks trying to discuss and work out such feelings. He hoped this interim period could be profitable for the patient, that she might use the environmental situation and the milieu program. He suggested that the personnel should recognize that Mrs. Irwin might feel abandoned but also be able to point out to her that this was not realistic. Dr. Doren concluded the note with the statement that her mother would continue to visit weekly and that other friends or relatives might visit, with Dr. Preston's approval.

Many of the older staff were unhappy with Dr. Doren's excessive attention to Mrs. Irwin and his repetitive reporting of therapeutic sessions with psychoanalytic interpretations. A nurse reported,

« One nurse said something to me one night, that she thought Dr. Doren was being very special to her [Irwin], very partial, that she was the only patient he had in psychotherapy in the hospital; and I said this surprised me; and I named the other patients he had in the cottage that were in psychotherapy; but as far as she was concerned this was the only patient he had; anytime he came on the ward, he sought her out, and you kept wondering whether there were some countertransference problems there . . . It's not customary for them [psychotherapists] to come up every day or every weekend to seek these people out and see how they're getting along and so on.

Dr. Doren, meanwhile, continued to feel that his engagement and pending absence were particularly crucial factors in Mrs. Irwin's course. He later noted that Mrs. Irwin felt intolerable rage relating to her narcissistic injury. The feeling that Dr. Doren might have a life separate from his concern with her was just too much for her. He also felt that Mrs. Irwin's motivations were, as she had expressed them a number of times in therapy, to cause the therapist very severe mental anguish, that this was her way of retaliating against her mother and her way of retaliating against the therapist as a consequence of his abandonment of her. Others thought the patient's feelings were related to Dr. Doren's attitudes toward the problem. For example, one said, "My impression of what he said to the patient is 'Yes, you are abandoned.'" And, in conferences, "I got this feeling that what he was saying about the patient was that this was appropriate distress on her part."

On the ward, throughout early June, Mrs. Irwin again began to express feelings of hopelessness. Wendy O'Toole and Sue Osborn, two adolescent patients on the ward, were constantly trying to escape. Mrs. Irwin joined them in this procedure, although her attempts were feeble. She felt her inability to escape as another evidence of her inadequacy at everything. The ward was in something of a tumult. An aide noted:

« Sue and Wendy were always eloping; and everybody knew it; and they were always getting away; and I think that made Mrs. Irwin feel, she could do the same thing—"these girls are doing it, I can get away too." . . . The last few weeks there, Sue and Mrs. Irwin sort of hung on each other there, they were buddies; but they weren't really. I think Mrs. Irwin was very much afraid of Sue; but she pretended she wasn't. They would talk in the lounge of what to do and where to go, and they had planned together to meet when they both escaped. I think Sue put a lot of escape ideas into Mrs. Irwin's head.

On June 16, Mrs. Irwin had a fairly comfortable morning on the ward. She went to her therapy hour at 11 A.M.

Dr. Doren reported that in this hour she cried, particularly in relation to her concern about Dr. Carpenter, his termination of treatment with her, and the fact that he hadn't insisted that she come to the hospital considerably earlier (she was talking about three years before). Dr. Doren saw this statement as meaning that she would have had some place to go on leaving the hospital had she come here before her divorce. Now she saw life outside the hospital as empty and alone, whereas before she would have had a husband and family. Dr. Doren felt too that her concern with the termination of therapy with Dr. Carpenter was, at this time, related to her feelings of abandonment by him.

At noon, "The patient looked in good shape." She received a visit from her teen-aged nephew, the first visitor other than her mother and sister. The nurses' notes stated: "About five minutes after he arrived he went out again to get a box of candy which he had promised her . . . He returned in ten minutes and the two continued a pleasant visit."

A nurse noted retrospectively:

« I wasn't there when he came, but from what they told me, she asked him to go out and get her some candy. So they let him out. He came back, I guess Betty let him in; and he had the package, which she didn't check—our goof. I came back on the ward a little later in time to cut their visit—it was over. I should have sensed something was wrong, but I wasn't sure what. I let him out the door. He was a very, very nervous kid, extremely so, and I thought, what the hell is coming off here—did she upset him, or what's this kid upset about? Before I opened the door he said goodbye, she said goodbye, and this went about six or seven times: goodbye, goodbye, goodbye. I sensed something was wrong but I didn't think about it too much anymore.

Afterward, "She did pretty well. I remember spending some time with her after the visit; she didn't seem too concerned."

In the evening, the nurse in charge gave specific orders: "I said that at least three or several people—more than two, I know that—should be at the back door when any patient at all left." She gave such instructions "because you can't hold Sue with two people, it's impossible. I made a specific point of that the first part of the evening, because when I work with these people, most of them, I can predict just about what they're going to do for the evening. I did that night. That's why I made a special point of telling them that they should be careful, and that when they open the door, they should have these people there." She noted at that time that she was, "talking about Sue going out." "I wasn't particularly concerned about Mrs. Irwin at that particular time." An aide who was on duty that evening described what occurred:

« There was this tremendous air of intense anxiety on the ward with these two girls up, with Wendy and with Sue at that time; and Mrs. Irwin was there. I had Sue, as I recall, and Steve had Mrs. Irwin. At any rate, I remember, about ten minutes before the back door was opened and they got out, we were all standing in the hall. Wendy and I went into the lounge. Sue was always getting in Mrs. Irwin's room, and they were sitting in there kibitzing. We had to break this sort of thing up. Mrs. Irwin was tremendously anxious with this tremor most of the time, and Sue was just reinforcing it with talk of shock—any sort of talk that would contribute to this anxiety of hers, making the whole thing very hard to deal with when this group was together, and especially in the hall when there was a tremendous management problem.

And then, as I recall, we were in the lounge—Sue was evidently—well, I don't know—I lost track of her for three or four minutes there, I didn't know where she was at the time. Whether or not I didn't want to know, or whether or not I didn't know—at any rate, she happened to get in [the] room down at the end, which had been left open. And this is one point I had, whether or not architectural things like this matter—this locking of doors I think would be tremendously important—something I feel sometimes isn't practiced in— well, here's a good example; she managed to get in this opened room . . . someone had neglected to lock it on leaving. This was one thing that I put in my report . . . Had this door not been open, maybe it could have happened anyway, maybe it could have happened the next day, anything. Then, of course, the [ward back] door was opened, and I think—well, Steve and Mrs. Irwin were going out for a walk, and Sue took off. She was gone, and Steve was after her, and no one thought of Mrs. Irwin's seeing her opportunity and obviously [Mrs. Irwin] was gone. I was clear down at the other end of the ward, and I heard this scuffling. I was up there outside helping Steve with Sue. And that's about all . . .

Mrs. Irwin's escape occurred at about 7:30 P.M. It is noteworthy that the instructions of the charge nurse were not carried out. Mrs. Irwin was pursued, but not found. A progress note, written on June 19, stated that the following measures were taken immediately. (1) Dr. Preston, who was on call, was notified. He in turn called Dr. Doren. (2) The local police and county sheriff were notified and provided with a description of the patient. (3) Four staff members searched the area by car and on foot until 10:30 P.M. The police were also searching the area. In addition, further search was made the next morning, in daylight, without success.

About an hour and a half after the elopment, Mrs. Irwin's brother-in-law telephoned. It was his son who had visited Mrs. Irwin earlier that day. The nurse in charge at that time reported the conversation:

« He said that the boy had told him in strict confidence that he had brought this [a bottle of iodine] in and had got to wondering about it. Maybe it was something he should tell somebody. And I thought, "How could anyone be so dumb?" Then he told me that he had brought this bottle to the patient, and I anticipated maybe an ounce or so you know. But when we found the pint [of iodine under her pillow], I said I got fooled again. It was something I could hardly believe.

Mrs. Irwin's mother was telephoned on June 17, the morning

following the elopement. She reported that between 10:00 and 10:30 P.M. the night before someone had rung the doorbell to her apartment but that she had been slow in answering because she had the radio on and wasn't quite sure that she had heard the bell. When she did open the door, there was no one in sight. She felt quite strongly that it might have been the patient.

On June 18, Dr. Carpenter, Mrs. Irwin's ex-analyst, reported a couple of long-distance calls, one to his office and one to his home; they came in while he was between these two locations. It was not known where the calls originated, and the attempt to reach him was not repeated. Dr. Carpenter speculated that the calls might have been from Mrs. Irwin or a companion. His attempts to trace the calls were unsuccessful.

Dr. Doren reported an eerie coincidence:

« On that weekend . . . I was first aware of it about Friday. Friday, Saturday, and Sunday, there was a lot of difficulty with my phone; it would go dead spasmodically, and a number of people tried to call and were not able to get me—and at times it would work. I got the phone company out on either Saturday or Sunday, or both, I think. There was some short in a cable, in one of the wires in one of the cables, ending up with my number. When somebody would dial my number, it would ring in the house across the street, not my house . . . isn't this just fate? And this was finally straightened out, too. But I would be surprised in my mind if Mrs. Irwin had not tried to call me . . . whether this was true, that she tried to call me, I have no idea. But if she had, it would have been just like rolling dice—the chances of hers being one of the calls that might have gotten through were slim.

On Monday, June 23, Mrs. Irwin's sister called the hospital to report that the patient had been found dead by suicide. Mrs. Irwin had gone to a distant city, where she registered in a hotel on the evening of June 21. She was found dead in the bathtub the following evening. The coroner reported she had taken a large amount of nonprescription sleeping pills and subsequently had drowned. She left three notes, two handwritten, one typed. All three were addressed to her mother. The longest read:

« Dearest Mother, There is so much I want to tell you—you've been so wonderful to me through all the years. But you know it just didn't work to keep pouring more thousands into Crest. Eventually I'd wind up at State. I hope you understand all this. I realize I'm being selfish in doing this but I guess I just can't help it. I've not been able to think of anything else even when I try. I don't know how to express my appreciation for all that's been given me. Don't know what's happened to me.

Love,
Miriam

Chapter IX

RECAPITULATION:
THE PREVENTION OF SUICIDE

WE HAVE THEORIZED THAT IN ORDER FOR AN ACTUAL suicide to take place, certain conditions must prevail in the "field." An individual comes to feel that his future is devoid of hope; he, or someone else, brings the alternative of suicide into his field. He attempts to communicate his conviction of hopelessness to others, in an effort to gain their assurance that some hope still exists for him. The character of the response at this point is crucial in determining whether or not suicide will take place. For actual suicide to occur, a necessary (although not sufficient) aspect of the field is a response characterized by helplessness and hopelessness. The helpless-hopeless response usually is communicated through an implicit or explicit expectation that the troubled person will kill himself.

This conception stemmed from the events described in the major part of this volume. In Chapter I the use of this thesis as a frame of reference in examining much of the literature relating to suicide lent support to the theory. We have described the setting in which the epidemic took place, as well as the unique experiences of the persons intimately involved. Each of the cases substantiates the appropriateness of our theory: the responses of all the emotionally significant people to the cries for help were decisive in each situation. Those who committed suicide found their worlds pervaded by anxiety about suicide, and by helplessness; no person in the immediate environment was hopeful and confident immediately prior to the suicide. The facts indicate that suicide did not take place—although it was possible—until the individual's aloneness was absolute; until all possible roads to hope were closed.

Certain factors applied for all the epidemic group. All these persons were acutely disturbed and suffered with feelings of anguish and panic prior to their coming to Crest. The reputation of Crest Hospital was excellent. The decline of the hospital was not publicly known. It was a fine, expensive, private hospital; the patients and their families saw Crest as a place that could help. Had the hospital remained as a representative of hope, the suicide epidemic might not—and we obviously believe, would not—have occurred.

Attitudes of hopelessness and helplessness permeated the entire hospital. Although individual suicides may well take place in a hospital in which the general atmosphere is not negative— for example, a hopeless situation may develop around a particular patient—the problem here is an epidemic of suicides. The history of the institution reveals (Chapter II), that the hospital's identity and ideological orientation had been damaged severely by late 1959. In our case studies we described in detail the atmosphere in the hospital in the months prior to the suicide epidemic. The atmosphere and its effects were best illustrated in the account of Mr. Ullman.

Mr. Ullman had a unique position in the cases detailed. He did not kill himself; he escaped. His case was the prologue to the epidemic. But it was in the transactions surrounding Mr. Ullman that, for the first time, the issue of suicide entered the hospital atmosphere as a subject of intense anxiety. Mr. Ullman's treatment became a test of the adequacy of a new way at Crest. The rise and decline of the idea, "psychological treatment for psychological illness," at Crest created staff distress; the coming of the new medical director in the fall of 1959 and his differing approach to treatment created other uncertainties. Shortly after Mr. Ullman's admission, his brother imparted to the hospital staff members his feeling about the intensity of Mr. Ullman's "drive" to suicide. The staff's feeling of inadequacy in dealing with the alleged suicide danger was unlike any past situation at Crest. However, although there was desperation among the staff, there was hope that Dr. Doren's "new way," even though it was considerably different from the old "Crest way," might work. Dr. Preston, as well as the director of nursing, Miss Nelson —both of them seasoned Crest employees who were vitally identified with its "way"—were ready to accept even a fundamental change. Miss Nelson said, "I had said to myself that I would have to accept the idea of shock treatment. I felt sure Doren was oriented this way, that I would have to change." Dr. Preston recalled:

« Well, part of shock treatment too had to do with the need to become a different kind of hospital. We can no longer be a . . . hospital where organic treatments are not used . . . [we have to change as] part of getting more patients, increasing our census. . . . We've got to change our approach —I mean this was something that Doren was saying.

Mr. Ullman was treated with electric shock. His subsequent suicide attempt defined the shock treatment as a failure. Mr. Ullman's suicide attempt depleted the hopes of the very vulnerable Crest staff. Anxiety about suicide increased markedly. With hope gone, and fear of suicide dominant, the setting for the suicide epidemic was complete.

Now we must explore the question: Why did Ullman not commit suicide? The theory, of course, proposes only necessary —not sufficient—conditions. The necessary conditions may not have prevailed for Ullman. Hope was higher in the hospital prior to his attempt at suicide. Also, shortly after his attempt, arrangements were begun for his transfer to another, highly reputed, hospital. Earlier Ullman and his family had seriously considered this latter hospital, settling ultimately on Crest because of its location. It follows that Ullman may have had very real hopes regarding the new hospital to which he anticipated transfer.

The history of the hospital and the events of the Ullman case graphically illustrate what was happening in the hospital prior to the epidemic. It is strikingly significant that no patient committed suicide before Ullman's attempt on December 23, 1959. All patients in the epidemic group had been in the hospital for a considerable time before that. Mr. Einston had come to Crest on March 6, 1959. The admission dates of the others were as follows: Mr. Oakson, September 19, 1959; Mrs. Irwin, October 28, 1959; and Mrs. Arlington, November 1, 1959.

After Mr. Ullman's suicide attempt, there was conflict and confusion within the professional group. Hope was decreased, and anxiety high, especially concerning the danger of suicide. This situation in the hospital, affecting all staff members including the professional staff, was part of the field of each patient in the epidemic group. The condition of the hospital was the source of the epidemiological nature of the subsequent events. The anxiety and fearful expectations of the ward staff and the therapists, the inadequacy of the staff in helping involved relatives of patients, the tendency of patients to identify with one another, and of the staff to make similar identifications, all contributed to the atmosphere which elicited the process. Once the process had started with Ullman, it spread.

Although the patients in the epidemic group shared the same setting, each had his individual world, with its unique aspects, such as his own particular family and his own particular interactions with his therapist. Although the epidemic had its source in the hospital setting, the significant people outside the hospital also played their parts.

Mr. Einston was the first patient to commit suicide. From the point of view of the hospital staff, and his therapist, he had made considerable progress. Prior to Christmas, his behavior in the hospital was much improved, his talk hopeful. He was thinking positively of the future, having made plans to return to school.

At home, however, he was seen very differently; and it is clear that he behaved very differently. With his parents and sister he behaved in a suffering manner. They believed that he was preoccupied with the idea of suicide and felt helpless to deal with the suicide danger. On Einston's last visit home, shortly before Christmas, the family hid some possible weapons, were anxious about others, and were eloquently aware of their inability, in their situation, to protect their son adequately against what they saw as a danger of suicide. They felt that he should not be allowed to go on visits from the hospital.

Thus, prior to Christmas, expectations of suicide, combined with helplessness, were what Einston found at home. And he facilitated this attitude through his behavior and communications. At the hospital, where the expectations were relatively hopeful, Einston's behavior reflected the positive attitude. His behavior was not, however, merely a reflection of expectations; rather, a reciprocal, feedback process existed in both situations. Unfortunately, the communication between the hospital and the parents was very poor. For the many reasons elaborated in the text, the parents were never able to communicate to the hospital staff the extent of their concern and the basis for it. Too often their communications were seen as a reflection of their pathology and pathological involvement with their son. While the relatives were expecting and fearing suicide and felt helpless, the hospital and therapist still offered hope.

Mr. Einston returned to the hospital, after his disturbed and disturbing visit home, on the day of Mr. Ullman's suicide attempt.

Anxiety pervaded the hospital. Many members of the staff now saw Einston in a different light than before his departure; he appeared to them exhausted, dragging, unhappy. A number of the ward staff thought he should not be given as much freedom as he had been receiving. The medical director explicitly suggested to Einston's therapist that the pace of Einston's freedom should be slowed. The confidence in Einston had decreased. Immediately after Ullman's attempt, staff perception could not have been normally "objective."

Einston's therapist, who was also Ullman's therapist, disregarded the staff warnings. While he was not aware of the specifics of Einston's behavior at home, he knew that something uncomfortable was happening in the family interchange. He did raise the issue directly with Einston, of his parents' not wanting him at home. If the relationship between Einston and his therapist or any one person had remained stable and characterized by hope, suicide probably would not have occurred.

While Dr. Preston had been a major source of hopefulness for Einston, he and Einston had had chronic problems of communication throughout their experience together. At just this time, the therapist felt that Einston was again withholding something of significance in the therapy situation. Finally, the shock of his experience with Ullman increased Dr. Preston's anxiety about Einston. Thus, at this critical time the support and investment of his therapist were withdrawn from Einston. In Einston's desperate state then, there was no one who was understanding, hopeful, and confident. He had communicated his "cry for help" clearly to his parents, and more subtly to the hospital. The response was helpless anxiety from the parents: they who loved him did not want him with them. Moreover, the parents felt hostility toward the hospital and an acute lack of confidence in the hospital's ability to be helpful. The hospital's response to Einston was anxiety. Such a situation had not prevailed before Ullman's attempt. Einston was alone, cut off from help and hope; and it was at this time—and not earlier—that he carried out his plans to commit suicide.

Mr. Oakson, the second in the epidemic of suicide, was considerably older than the other members of the group. In his case alone suicide had not been an explicitly considered problem. His therapist later said that he had thought of the possibility of the patient's committing suicide, but not seriously. Rather, he thought that the greater possibility, if Mr. Oakson should become acutely aggressive, was that he would harm his wife.

Mr. Oakson had left the hospital on the 24th, the day after Ullman's suicide attempt, for his Christmas holiday, returned on the evening of the 25th, and left again on the 27th planning to return for interviews only. Oakson returned for therapy hours on January 6 and 7; in the interim Mr. Einston had committed suicide. In these interviews Mr. Oakson repeated his desire to be discharged from the hospital while continuing psychotherapy. He agreed "that if things did not go well he would be readmitted." His therapist wrote:

« Continuation of [hospitalization] under the circumstances would continually stimulate his regressive tendencies to such a degree that it might be difficult to bring about his discharge except after a much longer period of time. It may be that he will have to return, but I felt that there was a reasonable chance that he could make the grade at home with follow-up interviews here.

He felt that there was a great danger that if Mr. Oakson had to return to the hospital he would become completely regressed "and likely never to come out of it." The therapist also indicated that, at this time, he was hoping Oakson would not find out about Ullman and Einston, feeling that it would be bad for him. He wondered, in retrospect, if this might have resulted in his being particularly anxious and withdrawing from Oakson.

Mr. Oakson saw himself as being in a situation of conflict. He was pressing the hospital to send him home, but not because he had confidence in this alternative. He felt the need to establish himself as an adequate man, while at the same time he feard that his dependence would necessitate continued hospitalization, with the consequence that he would be sent to a state hospital for life. This last fear, which desperately troubled him, was not a delusion. The financial situation of the Oakson family was such that if continued hospitalization was felt to be necessary, the state hospital would be the only choice. This had been openly discussed between Mr. Oakson and his therapist. Thus, Oakson's going home was seen as crucial both by his therapist and himself; they agreed he would either recover or end up "completely regressed" in a state hospital. But the therapist felt there was a reasonable chance that he would recover; and Mr. Oakson shared his view. Hope still existed.

Mrs. Oakson believed that her husband should be in the hospital. She felt that the hospital had not yet given him sufficient assistance. Her conviction that her husband's behavior was a causal factor in her heart difficulties also influenced her feeling that he should not return home.

Mr. Oakson returned home to find his wife suffering with one of her heart attacks. He wanted to call a physician, but his wife said he should not. Feeling helpless, Mr. Oakson telephoned his therapist, who supported his proposed action.

At home he was preoccupied with the fear of being sent to a state hospital. Psychotic symptoms returned in full. Mrs. Oakson became very frightened; for the first time, she called on their son for help. Mrs. Oakson became increasingly more uncomfortable and, on the night of the 16th, it was reported she felt "more helpless than she ever had before." In response to his request that she join her husband for a walk, she told him to take a pill. As the therapy hour at Crest approached, the alternatives for Mr. Oakson were limited. He had failed to make the grade at home, where he was not wanted. Going to his therapy hour meant re-hospitalization, with the expectation of complete regression and transfer to a state hospital. As in Einston's case, there was no source of hope and confidence.

The third person to commit suicide was Mrs. Arlington. As she entered the hospital following a suicide attempt, the possibility of actual suicide was a consideration in her treatment. However, attitudes about her suicide "drive" varied considerably. Some saw her as especially in danger of suicide, while others felt that her attempts were histrionic—as if she were making them "in Yankee Stadium at home plate." Mrs. Arlington had opportunities to commit suicide, or to make serious attempts at suicide, on January 5 and 8, the days she was away from hospital supervision. But at this time, hope still existed for her with her therapist, with some members of the hospital staff and her hospital physician, and with her husband. However, her husband had been withdrawing, as Mrs. Arlington was aware. When, on the 8th, she pressed him about the possibility of their making a go of the marriage, and he could offer no assurance, she acutely felt his desire to be rid of her and the marriage. Turning from this blind alley, Mrs. Arlington encountered another; for as a consequence of her escape on the 8th, her relationship with her therapist was ended. Her former therapist, Mrs. Clift, to whom she might have turned, had, at the last crisis, admitted her helplessness. Only the hospital remained for her.

Her situation at the hospital was not a happy one. She was disliked by many of the staff members, including her hospital physician. Moreover, after the termination of her therapy, there was no new therapist available. It was reported that nobody wanted to treat her. A conference had been planned to review her situation; but the major item on the conference agenda was the relationship between Mr. Arlington and Mrs. Clift. New plans for Mrs. Arlington were vague and it was hoped that something would come out of the conference. Moreover, the hospital was fraught with anxiety consequent on the suicides of Einston and Oakson, which had followed the trauma of Mr. Ullman's suicide attempt. This anxiety and uncertainty led in part to the prescribing of Thorazine by Dr. Preston. He, however, did not even at this time consider Mrs. Arlington a real suicide risk; he did not expect her to commit suicide, nor did he feel helpless in relation to a danger of her committing suicide. Thus, even though suicide precautions had been prescribed on January 8, they had been eased on January 17. Dr. Preston's attitudes and behavior were one positive factor. One further source of hope remained for Mrs. Arlington in her friend, Mr. Einston. Before her final day we do not know what Mrs. Arlington knew or believed about Mr. Einston's fate; but on that final day she discovered with certainty what she must at least have suspected, that Harry Einston was dead. She reacted to this knowledge very intensely; she is reported to have said that day that Harry was her hope.

The last thread of confidence was broken by the treatment she received on January 19. Dr. Preston, at two in the morning of that day, had acted with confidence. Mrs. Arlington was disturbed, but he controlled the decisions about what was to be done. He was confidently in charge, if somewhat cavalier in manner. His absence as the day unfolded may have been crucial; for it appears that he alone was confident, the notes of the ward staff eloquently expressing its anxiety. The shots of Compazine, and more particularly the use of restraints for the first time, accompanied as they were with the reinstitution of full suicide precautions, clearly indicate that the helpless expectation of suicide pervaded her field. It was at this point, and not before, that Mrs. Arlington committed suicide.

The final case in the epidemic group was Mrs. Irwin. Her relationships with her relatives were, at best, superficial. There seemed to be an agreement between Mrs. Irwin and her mother that nothing important was to be communicated between them. Mrs. Irwin's mother and sister were both helpless, seeing Mrs. Irwin as self-destructive but feeling that there was no way in which they could serve her. They believed that psychiatrists had to take the responsibility; others must avoid significant, emotionally loaded interchange because, they had heard, this could only interfere with the treatment process. The extremity of the mother's avoidance and denial was illustrated on the birthday trip to the airport. Mrs. Irwin had some hope of getting together once again with her ex-husband; but this vestige was destroyed when the husband failed to respond to her gift and letter of Valentine's Day.

Mrs. Irwin's therapist was anxious about her and about the danger of her suicide. He felt that a special danger was presented by his engagement and business trip, which Mrs. Irwin might interpret as a desertion. With other members of the hospital staff, the therapist saw Mrs. Irwin's life as empty, her future discouraging.

The ward staff may have added the final blow in this case. Mrs. Irwin had made many suicide gestures to which the ward staff had, in the past, responded effectively. The new helplessness of the ward staff was dramatically conveyed when the staff failed to prevent Mrs. Irwin's nephew from bringing her a pint bottle of iodine, which she secreted under her pillow. It is the unanimous opinion of those involved that, had Mrs. Irwin not escaped that night, she would have killed herself in her hospital room, while on suicide precautions. As with the others in the suicide group, Mrs. Irwin's world was filled with the expectation of suicide and with the sense of the helplessness of others to prevent it. In no person was there hope and confidence.

To summarize, suicide occurred in each case when, and only when, all significant hopeful relationships were broken. The patient, after communicating, testing, and searching for hope, then felt that he was alone in an empty world.

Our data give powerful support to a field-theoretical, transactional view of emotional disturbance, and to the potential significance of such a view in the treatment of those who become emotionally disturbed. The data, too, raise serious question about the adequacy of the point of view, most popular today, which regards emotional disturbance as "illness." It seems clear that emotional disturbance, even the most severe, cannot be understood unless the field in which it develops and exists is examined. The manifestations of difficulty in the disturbed individual have meaning, and change meaning, dependent on aspects of the field. The significant aspects of the field usually are interpersonal; thus, the emotionally important individuals in the disturbed person's field—family, close friends—make up the major significant factors. The increased egocentricity that accompanies emotional disturbance makes the closer relationships more difficult, and more intensely meaningful. At times, significant aspects of the field may be more widespread. Insofar as help for the individual is concerned, one can do a good deal about the limited field, but less about the broader one.

In our group of cases, when the significant figures were joined in helplessness and hopelessness, the results were disastrous. The behavior of the disturbed individuals was influenced powerfully by the atmosphere in the field. This is not to say that the atmosphere is all—that the individual does not bring his own predispositions into the field. Clearly he does. But the predisposition to suicide is only one of many. To escape from the torture of his apparently hopeless world, the acutely disturbed individual may commit suicide—but he may also withdraw by becoming thoroughly psychotic or by developing a severe psychosomatic ailment. Selection from among these predispositions is a function of the social field. The more acute the disturbance, the more intense the anxiety, the more severe the need, then the more vulnerable the person to influence by those significant people in the field. In the ten years of Crest's history described, many individuals brought into the field the explicit possibility of suicide. Actual suicide occurred, however, only when helpers in an atmosphere of helplessness focused upon these particular dispositions.

It is not necessary that the individual bring suicide into the field; suicide as a possibility may sometimes be brought by others. Most commonly, the individual introduces the alternative of suicide into the field, which increases the possibility of his being expected to commit suicide. In this context two questions arise which need further study: One, why do some individuals, and not others, consider suicide explicitly? We have found those intrapsychic analyses which have appeared in the literature unfruitful sources for the answer. Two, why are some patients more vulnerable than others to the alternative of suicide brought in from the setting? After all, all of Crest's patients did not commit suicide.

We have stated that the selection from the manifold predispositions of the patient is a function of the social field. We think that this conceptualization is applicable to the general problem of choice of symptom in its broadest sense. In our view, those who actually commit suicide respond to the expectation that they will kill themselves. The disturbed behavior—the symptom —is focused through expectations. This same process may underlie the course and the treatment of, for example, those who are diagnosed as acute schizophrenics and who later become chronic hospital occupants. We might hypothesize that when they are acutely crying for help, their worlds become filled with negative expectations, with the expectation that they are not salvageable. We reject the idea that "schizophrenic behavior" can be fruitfully interpreted as essentially a consequence of an intrapersonal illness, just as in Chapter I we rejected the idea that suicide can be usefully defined as an "illness." Although the popular professional view of those disturbed individuals diagnosed schizophrenia, and of those who commit suicide, is that they are suffering from an illness, there has been no demonstration so far that this frame of reference is more productive than the psychosocial-transactional orientation we offer in its stead.

What are the implications in our text for the general problem of suicide? We leave out of consideration what has been called "rational suicide." We believe such suicides occur; that is, we do not agree with the assumption that all those who commit suicide are emotionally disturbed. Rational suicides are distinguished by their purpose: they are not committed in a state of desperate hopelessness but to achieve a specific goal, a goal falling in the realm of general human understanding. For example, we see Socrates' death as rational; he, as he explained, was supporting the integrity of established government in killing himself. The Kamikaze pilots in World War II and the Vietnamese Buddhists in 1963 killed themselves for specific social purposes. The leaders of the Suicide Prevention Center in Los Angeles (Shneidman, Farberow, and Litman, 1961) point up the particular "mistaken notion" that all suicidal persons are insane. They too consider some suicides as rational. They add, and we agree, "The majority of persons who commit suicide are tormented and ambivalent."

We are centrally concerned with the prevention of suicide. Most of those who actually suicide make a prior communication of their intent. We suggest that the answer to the cry for help is crucial. Robins, *et al* (1959), have pointed out that when faced with a "suicidal person": "no clear cut information is available to physicians or to the public as to what should be done in this situation." We conclude definitely that something can be done. The situation facing any of us—whether we be therapist, physician, friend, or relative—when a person talks, threatens, or attempts suicide, is by no means hopeless; nor are we, whoever we are, helpless. The individual is desperate, lonely, frantic—asking for hope and help. We—again any of us—can respond helpfully to this need in the individual. We can empathize with and recognize his terror explicitly, and not succumb to terror ourselves. We can make it clear that changes are possible, that changes in his life situation can be made, that we will do what we can to help bring about desired changes.

Changes can be of many sorts. Guiding the disturbed individual into a treatment situation is certainly a compellingly reasonable change. Still other changes, of a personal and individual nature, can be made. It is not necessary at this time that the changes be directed toward a special "real" or "deep" problem of the individual. Changes of job, friends, or family, or changes within the job or family situation may be effective in some cases. The therapeutic power of the action toward change depends upon the clarity of the communication of hopefulness.

In our emphasis on action we do not mean to belittle the effectiveness of words. Sympathetic and hopefully confident words from a person in whom one has confidence may be of powerful help in a crisis. Suicide prevention centers around the world which can be phoned at any hour of the day or night by people in suicidal crises use both words and action. The effectiveness of these Centers depends on the self-assurance of the staffs; their purpose is to help and they know that help is possible. Hopefulness then is basic to all their communications.

In considering the response to the suicide crisis the necessary hopefulness can be communicated in a variety of ways; the exact form of the communication is less important than the message it conveys. As is clear from the ten years of the history of the use of suicide precautions at Crest, they can be used both negatively and positively. Whether or not they are used is far less important than the atmosphere within the hospital. What is true in the hospitals is as true for the families of those in a suicidal crisis. For example, families of mental hospital patients who may have threatened or attempted suicide should be advised to deal with their relative as competent, to expect him to return, in not too long a time, to his role responsibilities. They should know that there will be disturbances and difficulties, but these do not mean that suicide is inevitable or that hope is inappropriate.

We can *expect* that there is hope in such crisis situations as we have been discussing. When faced with a person considering suicide, there is a choice between positive and negative expectations, neither of which are substantially supported by fact or truth. This sort of choice is little different from most of life's choices; they are characterized by ambiguity, and the outcome is vague rather than clear. Yet, in the face of suicide attempts or threats, the negative choice is too prevalent, at least among those who give professional counsel. We believe this choice stems in good part from the "illness" approach which we have criticized. Such an approach divides humanity into two categories, the prone and the non-prone, in which the prone are the sick ones, the weaklings, helpless and worthy of concern rather than respect, to be dealt with more properly as objects—of our sympathy—than as responsible human beings. But when one deals with an individual as a human being, as a person, one communicates respect. And respect has implicit positive expectations; it says: you can cope, you can choose. An attitude of respect for the *person* who is the disturbed individual may be the crucial necessary difference. Certainly the expectation that a person will commit suicide—that he is being driven, and is helpless in the face of these drives—and that the respondent is totally responsible (Robins, *et al,* 1959) does not have the character of respect for the individual.

This point was eloquently made by Carl Rogers (1961) in commenting on the treatment of Ellen West, a woman who committed suicide, and whose case was reported in great detail (Binswanger, 1958). Mrs. West was hospitalized, at age 33, after much treatment and four suicide attempts. In the hospital, suicide preoccupation and threats continued. At the hospital, the feeling was that release meant certain suicide. There were consultations, what Rogers (1961) called the "comic-tragic argument over her diagnosis." ". . . then comes the last final, incredible decision. She is suicidal, schizophrenic, and hopeless for treatment. Therefore we will discharge her and let her commit suicide." Binswanger (1958) wrote that he and his renowned consultants all agreed "that no definitely reliable therapy is possible. We therefore resolved to give in to the patient's demands for discharge." Ellen West, who had said, "I scream but they do not hear me," went home and, on her third day at home, killed herself. In Ellen West's case, actual suicide did not take place until—like the people we have described—total hopelessness was made explicit and definite. While hope existed—and treatment went on for many years—although the apparent desire for suicide existed in Ellen West, actual suicide did not occur.

We do not wish to imply here that hope and possibilities resolve all conflicts or that they will necessarily avoid the actual suicide. Respect, however, may avoid the actual suicide, and may be more broadly helpful.

In applying his theory of psychotherapy to the case of Ellen West, Rogers (1961) wrote:

« The greatest weakness [in the treatment], in my opinion, is that no one involved in her treatment seems to have related to her as a *person;* a person worthy of respect, a person capable of autonomous choice, a person whose inner experiencing is a precious resource to be drawn upon and trusted. Rather, she seems to have been dealt with as an object.

He concluded:

« For myself, I draw certain lessons from this case of Ellen West. The first is that in every respect in which we make an object of the person—whether by diagnosing him, analyzing him, or perceiving him impersonally in a case history—we stand in the way of our therapeutic goal. To make an object of a person has been helpful in treating physical ills. It has not been successful in treating psychological ills. We are deeply helpful only when we relate as persons, when we risk ourselves as persons in the relationship, when we experience the other as a person in his own right. Only then is there a meeting of a depth which dissolves the pain of aloneness in both client and therapist.

Too often, in responding to the cry of another human being on the brink of suicide, a person—friend or physician, therapist or parent—acts as if his answer will not influence the other. Too often, the consequences are proof that his conduct is the key to the other's future. After hearing the cry for help, one cannot avoid being fundamentally involved. We are none of us alone, neither clients nor therapists. If we live and act with this awareness, then none of us will reach the end of hope.

REFERENCES

Binswanger, Ludwig. The Case of Ellen West. In May, R., Angel, E., and Ellenberger, H. F. (Eds.), *Existence*. New York: Basic Books, 1958, pp. 237-364.

Robins, E., Gassner, S., Kayes, J., Wilkinson, R. H., and Murphy, G. E. The Communication of Suicidal Intent: A Study of 134 Consecutive Cases of Successful (Completed) Suicide. *American Journal of Psychiatry,* 115: 724-733, 1959.

Rogers, Carl. The Loneliness of Contemporary Man as Seen in "The Case of Ellen West." *Annals of Psychotherapy,* 2: 22-27, 1961.

Shneidman, Edwin S., Farberow, Norman L., and Litman, Robert E. The Suicide Prevention Center. In Farberow, N. L., and Shneidman, E. S. (Eds.), *The Cry for Help*. New York: McGraw-Hill, 1961, pp. 6-18.